RECOGNIZING

NATIVE

SHRUBS

STACKPOLE BOOKS Harrisburg, Pennsylvania

RECOGNIZING NATIVE SHRUBS

Text and Illustrations by

WILLIAM CAREY GRIMM

Library of Congress catalog card number: 66-12781

Printed in the USA by The Telegraph Press, Harrisburg, Pa.

To my wife

RUTH CURTIS GRIMM

PREFACE

Since the appearance of the author's *Shrubs of Pennsylvania* in 1952, many persons have expressed a desire for an illustrated popular manual which would cover a wider range. The present work has therefore been prepared, covering the native shrubs and woody vines of the eastern United States from the Canadian border south to the Gulf Coast and northern Florida, and from the Mississippi Valley eastward to the Atlantic Coast.

Most of the illustrations have been made from material collected by the author, but in some cases the drawings were made from herbarium specimens or from photographs. Thanks are due the University of North Carolina, University of Georgia, University of Tennessee, and Clemson University for the loan of specimens of various southeastern shrubs. Dr. Wilbur H. Duncan of the University of Georgia and Dr. Harry E. Ahles of the University of North Carolina have been most helpful, not only in supplying needed specimens but in many other ways.

For various material, I am also indebted to the following persons: Mr. Gurdon L. Tarbox, Jr., of Brookgreen Gardens, Murrells Inlet, S. C.; Mr. Arthur Stupka of Gatlinburg, Tennessee; Dr. O. M. Freeman of Tryon, N. C.; Dr. Thelma Howell of the Highlands Biological Station, Highlands, N. C.; Mr. W. J. Barker of Clemson, S. C.; Mr. C. Garvin Hughes of Hickory, N. C., Mr. James B. Shuler, Jr., of Greenville, S. C., Mr. E. F. Johnson of McClellanville, S. C., and Mr. Joe Morton of Waycross, Ga.

Although this is a popular book intended for the layman, scientific names could not be dispensed with. Many of the shrubs, like other wild plants, are known by a number of popular or local names; others have no common name at all. While botanists are not in general agreement on some of the scientific names, an effort has been made to use those which are now most widely accepted. In some cases the scientific names vary from those used in *Gray's Manual of Botany* and Small's *Manual of the Southeastern Flora*.

W. C. G.

7

CONTENTS

9

PAGE GUIDE
TO SHRUB FAMILIES

USING THIS BOOK
TO RECOGNIZE SHRUBS

To most people a shrub is a bush. It is a woody plant smaller than a tree, with several stems growing together in a clump. Sometimes an arbitrary height of twenty feet is set as the maximum height for a shrub. The distinction between shrubs and trees, however, is often very vague, and some woody plants can justifiably be considered as both trees and shrubs. Some of the larger shrubs often have a single stem or trunk a short distance above the ground. On the other hand, there are trees which commonly have several trunks growing together in a clump. Botanists also consider woody vines as being shrubs. Then, too, we often run into difficulty in distinguishing herbaceous plants from shrubs. Some plants are intermediate between the two. They have stems which are at least partly woody, especially toward the base, and they are often called "semiwoody" plants or "sub-shrubs." Woody vines are included in the present work, and so are some of these so-called "sub-shrubs."

Our native shrubs are useful in many ways. They help to prevent the erosion of the soil and of stream banks; they provide much needed cover for wildlife. A great many species also provide food for the wild creatures of our fields and woods. Some produce fruits which are enjoyed by human beings as well, or which have some medicinal value. The beauty of many of our native shrubs all too often is not appreciated. Most of the ornamental shrubs which we plant about our homes and in our gardens are shrubs from foreign lands. Very few native American species are ever listed in the nursery catalogs, though many are singularly attractive and well worth introducing into our home grounds and gardens. Some of them will thrive in places where most cultivated shrubs refuse to grow—on dry barren soils or in very wet environments.

One way to use a book such as this is to thumb through it until you find the name of the plant in question, and there is really nothing wrong

13

about this method. Another way is to use a key; this usually turns out to be a shortcut to identification. Two sets of simple keys are provided in this book. One is a key to the genera of shrubs when leaves, and perhaps fruits, are present. The other is a key to the genera of leaf-losing shrubs in winter condition, when the leaves are absent. In addition, keys to most of the larger genera are provided in the Appendix.

To find a particular shrub, it is first necessary to determine which key should be used. To determine this, consult the information which immediately follows this Introduction. For instance, if the plant is a *woody vine,* you will be directed to use Key II; if it is a *trailing shrub,* or a dwarf one less than a foot high, you will be told to use Key I. The keys have two alternatives bearing the same number. The user should begin with the first step, which is number 1. At each step, or set of numbers, a choice must be made between each pair of characteristics. Of course it is necessary to make accurate observations and correct choices at each progressive step in the key until the genus name of the plant is finally determined. Sometimes it will be necessary to take many steps through a key before arriving at the genus name, while at other times the steps may be relatively few.

As this book is intended for the layman, technical terms have been avoided as much as possible. It should therefore be useful to anyone who has an interest in, and wishes to identify, native shrubs. A few of the particularly difficult genera, such as the blackberries (*Rubus*) and hawthorns (*Crataegus*), are treated here in only a very general sort of way. Even professionally trained botanists find them most exasperating. The average person can hardly be expected to do better than recognize them as blackberries or hawthorns.

While most of the characteristics used for identification are ones which can be easily seen with the unaided eye—or sometimes even detected by the nose—the use of such characteristics was not always possible. A good hand lens is therefore quite an asset. This is epecially true in trying to identify the leaf-losing shrubs in winter, when we often have to rely on characteristics that are not easily seen with the unaided eye. Usually it is necessary to use a hand lens to determine the number and arrangement of the bundle scars within the leaf scars, or other minute details.

For convenience, the text describing each shrub is placed on the page opposite the illustration. While the descriptions are necessarily brief, they will tell you what you need to know in order to identify a given shrub. Identification, as far as possible, is based upon leaf characteristics.

Times of flowering and fruiting are included. In the case of wide-ranging species, the earliest month mentioned is when the shrub usually blooms in the southern portion of its range; the latest month is when it usually finishes blooming in the north. The time of blooming is, of course, later at higher elevations in the mountains than in the lowlands in the same latitude.

The range of the shrub is also useful in arriving at an identification. If the shrub has a distinctly northern range, obviously it can be eliminated when you are trying to identify shrubs in the south; and strictly southern species need not be expected to occur in the north. Some shrubs are found only in the mountain regions; others in the coastal lowlands. Such facts are given in the text.

The beginner will undoubtedly find occasional shrubs which he will be unable to identify. If possible consult a local botanist or other person who is familiar with the local plants. Should such a person not be available, botanists at the various colleges and universities will be more than glad to help you make correct identifications. Fresh specimens may be sent to them by mail, wrapped in plastic wrap or waxed paper to prevent their withering before arrival. If dried specimens are sent, they should be carefully pressed while still fresh and the parts well arranged and flattened out. Specimens may be dried between blotters or folded newspapers, then securely wrapped and sent by parcel post. Address them to the Department of Botany at the institution of your choice. Your specimens may be a valuable addition to the collection of plants in the college or university herbarium, so always state when and where they were collected.

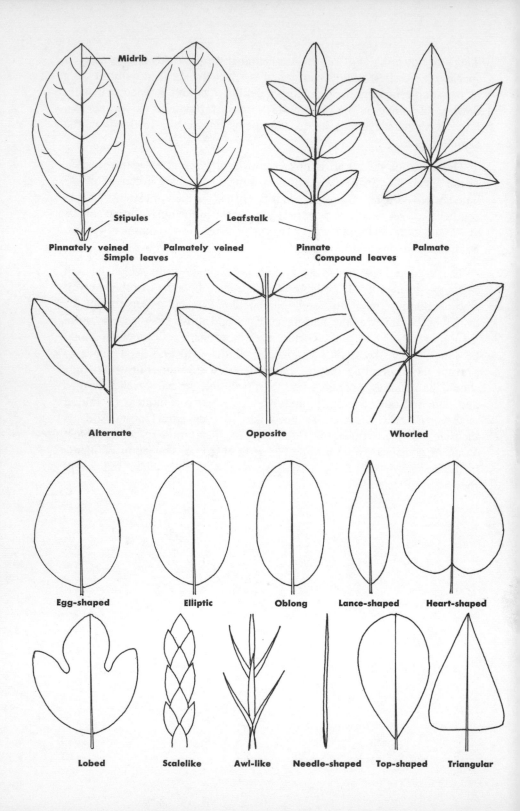

Midrib

Stipules   **Leafstalk**

Pinnately veined   **Palmately veined**   **Pinnate**   **Palmate**
Simple leaves   **Compound leaves**

Alternate   **Opposite**   **Whorled**

Egg-shaped   **Elliptic**   **Oblong**   **Lance-shaped**   **Heart-shaped**

Lobed   **Scalelike**   **Awl-like**   **Needle-shaped**   **Top-shaped**   **Triangular**

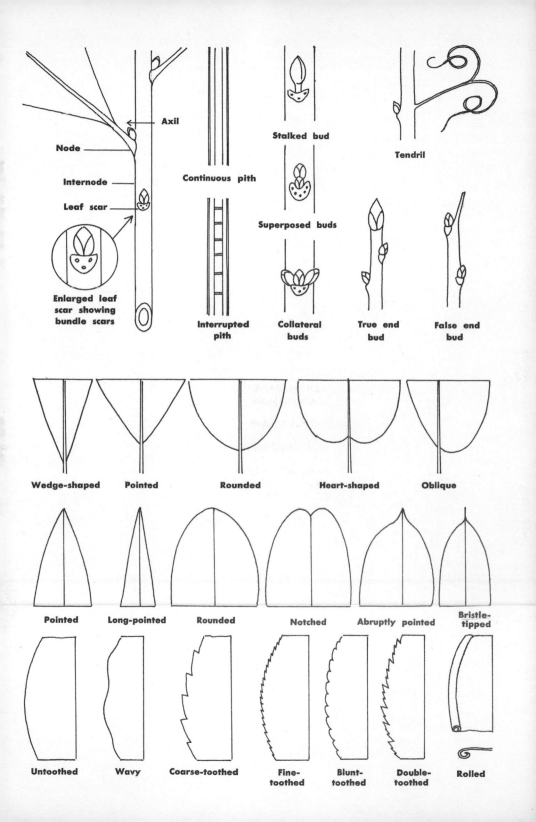

Axil

Node

Internode

Leaf scar

Enlarged leaf
scar showing
bundle scars

Continuous pith

Interrupted
pith

Stalked bud

Superposed buds

Collateral
buds

Tendril

True end
bud

False end
bud

Wedge-shaped   Pointed   Rounded   Heart-shaped   Oblique

Pointed   Long-pointed   Rounded   Notched   Abruptly pointed   Bristle-tipped

Untoothed   Wavy   Coarse-toothed   Fine-toothed   Blunt-toothed   Double-toothed   Rolled

KEYS TO THE
GENERA OF SHRUBS

Shrubs with the leaves present

PROSTRATE, TRAILING, OR ERECT SHRUBS
LESS THAN ONE FOOT HIGH

1 Stems fleshy and jointed, usually armed with slender spines; leaves small, scalelike and soon shed, bearing in their axils clusters of barbed hairs   PRICKLY-PEARS *(Opuntia)*   160
1 Stems and leaves otherwise—2

    2 Leaves scalelike, awl-like, needle-like, or flattened but not over ⅛ inch wide—3
    2 Leaves with broader blades, usually over ⅛ inch wide—10

3 Leaves scalelike or awl-like, the bases often overlapping—4
3 Leaves neither scalelike nor awl-like—5

    4 Plants green and more or less hairy, or densely woolly and whitish; flowers yellow   HUDSONIAS *(Hudsonia)*   200
    4 Plants smooth, mosslike, with leaves in 4 rows; flowers pink or white   MOSS-PLANT *(Cassiope)*   232

5 Leaves opposite—6
5 Leaves alternate—7

    6 Leaves narrow and flat or almost needle-like, with clusters of smaller leaves in the axils; flowers yellow
          ST. JOHN'S-WORTS *(Hypericum)*   199
    6 Leaves never with axillary clusters of smaller leaves, not needle-like but with margins inrolled; flowers white or pink, bell-shaped   ALPINE-AZALEA *(Loiseleuria)*   220

7 Leaves flat, margins rough or minutely toothed
          MOUNTAIN-HEATH *(Phyllodoce)*   224
7 Leaf margins more or less rolled inward beneath—8

    8 Leaf margins untoothed   CROWBERRIES *(Empetrum)*   163
    8 Leaf margins minutely toothed—9

9 Leaves under ¼ inch long, sides parallel
          BROOM-CROWBERRY *(Corema)*   163
9 Leaves over ¼ inch long, broader toward tip
          MOUNTAIN-LOVER *(Pachystima)*   176

    10 Leaves compound—11
    10 Leaves simple—17

11 Stem or leafstalks prickly or bristly—12
11 Stems and leafstalks entirely unarmed—14

    12 Leaflets untoothed; pairs of short spines often present at the bases of the leafstalks; fruit a flattened pod
          LOCUSTS *(Robinia)*   156
    12 Leaflets toothed; fruits other than pods—13

13 Stipules joined to leafstalks half or more of their length
          ROSES *(Rosa)*   143
13 Stipules not joined to the leafstalks or merely attached at the base
          BLACKBERRIES *(Rubus)*   139

14   Leaflets **3—15**
14   Leaflets 5 or more—**16**

15   Leaflets less than ½ inch wide, 3-toothed at the broad **tip**
                    CINQUEFOILS *(Potentilla)*   136
15   Leaflets broader, usually egg-shaped, pointed at tip and with a few large teeth on the margin   POISON-IVY *(Rhus)*   167

    16   Interior of stems bright yellow; leaflets usually 5, coarsely cut-toothed and often deeply cleft
                    SHRUB YELLOWROOT *(Xanthorhiza)*   104
    16   Interior of stems not bright yellow; leaflets 7 to 11, untoothed, elliptic or egg-shaped   LOCUSTS *(Robinia)*   152

17   Leaves opposite or sometimes in 3's—**18**
17   Leaves alternate—**24**

    18   Leaf margins toothed—**19**
    18   Leaf margins not toothed—**20**

19   Plant with a mintlike odor; leaves shallowly toothed, usually less than ½ inch wide   BASILS *(Satureja)*   256
19   Plant not aromatic; leaves sharply and finely toothed, usually over ½ inch wide; branchlets green and 4-sided
                    STRAWBERRY-BUSHES *(Euonymus)*   176

    20   Leaves with minute clear or black dots; flowers yellow—**21**
    20   Leaves otherwise; flowers not yellow—**22**

21   Flowers 4-petalled; fruit a capsule enclosed by a pair of large heart-shaped sepals   ST. PETER'S-WORTS *(Hypericum)*   192
21   Flowers 5-petalled; fruit a capsule with 5 sepals at the base
                    ST. JOHN'S-WORTS *(Hypericum)*   192

    22   Leaves very white beneath; branchlets 2-edged
                    LAURELS *(Kalmia)*   224
    22   Leaves not noticeably whitened beneath; branchlets not 2-edged—**23**

23   Leaves oval or elliptic, leathery, very short-stalked; plant bushy or prostrate; fruit a capsule   SANDMYRTLES *(Leiophyllum)*   212
23   Leaves roundish or heart-shaped, scarcely leathery, distinctly stalked; plant trailing; fruits red, berry-like
                    PARTRIDGEBERRY *(Mitchella)*   260

    24   Leaves lobed   CURRANTS *(Ribes)*   120
    24   Leaves not lobed—**25**

25   Largest leaves less than 1 inch long—**26**
25   Largest leaves more than 1 inch long—**37**
    26   Leaf margins conspicuously toothed—**27**
    26   Leaf margins untoothed or the teeth very inconspicuous—**30**

27   Leaves thick, leathery, evergreen; branchlets strongly angled
                    HUCKLEBERRIES *(Gaylussacia)*   235
27   Leaves and branchlets otherwise—**28**

    28   Buds covered with a solitary hoodlike scale
                    WILLOWS *(Salix)*   80
    28   Buds with 1 or more pairs of visible scales—**29**

29 Plant low and trailing   BEARBERRIES *(Archtostaphylos)*   235
29 Plant erect or bushy, over 6 inches high
                                  BLUEBERRIES *(Vaccinium)*   239

   30 Leaves with minute black dots beneath
                                  MOUNTAIN-CRANBERRY *(Vaccinium)*   247
   30 Leaves not black-dotted beneath—31

31 Lower leaf surface with minute brown scales
                                  RHODODENDRONS *(Rhododendron)*   212
31 Lower leaf surface otherwise—32

   32 Shrubs upright or bushy, over 6 inches high—33
   32 Shrubs trailing or with upright branches less than 6 inches
      high—34

33 Largest leaves less than ½ inch long; whole plant bristly-hairy;
fruit a capsule   LAURELS *(Kalmia)*   224
33 Largest leaves over ½ inch long; plants smooth or somewhat
hairy; fruit a berry
                  BLUEBERRIES AND BILBERRIES *(Vaccinium)*   239

   34 Plant with a wintergreen odor; lower surfaces of the leaves
      with some stiff brown hairs; berries white, bristly
                          CREEPING-SNOWBERRY *(Gaylussacia)*   232
   34 Plant not aromatic; leaves otherwise; berries not white—35

35 Leaves whitened beneath   CRANBERRIES *(Vaccinium)*   247
35 Leaves merely paler green beneath—36

   36 Leaf margins rolled inward on the lower side; plant of
      the southeastern coastal plain
                                  BLUEBERRIES *(Vaccinium)*   239
   36 Leaf margins flat; plant of northeast and Canada
                                  BEARBERRIES *(Arctostaphylos)*   232

37 Leaf margins conspicuously toothed—38
37 Leaf margins untoothed or the teeth very inconspicuous—41

   38 Leave more or less clustered at tips of stems or almost in
      whorls—39
   38 Leaves well spaced along the stem—40

39 Plant with a wintergreen odor; leaves oval and with a few bristly
teeth on the margin; fruits berry-like, red
                                  TEABERRY *(Gaultheria)*   232
39 Plants not aromatic; leaves egg-shaped to lance-shaped or
broadest above the middle; fruits otherwise
                                  PIPSISSEWAS *(Chimaphila)*   211

   40 Leaves 1½ inches or more long, toothed above the middle;
      branchlets lustrous brown, the main stems prostrate
                                  CHERRIES *(Prunus)*   148
   40 Leaves less than 1½ inches long, the margin finely toothed
      throughout; branchlets otherwise; plants bushy
                  BILBERRIES AND BLUEBERRIES *(Vaccinium)*   239

41 Stems trailing or low climbing—42
41 Stems more or less erect—43

42   Leafstalks with a pair of tendrils at base; fruit a berry; plants woolly or smooth, sometimes bristly or prickly
                                      GREENBRIERS *(Smilax)*   72

42 Leafstalks never with tendrils; stems with bristly brown hairs and leaf margins hairy-fringed; fruit a capsule
                    TRAILING-ARBUTUS *(Epigaea)*   231

43 Leaves with small yellow resin dots, at least beneath—44
43 Leaves never resin-dotted—45

    44   Leaves spicy-aromatic when crushed, the margins usually toothed; fruit a wax-coated nutlet
                            WAX MYRTLES *(Myrica)*   79
    44   Leaves not aromatic, margins untoothed; fruit a berry
                      HUCKLEBERRIES *(Gaylussacia)*   235

45 Leaves minutely black-dotted beneath
                      STAGGERBUSH *(Lyonia)*   228
45 Leaves not black-dotted beneath—46

    46   Branchlets and lower leaf surfaces strongly whitened; leaf margins rolled inward on lower side
                      BOG ROSEMARY *(Andromeda)*   224
    46   Branchlets and lower leaf surfaces very slightly if at all whitened; leaf margins flat or but slightly rolled—47

47 Branchlets velvety hairy or minutely warty-dotted
                      BLUEBERRIES *(Vaccinium)*   239
47 Branchlets otherwise—48

    48   Leaves mostly rounded at tip, lustrous and wrinkled-veiny above, evergreen; fruit a whitish "plum"
                      DEER-PLUM *(Chrysobalanus)*   144
    48   Leaves otherwise; fruit a capsule—49

49 Leaf margins slightly rolled inward on the lower side, the leaves finely hairy beneath; capsules globe-shaped   LAURELS *(Kalmia)*   223
49 Leaf margins flat, hairy-fringed, the leaves with scattered stiff hairs along the midrib beneath; capsules oblong
                      AZALEAS *(Rhododendron)*   215

KEY II

CLIMBING OR SCRAMBLING SHRUBS (VINES)

1 Climbing by means of tendrils or twining leafstalks—2
1 Climbing by other means—10

    2   Climbing by twining tendril-like leafstalks
                      CLEMATIS *(Clematis)*   103
    2   Climbing by means of true tendrils—3

3 Leaves simple—4
3 Leaves compound—8

KEY III

ERECT SHRUBS ONE FOOT OR MORE HIGH WITH COMPOUND LEAVES

5 Leaves more than once compound ARALIAS *(Aralia)* 203
5 Leaves merely compound—6

    6 Branchlets with a lemon- or limelike odor when bruised
                        PRICKLY-ASHES *(Xanthoxylum)* 159
    6 Branchlets not aromatic—7

7 Leaflets with untoothed margins LOCUSTS *(Robinia)* 152
7 Leaflets with toothed margins—8

    8 Stipules joined to the leafstalks half or more of their length
                              ROSES *(Rosa)* 143
    8 Stipules otherwise
          RASPBERRIES AND BLACKBERRIES *(Rubus)* 139

9 Leaflets 3—10
9 Leaflets 5 or more—12

    10 Stalk of the end leaflet distinctly longer than the other two,
       leaflets usually coarsely toothed or lobed
               POISON-IVY AND POISON-OAK *(Rhus)* 167
    10 Stalk of the end leaflet little if any longer than the other
       two—11

11 Leaflet margins coarsely toothed; branchlets aromatic if bruised
   or broken SUMACS *(Rhus)* 167
11 Leaflet margins untoothed or the teeth obscure; plant very ill-
   scented if bruised or broken HOPTREE *(Ptelea)* 159

    12 Leaflets usually 5—13
    12 Leaflets 7 or more—15

13 Leaflets radiating from the summit of the leafstalk
                        BLACKBERRIES *(Rubus)* 139
13 Leaflets arranged along an extension of the leafstalk—14

    14 Stems bright yellow inside; leaflets sharply cut-toothed and
       often deeply cleft SHRUB YELLOWROOT *(Xanthorhiza)* 104
    14 Stems otherwise; leaflets untoothed, narrow, silky-hairy, and
       1 inch or less long CINQUEFOILS *(Potentilla)* 136

15 Extension of the leafstalk winged between the leaflets
                            SUMACS *(Rhus)* 164
15 Extension of the leafstalks otherwise—16

    16 Leaflet margins sharply toothed—17
    16 Leaflet margins untoothed—18

17 Branchlets velvety-hairy, or smooth and whitened with a bloom,
   exuding a milky sap when cut; leaflets whitened or green and
   hairy beneath SUMACS *(Rhus)* 164
17 Branchlets and leaves otherwise; buds gummy
                      MOUNTAIN-ASH *(Sorbus)* 132

    18 Leaflets usually less than 2 inches long—19
    18 Leaflets mostly over 2 inches long—20

26

19   Flowers and small 1- or 2-seeded pods in rather long and narrow end clusters; leaflets usually with minute clear dots or densely hairy   **INDIGOBUSHES** *(Amorpha)*   **151**

19   Flowers and 2- to 3-inch flattened pods in axillary clusters; leaflets otherwise   **LOCUSTS** *(Robinia)*   **152**

    20   Leafstalks red or tinged with red; leaflets 2 to 3 times as long as broad; fruits small, whitish, in drooping axillary clusters   **POISON SUMAC** *(Rhus)*   **164**

    20   Leafstalks otherwise; leaflets 4 or more times as long as broad; fruits rather large, yellowish, in more or less erect end clusters   **SOAPBERRIES** *(Sapindus)*   **180**

KEY IV

SHRUBS MORE THAN ONE FOOT HIGH WITH OPPOSITE OR WHORLED SIMPLE LEAVES

1   Leaves awl-like, needle-like, or very narrow and less than ⅛ inch wide—2

1   Leaves with distinct blades more than ⅛ inch wide—4

    2   Leaves arranged in 3's, awl-like, stiff, and sharp at the tip   **JUNIPERS** *(Juniperus)*   **68**

    2   Leaves opposite, very narrow or sometimes almost needle-like; with clusters of smaller leaves present in the axils—3

3   Leaves almost needle-like or flattened, smooth; flowers yellow; fruit a capsule with 5 sepals at the base   **ST. JOHN'S-WORTS** *(Hypericum)*   **192**

3   Leaves club-shaped, grayish-downy; flowers pale bluish; fruit a seedlike nutlet, usually grouped in 4's and within the persistent calyx   **CONRADINA** *(Conradina)*   **256**

    4   Leaves lobed or with toothed margins—5

    4   Leaves neither lobed nor with margins conspicuously toothed—21

5   Leaves lobed or both toothed and lobed—6

5   Leaves not lobed but the margins toothed—9

    6   Main veins of the leaves arising along a midrib—7

    6   Main veins of the leaves radiating from the summit of the leafstalk—8

7   Leaves usually less than 4 inches long, downy beneath, wavy-lobed; branchlets very slender.   **SNOWBERRIES** *(Symphoricarpos)*   **267**

7   Leaves usually over 4 inches long, rather leathery, lobed like an oak leaf, densely tawny-woolly beneath   **HYDRANGEAS** *(Hydrangea)*   **115**

8 Leafstalks usually with stipules at the base or glands at the summit, or the lower leaf surfaces minutely black-dotted or densely hairy   VIBURNUMS *(Viburnum)*   268

8 Leafstalks with neither stipules or glands, the lower surface smooth or minutely downy   MAPLES *(Acer)*   179

9 Leaf margins with large and coarse teeth averaging 5 or fewer to the inch of leaf margin—10

9 Leaf margins with smaller and finer teeth—14

    10 Leaves with prominent and rather straight veins which end in the marginal teeth   VIBURNUMS *(Viburnum)*   268

    10 Leaves with branching veins which do not end in the marginal teeth—11

11 Leaf margins with a few bluntish or wavy teeth; leaves grayish green with silky hairs   SEA-OXEYE *(Borrichia)*   276

11 Leaf margins with rather sharply pointed teeth—12

    12 Leaves without evident stalks   MARSH ELDERS *(Iva)*   275

    12 Leaves with evident stalks—13

13 Leafstalks usually less than ½ inch long; marginal teeth usually widely spaced   MOCK-ORANGES *(Philadelphus)*   112

13 Leafstalks usually 2 or more inches long   HYDRANGEAS *(Hydrangea)*   116

    14 Branchlets 4-sided and green   STRAWBERRY-BUSHES *(Euonymus)*   175

    14 Branchlets otherwise—15

15 Branchlets with hairy-lined ridges running down from a line between the leaf bases; leaves hairy-fringed; fruit a capsule   BUSH-HONEYSUCKLES *(Diervilla)*   260

15 Branchlets, leaves, and fruits otherwise—16

    16 Largest leaves less than 1 inch long—17

    16 Largest leaves more than 1 inch long—18

17 Leaves with clusters of smaller leaves in the axils; plant usually less than 2 feet high and with a pleasant odor   BASILS *(Satureja)*   256

17 Leaves otherwise; plant with straggling stems and often short spiny branchlets; not aromatic; fruits berry-like   SAGERETIA *(Sageretia)*   180

    18 Leaves whitish-woolly beneath; fruits berry-like, magenta purple   BEAUTYBERRY *(Callicarpa)*   255

    18 Leaves otherwise; fruits not berry-like, with a large stone—19

19 Leaves roundish heart-shaped, 4 or more inches wide   VIBURNUMS *(Viburnum)*   268

19 Leaves smaller—20

20   Leafstalks winged or grooved on the upper side; the leaf margins toothed quite to the base
VIBURNUMS *(Viburnum)*   268

20   Leafstalks otherwise; the leaf margins finely and often inconspicuously toothed above the middle
SWAMP-PRIVETS *(Foresteria)*   252

21   Plant parasitic, growing on the branches of deciduous trees
MISTLETOE *(Phoradendron)*   100

21   Plants rooted in the soil—22

22   Leaves with the main veins curving, tending to parallel the margin and to meet at the tip   DOGWOODS *(Cornus)*   204

22   Leaves with the veins otherwise—23

23   Leaves leathery in texture—24
23   Leaves very slightly if at all leathery—26

24   Leaves usually less than ½ inch long
SANDMYRTLES *(Lyonia)*   212

24   Leaves larger—25

25   Leaves mostly less than 2 inches long, often in whorls of 3; fruits globe-shaped and long-stalked capsules   LAURELS *(Kalmia)*   223

25   Leaves 2 inches or more long, always opposite; fruit an olive-like drupe   DEVILWOOD *(Osmanthus)*   255

26   Leaves commonly with clusters of smaller leaves in the axils—27

26   Leaves otherwise—29

27   Flowers red; fruit a seedlike nutlet usually in groups of 4 and enclosed within a persistent calyx   BASILS *(Satureja)*   256

27   Flowers yellow; fruit a capsule; leaves with minute clear or black dots—28

28   Flowers 4-petalled; capsule enclosed with a pair of large heart-shaped sepals   ST. PETER'S-WORTS *(Hypericum)*   192

28   Flowers 5-petalled; capsules with 5 sepals at the base
ST. JOHN'S-WORTS *(Hypericum)*   192

29   Leaves and branchlets spicy-aromatic when bruised; fruit a large, leathery, pear-shaped pod containing large seeds
STRAWBERRY SHRUB *(Calycanthus)*   107

29   Leaves and branchlets not aromatic; fruits otherwise—30

30   Branchlets and lower leaf surfaces coated with silvery-white star-shaped hairs and rusty scales
BUFFALOBERRY *(Shepherdia)*   203

30   Branchlets and lower leaf surfaces otherwise—31

31   Leaves often arranged in 3's—32
31   Leaves always opposite—33

32   Leaves lance-shaped; fruit an urn-shaped capsule in the leaf axils; plant woody chiefly toward the base
SWAMP LOOSESTRIFE *(Decodon)*   200

32   Leaves oval, elliptic, or egg-shaped; flowers and fruits in long-stalked dense, ball-shaped heads
BUTTONBUSH *(Cephalanthus)*   259

33 Largest leaves usually more than 4 inches long—34
33 Largest leaves usually less than 4 inches long—35

34 Leaves rusty-hairy beneath; fruit a large roundish capsule
PINCKNEYA *(Pinckneya)*   259
34 Leaves at most pale downy beneath; fruit an olive-like
drupe   FRINGETREE *(Chionanthus)*   255

35 Leaves stalkless or very nearly so, broadest at the tip and tapering to the base, sometimes obscurely toothed above the middle
VIBURNUMS *(Viburnum)*   268
35 Leaves with more or less evident stalks—36

36 Leafstalks grooved above or slightly winged; buds elongate,
with one pair of rusty-scurfy scales
VIBURNUMS *(Viburnum)*   268
36 Leafstalks neither grooved nor winged; buds otherwise—37

37 Leaves broadly pointed, blunt, or rounded at the tip; fruit a
many-seeded berry—38
37 Leaves sharply pointed at the tip; fruits 1-seeded—39

38 Leaves but slightly longer than broad; berries in more or
less dense axillary or end clusters
CORALBERRY AND SNOWBERRIES *(Symphoricarpos)*   267
38 Leaves usually distinctly longer than broad; berries on long
axillary stalks, in distinct pairs or the pairs sometimes more
or less united   HONEYSUCKLES *(Lonicera)*   260

39 Leaves lance-shaped, broadly pointed or roundish at base; shrub
more than 3 feet high, with greenish branchlets
BUCKLEYA *(Buckleya)*   100
39 Leaves oval or egg-shaped, pointed at base; shrub less than 3 feet
high, with purplish-brown branchlets   NESTRONIA *(Nestronia)*   100

KEY V

ERECT SHRUBS ONE FOOT OR MORE HIGH WITH ALTERNATE SIMPLE LEAVES

1 Leaves 1 foot or more wide, fanlike and folded, and with long
leafstalks; more or less clustered on a short, trunklike stem—2
1 Leaves less than 1 foot wide, neither fanlike nor folded—4

2 Leafstalks edged with sharp sawlike teeth
SAW-PALMETTO *(Serenoa)*   68
2 Leafstalks smooth-edged—3

3 Stems armed with long needle-like spines
NEEDLE-PALM *(Rhapidophyllum)*   68
3 Stems unarmed   PALMETTOS *(Sabal)*   68

4 Leaves grasslike; or long and narrow, stiff, swordlike or
dagger-like—5
4 Leaves otherwise—6

5 Plants bamboo-like; leaves grasslike; flowers not showy; fruits grainlike   CANE *(Arundinaria)*   71
5 Plants with clusters of stiff and narrow or dagger-like leaves; flowers creamy white, large and showy; fruits capsules
                                                              YUCCAS *(Yucca)*   71

    6 Leaves very narrow, more or less stiff, less than ⅛ inch wide—7
    6 Leaves with broader blades more than ⅛ inch wide—9

7 Leaves flat, with parallel margins and pointed tips, usually over ½ inch long   YEWS *(Taxus)*   68
7 Leaves with a deep longitudinal groove on the lower side, usually less than ½ inch long, often nearly whorled—8

    8 Leaves ¼ to ½ inch long; branches stiffly erect; plant aromatic   SANDHILL ROSEMARY *(Ceratiola)*   163
    8 Leaves ¼ inch or less long; branches spreading; plant not aromatic   BROOM-CROWBERRY *(Corema)*   163

9 Leaves lobed or both toothed and lobed—10
9 Leaves not lobed, the margins either toothed or untoothed—18

    10 Leaves aromatic when crushed—11
    10 Leaves not especially aromatic when crushed—12

11 Leaves long and narrow, with deep rounded lobes on each side of the midrib   SWEETFERN *(Comptonia)*   76
11 Leaves broad, mitten-shaped or 3-lobed   SASSAFRAS *(Sassafras)*   212

    12 Leaves large, 4 inches or more wide—13
    12 Leaves smaller, less than 4 inches wide—14

13 Branches and veins on the lower surface of the leaves prickly
                                              DEVIL'S-CLUB *(Oplopanax)*   204
13 Branches and leafstalks covered with sticky-glandular and reddish hairs   RASPBERRIES *(Rubus)*   139

    14 Main veins of the leaves radiating from the summit of the Leafstalk—15
    14 Main veins of the leaves arising along a midrib—16

15 Leaves often clustered on lateral spurs; bark not freely peeling; fruit a berry   CURRANTS AND GOOSEBERRIES *(Ribes)*   116
15 Leaves not clustered on lateral spurs; bark peeling in papery layers; fruits inflated papery pods   NINEBARK *(Physocarpus)*   124

    16 Branches without spines or thorns; fruit an acorn
                                                              OAKS *(Quercus)*   96
    16 Branches spine-tipped or with slender thorns; fruits apple-like—17

17 Branches often spine-tipped or spurlike; fruits greenish, about 1 inch in diameter   CRAB APPLES *(Malus)*   132
17 Branches with slender thorns; fruits smaller, usually red or yellowish   HAWTHORNS *(Crataegus)*   132

    18 Leaf margins toothed—19
    18 Leaf margins untoothed—67

19 Leaves often paired or clustered on lateral spurlike branches—20
19 Leaves not in such pairs or clusters—22

    20 Leaves in pairs; catkins often present; fruits small nutlets borne in conelike structures   **BIRCHES** *(Betula)*   91
    20 Leaves in clusters; catkins absent; fruits berry-like—21

21 Branchlets with 3-parted spines, the interior yellow; fruits oval-shaped, pulpy berries in drooping clusters
                                        BARBERRIES *(Berberis)*   107
21 Branchlets unarmed, the interior not yellow; fruits with large, bony, seedlike nutlets   **HOLLIES** *(Ilex)*   168

    22 Leaves with minute yellow resin dots at least on the lower surface, usually aromatic when crushed
        SWEETGALE AND WAX MYRTLES *(Myrica)*   76
    22 Leaves not resin-dotted—23

23 Leaves with 3 prominent veins from near the base—24
23 Leaves with one prominent midrib from which smaller veins branch—25

    24 Leaf margins finely toothed, the leaf bases quite symmetrical   **REDROOTS** *(Ceanothus)*   183
    24 Leaf margins coarsely toothed, the bases not symmetrical   **HACKBERRIES** *(Celtis)*   99

25 Branches spine-tipped or with slender thorns—26
25 Branches not armed—28

    26 Fruits with a large stone surrounded by flesh
                              PLUMS *(Prunus)*   144
    26 Fruits apple-like—27

27 Fruits greenish, about 1 inch in diameter; branches often spine-tipped   **CRAB APPLES** *(Malus)*   132
27 Fruits usually red or yellowish; branches with slender thorns
                      HAWTHORNS *(Crataegus)*   132

    28 Leaves leathery in texture; usually evergreen—29
    28 Leaves not leathery; mostly deciduous—38

29 Leaves coarsely wavy-toothed; fruit an acorn   **OAKS** *(Quercus)*   96
29 Leaves with small or obscure teeth; fruit not an acorn—30

    30 Leaves spine-tipped or with a few bristly or spiny teeth above the middle   **HOLLIES** *(Ilex)*   175
    30 Leaves otherwise—31

31 Leaves with minute black dots on the lower surface
                      FETTERBUSHES *(Pieris)*   231
31 Leaves not black-dotted beneath—32

    32 Leaves usually broadest toward the rounded or indented tip; fruit a whitish "plum"   **DEER-PLUM** *(Chrysobalanus)*   144
    32 Leaves broadest at or below the middle, not rounded at tip—33

33 Largest leaves more than 3 inches long—34
33 Largest leaves less than 3 inches long—35

    34 Sprawling or arching shrubs; fruit a capsule
                    LEUCOTHOËS *(Leucothoë)*   227
    34 Erect shrub or small tree; fruit not a capsule but rather dry
        and 1-seeded   SWEETLEAF *(Symplocos)*   252

35 Leaves with minute rusty and silvery scales
                  LEATHERLEAF *(Chamaedaphne)*   231
35 Leaves otherwise, usually quite smooth—36

    36 Leaf margins obscurely toothed; leaves often whitened beneath; fruit a capsule   ZENOBIA *(Zenobia)*   224
    36 Leaf margins with low or bluntish teeth; leaves not whitened beneath; fruits berry-like—37

37 Colony-forming shrubs less than 1½ feet high; branchlets angled; fruit a bluish berry   HUCKLEBERRIES *(Gaylussacia)*   235
37 Taller erect shrub; branchlets not angled, rather stiff and spiky; fruits usually red, with large seedlike nutlets   HOLLIES *(Ilex)*   168

    38 Leaf margins toothed mainly above the middle—39
    38 Leaf margins toothed quite to the base—42

39 Marginal teeth rather large and coarse, irregular, or wavy—40
39 Marginal teeth rather small and sharp—41

    40 Leaves wedge-shaped at base; fruits small achenes with long silky hairs   GROUNDSEL BUSHES *(Baccharis)*   276
    40 Leaves broadly pointed to roundish at base, the base often not symmetrical; fruit a 2-beaked woody pod
                  WITCH-ALDERS *(Fothergilla)*   123

41 Branchlets and lower leaf surfaces with starry-branched hairs; tall shrubs   SNOWBELLS *(Styrax)*   251
41 Branchlets and lower leaf surfaces smooth or nearly so; low shrubs; the leaf margins often double-toothed
                  SPIRAEAS *(Spiraea)*   124

    42 Leaf margins with coarse teeth, averaging 5 or fewer to an inch—43
    42 Leaf margins more finely and sometimes double-toothed—45

43 Leaves with veins ending in sharp marginal teeth
                  CHINQUAPINS *(Castanea)*   95
43 Leaf margins with bluntish, rounded, or wavy teeth—44

    44 Leaf bases not symmetrical; fruit a woody pod
                  WITCH-HAZEL *(Hamamelis)*   123
    44 Leaf bases quite symmetrical; fruit an acorn
                  OAKS *(Quercus)*   96

45 Aquatic shrub of cypress ponds with a spindle-shaped stem branching above; leaves rather crowded, narrow, minutely toothed, and yellowish green   STILLINGIA *(Stillingia)*   160
45 Shrubs otherwise—46

34

57 Leaves broadly pointed to roundish at base, with some starry-branched hairs on the lower surface; fruits winged
SILVERBELLS (Halesia) 251
57 Leaves wedge-shaped at base, smooth or nearly so; fruits oblong, 2-grooved capsules about ¼ inch long
VIRGINIA WILLOW (Itea) 115

58 Largest leaves 3 or more inches long—59
58 Largest leaves usually less than 3 inches long—61

59 Branchlets and lower leaf surfaces with small starry-branched hairs
PEPPERBUSHES (Clethra) 208
59 Branchlets and lower leaf surfaces with simple hairs, if any—60

60 Leaf margins hairy-fringed as well as toothed; fruit a capsule
STEWARTIAS (Stewartia) 192
60 Leaf margins toothed but not hairy-fringed; fruits berry-like
BUCKTHORNS (Rhamnus) 183

61 Leafstalks slender, usually ¼ inch or more long—62
61 Leafstalks moderate or stout, less than ¼ inch long—63

62 Fruits juicy, with about 10 small seeds; buds narrow, several times as long as wide
SERVICEBERRIES (Amelanchier) 128
62 Fruits rather dry, with large seedlike nutlets; buds short, not much longer than wide HOLLIES <i>(Ilex)</i> 168

63 Branchlets minutely warty-dotted, green or reddish, smooth or hairy BLUEBERRIES <i>(Vaccinium)</i> 239
63 Branchlets not warty-dotted—64

64 Largest leaves less than 2 inches long
BILBERRIES (Vaccinium) 239
64 Largest leaves usually 2 or more inches long—65

65 Leaf margins with small and rather obscure teeth; fruit a small roundish capsule MALEBERRY <i>(Lyonia)</i> 228
65 Leaf margins with sharp and quite conspicuous teeth—66

66 Leaves broadest near the often roundish base; fruit a juicy berry
SOUTHERN MOUNTAIN-CRANBERRY (Vaccinium) 244
66 Leaves broadest near or above the middle, pointed at base; fruits berry-like but with large seedlike nutlets
HOLLIES (Ilex) 168

67 Shrubs with thorns on the branchlets and with a milky sap
BUMELIAS (Bumelia) 248
67 Shrubs not thorny—68

68 Leaves or branchlets aromatic when bruised—69
68 Leaves and branchlets odorless or nearly so, or with an unpleasant odor—75

69 Sap gummy; leaves broadest above the middle and often indented at tip SMOKETREE <i>(Cotinus)</i> 163
69 Sap not gummy; leaves usually with pointed tips—70

70 Leaves with small yellowish resin dots, at least on the lower surface WAX MYRTLES <i>(Myrica)</i> 79
70 Leaves not resin dotted—71

71 Leaves more or less leathery—72
71 Leaves not leathery—74

72 Leaves less than 2 inches long; branchlets very slender; spicy-aromatic PONDSPICE *(Litsea)* 112
72 Leaves more than 2 inches long; branchlets moderate—73

73 Leaves whitened beneath; spicy-aromatic
MAGNOLIAS *(Magnolia)* 107
73 Leaves not whitened beneath; odor anise-like
PURPLE-ANISE *(Ilicium)* 108

74 Branchlets slender; leaves sharply pointed at tip; fruits red
SPICEBUSHES *(Lindera)* 111
74 Branchlets moderate; leaves broadly pointed or blunt at tip, some usually mitten-shaped or 3-lobed; fruits dark blue
SASSAFRAS *(Sassafras)* 112

75 Leaves heart-shaped; leafstalks swollen at summit; fruit a flattened pealike pod REDBUD *(Cercis)* 151
75 Leaves not heart-shaped and leafstalks not swollen at summit; fruits not pealike pods—76

76 Young branchlets and lower leaf surfaces densely coated with minute silvery scales ALABAMA CROTON *(Croton)* 160
76 Young branchlets and leaves otherwise—77

77 Leaves usually with clusters of smaller leaves in the axils—78
77 Leaves without axillary clusters of smaller leaves—79

78 Largest leaves scarcely ¼ inch long; fruits 3-lobed, 3-seeded capsules REDROOTS *(Ceanothus)* 183
78 Largest leaves often 1½ inches long, broadest near the blunt or rounded summit; fruit a berry
MATRIMONY-VINES *(Lycium)* 248

79 Largest leaves less than 1 inch long—80
79 Largest leaves usually more than 1 inch long—81

80 Leaves less than ½ inch long, stalkless or nearly so, rather crowded; both leaves and branchlets with bristly hairs; fruit a capsule LAURELS *(Kalmia)* 223
80 Largest leaves over ½ inch long, short-stalked, often downy beneath; branchlets minutely warty-dotted; fruit a berry
BLUEBERRIES *(Vaccinium)* 239

81 Leaves more or less leathery—82
81 Leaves not leathery—101

82 Branchlets ill-scented if broken; buds hairy and without visible scales; fruit a large pulpy berry with big seeds
PAWPAWS *(Asimina)* 108
82 Branchlets nearly or quite odorless if broken—83

83 Leaves densely rusty-woolly beneath, the margin strongly rolled inward on the lower side LABRADOR-TEA *(Ledum)* 212
83 Leaves not rusty-woolly beneath—84

84 Leaves densely coated with rust-colored scales or brown dots on the lower surface—85
84 Leaves otherwise—87

85 Leaves 2 to 4 inches long; branchlets with large end buds
                RHODODENDRONS *(Rhododendron)*   215
85 Leaves smaller; branchlets not with large end buds—86

    86 Leaves with minute silvery scales on the upper surface;
        flowers and fruits in the axils of leaflike bracts toward the
        ends of the branchlets   LEATHERLEAF *(Chamaedaphne)*   231
    86 Leaves smooth above; flowers and fruits in clusters on
        growth of the previous year   LYONIAS *(Lyonia)*   228

87 Branchlets 3-sided; leaves with a conspicuous vein paralleling the
    leaf margin, glandular-dotted beneath; shrub with spreading and
    arching branches   FETTERBUSHES *(Lyonia)*   228
87 Branchlets and leaves otherwise—88

    88 Leaves either spine-tipped or minutely black-dotted beneath;
        fruits berry-like but with large bony nutlets
                        HOLLIES *(Ilex)*   168
    88 Leaves neither spine-tipped nor black-dotted beneath—89

89 Leaves very white on the lower surface, the leaf margins strongly
    rolled inward on the lower side BOG ROSEMARY *(Andromeda)*   224
89 Leaves slightly if at all whitened on the lower surface, and leaf
    margins slightly if at all rolled inward on the lower side—90

    90 Leaves usually less than 3 inches long—91
    90 Leaves usually 3 or more inches long—97

91 Leaf blades more than 4 times as long as broad, tipped with a
    small bristle; fruit an acorn   OAKS *(Quercus)*   99
91 Leaves usually less than 4 times as long as broad; fruits other-
    wise—92

    92 Branchlets with large end buds; leaves often whitened and
        with small rusty hairs beneath AZALEAS *(Rhododendron)*   215
    92 Branchlets without large end buds—93

93 Leaves sharply pointed at tip and more or less twisted, standing
    rather upright along hairy branchlets   TAR-FLOWER *(Befaria)*   211
93 Leaves otherwise—94

    94 Branchlets minutely warty-dotted or hairy; fruit a berry
                    BLUEBERRIES *(Vaccinium)*   239
    94 Branchlets neither warty-dotted nor hairy; fruit a cap-
        sule—95

95 Leaves broadest about the middle and broadly pointed at both
    ends, often whitened beneath   ZENOBIA *(Zenobia)*   224
95 Leaves wedge-shaped at base, broadly or bluntly pointed at tip—
    96

    96 Shrub less than 3 feet high; leaves deciduous; capsules
        globe-shaped and long-stalked   LAURELS *(Kalmia)*   223
    96 Shrub taller or small tree; leaves evergreen; capsules 2- to
        4-winged, arranged in narrow clusters
                    BUCKWHEAT-TREE *(Cliftonia)*   168

97 Leaves more or less clustered near the ends of the branchlets—98
97 Leaves all well spaced along the branchlets—100

98 Branchlets with large end buds; fruit an oblong capsule ½ inch or more long
RHODODENDRONS *(Rhododendron)*   212

98 Branchlets without large end buds; capsules smaller, globe-shaped or egg-shaped—99

99 Leaves usually broadest near the middle and pointed at both ends; capsules globe-shaped and long-stalked
LAURELS *(Kalmia)*   223

99 Leaves usually broadest toward the blunt or rounded tip, wedge-shaped at base; capsules small, egg-shaped, in long and narrow clusters   SWAMP CYRILLA *(Cyrilla)*   167

100 Leaves broadest toward the roundish or indented tip, very veiny and lustrous above; fruit a whitish "plum"
DEER-PLUM *(Chrysobalanus)*   144

100 Leaves broadest about the middle, pointed at both ends, not lustrous or especially veiny above; fruit brownish, dry, 1-seeded   SWEETLEAF *(Symplocos)*   252

101 Leaves 6 to 12 inches long, broadest toward the tip and tapering to the base; buds hairy and without visible scales; branchlets ill-scented when broken; fruit a large pulpy berry with big seeds
PAWPAWS *(Asimina)*   108

101 Leaves usually less than 6 inches long—102

102 Leaves more or less clustered toward the tips of the branch-lets—103

102 Leaves all well spaced along the branchlets, or clustered on spurs—105

103 Leaves mostly oval-shaped, the main veins curving and tending to parallel the margin and meet at the tip
DOGWOODS *(Cornus)*   204

103 Leaves with veins otherwise, the margins usually hairy fringed; branchlets with large end buds—104

104 Leaves rough-hairy above, usually with chaffy scales on the veins beneath; branchlets rusty-hairy; fruit an egg-shaped capsule less than ¼ inch long   MENZIESIA *(Menziesia)*   220

104 Leaves usually smooth above, smooth or downy and with some stiff hairs along the midrib beneath; branchlets smooth, downy, or with scattered bristly hairs; fruits oblong capsules ⅜ inch or more long AZALEAS *(Rhododendron)*   215

105 Branchlets and lower leaf surfaces with starry-branched hairs; fruits pea-sized, dry, 1-seeded, grayish-downy
SNOWBELLS *(Styrax)*   251

105 Branchlets and lower leaf surfaces smooth or with simple un-branched hairs—106

106 Largest leaves more than 4 inches long—107

106 Largest leaves less than 4 inches long—109

107 Branchlets with large catkin-like flower buds toward the tip; fruits dry, wrinkled, 1-seeded   CORKWOOD *(Leitneria)*   76

107 Branchlets not with catkin-like flower buds—108

WINTER KEY TO LEAF-LOSING SHRUBS

1 Leaf scars and buds opposite or whorled—2
1 Leaf scars and buds alternate—39

    2 Climbing or twining vines—3
    2 Stems otherwise—8

3 Climbing by means of rootlets along the stems—4
3 Not with rootlets along the stems—5

    4 Leaf scars half-round, with a solitary C-shaped bundle scar
        TRUMPET CREEPER *(Campsis)*   **259**
    4 Leaf scars horseshoe-shaped, with 3 bundle scars
        CLIMBING-HYDRANGEA *(Decumaria)*   **115**

5 Climbing by means of tendrils—6
5 Scrambling or with twining stems—7

    6 Stems soft-woody, with longitudinal ridges; leaf scars hidden by persisting bases of the leafstalks
        VIRGIN'S-BOWERS *(Clematis)*   **103**
    6 Stems and leaf scars otherwise; the leaf scars with a solitary bundle scar   CROSSVINE *(Bignonia)*   **259**

7 Stems hollow inside between the nodes
        HONEYSUCKLES *(Lonicera)*   **263**
7 Stems with pith inside between the nodes
        TRACHELOSPERMUM *(Trachelospermum)*   **256**

    8 Stems prostrate or trailing—9
    8 Stems more or less erect—10

9 Twigs 2-edged or 2-winged   ST. PETER'S-WORTS *(Hypericum)*   **192**
9 Twigs more or less 4-sided or square
        STRAWBERRY-BUSHES *(Euonymus)*   **175**

    10 Buds naked, or without visible scales—11
    10 Buds with visible scales, or the buds not evident—13

11 Leaf scars with a solitary bundle scar; twigs roughish
        BEAUTYBERRY *(Callicarpa)*   **255**
11 Leaf scars with 3 or more bundle scars—12

    12 Leaf scars with 3 bundle scars   VIBURNUMS *(Viburnum)*   **268**
    12 Leaf scars with 5 or 7 bundle scars
        HYDRANGEAS *(Hydrangea)*   **115**

13 Twigs often spiny-tipped   SAGERETIA *(Sageretia)*   **180**
13 Twigs never spiny-tipped—14

    14 Twigs spicy-aromatic when broken
        STRAWBERRY-SHRUBS *(Calycanthus)*   **107**
    14 Twigs not aromatic—15

15 Twigs with a true end or terminal bud—16
15 Twigs without a true end or terminal bud—25

    16 Leaf scars with a solitary bundle scar—17
    16 Leaf scars with 3 or more bundle scars—20

17 Twigs rather stout, reddish brown and usually hairy; end bud much larger than the lateral ones PINCKNEYA *(Pinckneya)* 259

17 Twigs moderate or slender; end bud little if any larger than lateral ones—18

 18 Twigs 4-lined or 4-sided, usually green STRAWBERRY-BUSHES *(Euonymus)* 175

 18 Twigs otherwise—19

19 Twigs more or less coated with small rusty scales; buds stalked and with 2 visible scales BUFFALOBERRY *(Shepherdia)* 203

19 Twigs smooth except for conspicuous lenticels; buds with about 6 visible scales FRINGETREE *(Chionanthus)* 255

 20 Leaf scars large, shield-shaped or triangular, usually with 5 or more bundle scars but sometimes in 3 groups BUCKEYES *(Aesculus)* 179

 20 Leaf scars small or narrow, always with 3 bundle scars—21

21 Buds with 4 or more visible scales—22

21 Buds with only 2 visible scales—23

 22 Buds with but 2 pairs of visible scales VIBURNUMS *(Viburnum)* 268

 22 Buds with more than 2 pairs of visible scales MAPLES *(Acer)* 179

23 End bud flanked by a pair of persistent leafstalk bases DOGWOODS *(Cornus)* 204

23 End bud otherwise—24

 24 Tips of the opposing leaf scars meeting in a point MAPLES *(Acer)* 179

 24 Tips of the opposing leaf scars not meeting but sometimes connected with a transverse line VIBURNUMS *(Viburnum)* 268

25 Leaf scars indistinct, raised or covered by the persistent bases of the leafstalks—26

25 Leaf scars rather distinct, sometimes slightly raised—27

 26 Twigs very fine and usually downy; buds about 1/16 inch long; red berries often persisting CORALBERRY *(Symphoricarpos)* 269

 26 Twigs slender, smooth or nearly so; buds about ⅛ inch long HONEYSUCKLES *(Lonicera)* 263

27 Leaf scars with a solitary bundle scar—28

27 Leaf scars with 3 or more bundle scars—33

 28 Leaf scars often 3 at a node; buds buried in the bark and not visible BUTTONBUSH *(Cephalanthus)* 259

 28 Leaf scars always opposite; buds evident—29

29 Twigs prominently 2-angled or 2-winged below the leaf scars—30

29 Twigs otherwise—31

 30 Twigs 2-winged below the leaf scars ST. PETER'S-WORTS *(Hypericum)* 192

 30 Twigs 2-edged below the leaf scars ST. JOHN'S-WORTS *(Hypericum)* 192

45 Pith becoming somewhat chambered AMPELOPSIS *(Ampelopsis)*   184
45 Pith continuous; tendrils often ending in adhesive disks
                              CREEPERS *(Parthenocissus)*   187

    46 Stems aromatic when bruised or broken
                              SCHISANDRA *(Schisandra)*   108
    46 Not aromatic—47

47 Buds small, superposed on a silky area within the U-shaped leaf
scars   PIPEVINES *(Aristolochia)*   100
47 Buds and leaf scars otherwise—48

    48 Leaf scars very narrow and but slightly curved; stems
    usually with scattered prickles   ROSES *(Rosa)*   143
    48 Leaf scars otherwise; stems never with prickles—49

49 Leaf scars flanked with prominent knobs; buds silky-hairy
                              WISTERIAS *(Wisteria)*   156
49 Leaf scars and buds otherwise—50

    50 Buds small or sunken in depressions above the leaf scars—
    51
    50 Buds of moderate size and never sunken—53

51 Twigs downy; fruits red
                              RED-BERRIED MOONSEED *(Cocculus)*   104
51 Twigs smooth or nearly so; fruits blue or black—52

    52 Stems slender; fruits blue
                              COMMON MOONSEED *(Menispermum)*   104
    52 Stems moderate or rather stout; fruits black
                              CUPSEED *(Calycocarpum)*   104

53 Buds oblong and appressed; leaf scars raised
                              SUPPLEJACK *(Berchemia)*   180
53 Buds roundish and pointed outward; leaf scars not raised
                              AMERICAN BITTERSWEET *(Celastrus)*   176

    54 Stems prostrate or creeping—55
    54 Stems more or less erect—60

55 Buds small, often more than one above a leaf scar; twigs lustrous
reddish brown   CHERRIES *(Prunus)*   144
55 Buds moderate, always solitary; twigs otherwise—56

    56 Leaf scars covered by persistent leafstalk bases; stems
    prickly or bristly   BLACKBERRIES *(Rubus)*   139
    56 Leaf scars and stems otherwise—57

57 Buds densely hairy and without visible scales; leaf scars with 5
or more bundle scars   POISON-IVY *(Rhus)*   167
57 Buds with 1 or more visible scales; leaf scars with 3 bundle
scars—58

    58 Buds covered with a solitary hoodlike scale
                              WILLOWS *(Salix)*   80
    58 Buds with 2 or more visible scales—59

59 Buds usually with 3 visible scales; twigs glandular-warty or densely downy, with a very small green pith BIRCHES *(Betula)*   91
59 Buds with about 6 visible scales; twigs with a large pale pith and sometimes with a skunklike odor when broken
                         CURRANTS *(Ribes)*   116

    60 Plant with a solitary spindle-shaped stem and more or less erect branches above   STILLINGIA *(Stillingia)*   160
    60 Plants usually with several stems growing in a clump from the base, or with wide-spreading branches—61

61 Stems or twigs spine-tipped or with thorns, prickles, or prickly bristles—62
61 Stems or twigs never armed—75

    62 Leaf scars indistinct or hidden by persistent leafstalk bases—63
    62 Leaf scars quite distinct—64

63 Stems unbranched, usually arching, bristly or with broad-based prickles   RASPBERRIES AND BLACKBERRIES *(Rubus)*   139
63 Stems branched, yellow inside, with 3-branched spines at the nodes   BARBERRIES *(Berberis)*   107

    64 Branches often with sharp spinelike tips—65
    64 Branches otherwise—66

65 Leaf scars nearly half-round; twigs usually with a bitter almond-like taste   PLUMS *(Prunus)*   144
65 Leaf scars narrowly crescent-shaped; twigs otherwise
                    CRAB APPLES *(Malus)*   132

    66 Buds not evident, buried in the bark above the leaf scars; twigs bristly or with pairs of spines at the nodes
                    LOCUSTS *(Robinia)*   152
    66 Buds more or less evident above the leaf scars—67

67 Stems woody chiefly toward the base, very bristly; twigs nearly encircled by narrow leaf scars
            BRISTLY-SARSAPARILLA *(Aralia)*   203
67 Stems more or less woody throughout—68

    68 Twigs exuding a milky sap when cut
                  BUMELIAS *(Bumelia)*   248
    68 Twigs otherwise—69

69 Twigs very stout, ½ inch or more in diameter—70
69 Twigs more moderate or slender—71

    70 Twigs with broad-based stout prickles; fruits black
              HERCULES'-CLUB *(Aralia)*   203
    70 Twigs with slender prickles; fruits red
             DEVIL'S-CLUB *(Oplopanax)*   204

71 Twigs 5-angled, pale, slender; leaf scars with a solitary bundle scar   MATRIMONY-VINES *(Lycium)*   248
71 Twigs and leaf scars otherwise—72

44

72 Twigs with a lemon- or limelike odor when bruised or broken; buds hairy and without visible scales
PRICKLY-ASHES *(Xanthoxylum)* 159

72 Twigs not aromatic; buds with visible scales—73

73 Buds with rather fleshy red scales; twigs with sharp thorns ½ inch or more long HAWTHORNS *(Crataegus)* 132

73 Buds otherwise; twigs bristly or with shorter thorns or prickles—74

74 Leaf scars narrow and but slightly curved; twigs round
ROSES *(Rosa)* 143

74 Leaf scars crescent-shaped to U-shaped; twigs with lines or ridges running down below each leaf scar
CURRANTS AND GOOSEBERRIES *(Ribes)* 116

75 Leaf scars hidden by persistent leafstalk bases—76
75 Leaf scars otherwise—77

76 Bases of the leafstalks and the persistent stipules forming a sheath about the twig CINQUEFOILS *(Potentilla)* 136

76 Bases of the leafstalks otherwise RASPBERRIES *(Rubus)* 139

77 Leaf scars with a solitary bundle scar—78
77 Leaf scars with 3 or more bundle scars—103

78 Twigs with a spicy-aromatic odor when bruised or broken—79

78 Twigs not spicy-aromatic—80

79 Twigs very slender; terminal bud little if any larger than the lateral ones and often flanked by long-stalked flower buds
PONDSPICE *(Litsea)* 112

79 Twigs moderate; terminal bud much larger than the lateral ones
SASSAFRAS *(Sassafras)* 112

80 Twigs ending in a true end or terminal bud—81
80 Twigs without a true end bud, the tip dying back to a lateral bud—88

81 End bud usually much larger than the others, lateral buds solitary—82

81 End bud little if any larger than the others, lateral buds sometimes superposed—84

82 Outer bud scales about as long as the bud but falling off early, the inner scales downy or silky-hairy
PEPPERBUSHES *(Clethra)* 208

82 Outer bud scales much shorter than the bud, the scales all persisting—83

83 Bark soon shredding; fruit a capsule splitting into 4 parts
MENZIESIA *(Menziesia)* 220

83 Bark not soon shredding; fruit a capsule splitting into 5 parts
AZALEAS *(Rhododendron)* 215

84 Twigs showing interruptions in the pith when cut lengthwise—85

84 Twigs showing a continuous pith when cut lengthwise—86

97 Buds minute; fruits long-stalked capsules in end clusters
                                    LAURELS *(Kalmia)*   223
97 Buds 1/16 to ⅛ inch long—98

    98 Buds about ⅛ inch long, pointed at tip; fruits small globe-
        shaped capsules in branched clusters
                                    MALEBERRY *(Lyonia)*   228
    98 Buds usually smaller, blunt at tip; fruits not persisting
        SOUTHERN MOUNTAIN-CRANBERRY *(Vaccinium)*   244

99 Leaf scars distinctly raised—100
99 Leaf scars but slightly if at all raised—101

    100 Leaf scars with minute narrow stipule scars at each side;
         silvery-lined, cup-shaped fruit bases often persisting
                                    REDROOTS *(Ceanothus)*   183
    100 Leaf scars without such stipule scars; fruits small pods in
         groups of 3 to 5, in flat-topped or cone-shaped end clusters
                                    SPIRAEAS *(Spiraea)*   124

101 Leaf scars half-round; twigs purplish red, usually downy or
     whitened with a bloom   DEERBERRY *(Vaccinium)*   239
101 Leaf scars shield shaped or triangular; twigs smooth—102

    102 Buds roundish or egg-shaped; twigs often with minute black
         dots; fruit an urn-shaped capsule
                                    STAGGERBUSH*(Lyonia)*   228
    102 Buds cone-shaped; twigs sometimes whitened with a bloom;
         fruit a globe-shaped capsule   ZENOBIA *(Zenobia)* 224

103 Leaf scars with 3 bundle scars—104
103 Leaf scars with 5 or more bundle scars—136

    104 Twigs usually with catkins or catkin-like flower buds—105
    104 Twigs never with catkins or catkin-like flower buds—110

105 Twigs rather stout, about ¼ inch in diameter; large many-scaled
     flower buds present toward the tips of the twigs
                                    CORKWOOD *(Leitneria)*   76
105 Twigs much more slender—106

    106 Twigs spicy-aromatic when broken—107
    106 Twigs not spicy-aromatic—108

107 Twigs smooth; buds pointed   SWEETGALE *(Myrica)*   76
107 Twigs hairy; buds roundish   SWEETFERN *(Comptonia)*   76

    108 Catkins of 2 sizes, the smaller ones pistil-bearing; conelike
         fruiting bodies of the previous year often present
                                    ALDERS *(Alnus)*   92
    108 Catkins all more or less alike—109

109 Buds with 2 or 3 visible scales; twigs densely downy or glandu-
     lar-warty, some of them short and spurlike
                                    BIRCHES *(Betula)*   91
109 Buds with 4 or more visible scales, the flower-bearing ones
     usually larger; twigs more or less bristly-hairy
                                    HAZELNUTS *(Corylus)*   95

    110 Buds naked or without evident scales, rather hairy—111
    110 Buds with one or more visible scales—114

47

49

50

HOW PLANTS
ARE NAMED

Our modern method of naming plants was devised by the Swedish botanist Linnaeus in 1753. The first part of the scientific name is that of the genus to which a plant belongs, and it is always written with a capital letter. The second part is the name of the particular species, and it is customary to write this in lower case, even though it may be a geographical name or name of a person. Sometimes varieties, forms, or subspecies are recognized, and these names follow the species name. In this book only some of the more outstanding or distinct varieties or forms are recognized. Following the name of the plant it is customary to give the name of the author, or person who described the plant. In most cases these names are abbreviated.

The genus *Hydrangea* was first described by Linnaeus, as was the common Wild Hydrangea of eastern North America. Its name is therefore written *Hydrangea arborescens L.,* which indicates that the species was named by Linnaeus. Another hydrangea from the southeastern mountain region was originally named *Hydrangea radiata* by Thomas Walter, but modern botanists consider it to be but a subspecies of *Hydrangea arborescens;* and it is written *Hydrangea arborescens* ssp. *radiata* (Walt.) McClintock.

Scientific names are derived from various sources. Sometimes the generic names are simply the ancient Greek or Latin names for groups of plants: *Rosa* for the roses, *Vitis* for grapes, *Prunus* for the plums and cherries, etc. In quite a few cases the names signify some characteristic of the plant: *Xanthorhiza,* for example, means "yellow root." Again, the name may honor some person, as *Lyonia* for John Lyon; or some character from mythology, such as *Andromeda.* Specific names, too, often tell us of some distinctive characteristic: *acerifolium* means "with leaves like a maple," *macrocarpon* means "large-fruited," and *pubescens* tells us that perhaps the leaves, at least, are downy.

In the belief that many of you who will use this book will be interested in knowing the meanings of the scientific names, the following lists of generic and specific names have been included.

51

Acer—Latin name of the maples, from the Celtic, meaning hard.

Aesculus—Ancient Latin name of an oak or other mast-bearing tree.

Alnus—Ancient Latin name of the alders.

Amelanchier—French name of a related plant.

Amorpha—From a Greek word meaning deformed, alluding to the absence of four of the petals.

Ampelopsis—From two Greek words meaning grape and likeness.

Andromeda—Named for Andromeda, beautiful Ethiopian princess in Greek mythology.

Aralia—From the French-Canadian name *araile*.

Arctostaphylos—From two Greek words meaning a bear and a bunch of grapes.

Aristolochia—From two Greek words meaning best and delivery, in allusion to the supposed value in aiding childbirth.

Arundinaria—From the Latin word for a reed or cane.

Asimina—From the American Indian name *assimin*.

Baccharis—Name of some shrub apparently dedicated long ago to the wine god Bacchus and transferred to this genus by Linnaeus.

Befaria—Apparently named for José Bejar, professor of botany at Cadiz, Spain; but mispelled Befar by Linnaeus.

Berberis—Name latinized from the Arabic name for the fruits.

Berchemia—Named for Berthout van Berchem, an 18th-century Dutch botanist.

Bignonia—Named for Abbé Jean-Paul Bignon, once court librarian at Paris.

Borrichia—Named for Ole Borrich, 15th-century Danish botanist.

Brunnichia—Named for M. T. Brünnich, 18th-century Norwegian naturalist.

Buckleya—Named for Samuel B. Buckley, 19th-century American botanist.

Bumelia—Ancient Greek name of the ash.

Callicarpa—From two Greek words meaning beauty and fruit.

Calycanthus—From two Greek words meaning a calyx, or cup, and flower.

Calycocarpum—From two Greek words meaning a cup and fruit.

Campsis—From the Greek meaning curvature, alluding to the curved stamens.

Cassiope—Named for Cassiope, wife of Cepheus and mother of Andromeda.

Castanea—Ancient Latin name from the Greek *castana,* a chestnut.

Ceanothus—An obscure name used by Theophrastus.

Celastrus—Ancient Greek name for some evergreen tree.

Celtis—Classical Latin name of a species of lotus.

Cephalanthus—From two Greek words meaning a head and a flower.

Ceratiola—From the Greek word meaning a horn.

Chamaedaphne—From two Greek words meaning on the ground and laurel.

Chimaphila—From two Greek words meaning winter and to love.

Chrysobalanus—From two Greek words meaning golden and acorn, apparently in allusion to the yellow fruits of some species.

Clematis—Name used by Dioscorides for a climbing plant with long, lithe branches.

Clethra—Ancient Greek name of the alder.

Cliftonia—Named for Francis Clifton, an early English physician.

Cocculus—An old name meaning a small berry.

Comptonia—Named for Henry Compton, Bishop of London and patron of botany.

Conradina—Named for Solomon W. Conrad, early Philadelphia botanist.

Corema—From the Greek meaning a broom.

Cornus—From the Latin meaning a horn, alluding to the hard wood of some species.

Corylus—From the Greek meaning a helmet, alluding to the leafy involucres surrounding the fruits.

Cotinus—Ancient Greek name for the wild olive.

Crataegus—From the Greek meaning strength.

Croton—From the Greek meaning a tick, from the similarity of the seed to a tick.

Cyrilla—Named for Domenico Cirillo, 18th-century professor of medicine at Naples.

Decodon—From two Greek words meaning ten and tooth, referring to the calyx.

Decumaria—From the Latin meaning ten, alluding to the number of flower parts.

Diervilla—Named for Dr. N. Dierville, an early French traveler.

Dirca—Named for Dirce, wife of Lycus, in Greek mythology.

Elliottia—Named for Stephen Elliott, early South Carolina botanist.

Empetrum—From two Greek words meaning upon and a rock.

Epigaea—From two Greek words meaning upon and the earth.

Euonymus—From two Greek words meaning good name.

Forestiera—Named for Charles LeForestier, French physician and naturalist of Saint-Quentin.

Fothergilla—Named for Dr. John Fothergill, 18th-century physician and botanist of London.

Gaultheria—Named for Jean-Francois Gaulthier, early French physician and naturalist.

Gaylussacia—Named for Louis Joseph Gay-Lussac, early French chemist.

Gelsemium—From the Italian name of the true jasmine.

Halesia—Named for Stephen Hale, author of *Vegetable Staticks*.

Hamamelis—An ancient Greek name, probably of some plant producing flowers and fruits at the same time.

Hudsonia—Named for William Hudson, 18th-century English botanist.

Hydrangea—From two Greek words meaning water and vessel, alluding to the urn-shaped fruits.

Hypericum—Ancient Greek name of obscure meaning.

Ilex—Ancient Latin name of the Holly Oak.

Ilicium—From the Latin meaning allurement, alluding to the aromatic odor.

Itea—Greek name of the willow.

Iva—Old name of a medicinal plant.

Juniperus—Classical Latin name of the junipers.

Kalmia—Named for Peter Kalm, early Swedish botanist.

Ledum—From the Greek *ledon,* a plant yielding an aromatic resin.

Leiophyllum—From two Greek words meaning smooth and leaf.

Leitneria—Named for E. F. Leitner, German botanist killed in Florida during the Seminole War.

Leucothoë—Named for Leucothoë, daughter of Orchamus, King of Babylon.

Lindera—Named for Johann Linder, early Swedish botanist.

Litsea—A name of Chinese origin.

Loiseleuria—Named for Jean Auguste Loiseleur-Delongchamps, early French physician and botanist.

Lonicera—Named for Adam Lonitzer, early German herbalist.

Lycium—Ancient Greek name of a prickly shrub growing in Lycia.

Lyonia—Named for John Lyon, early American botanist and explorer.

Magnolia—Named for Pierre Magnol, early professor of botany at Montpellier.

Menispermum—From two Greek words meaning moon and seed.

Menziesia—Named for Archibald Menzies, early English surgeon and naturalist.

Mitchella—Named for Dr. John Mitchell, early American botanist.

Myrica—Latin name for the tamarisk, transferred to this genus by Linnaeus.

Nemopanthus—From the Greek, meaning a flower with a threadlike stalk.

Nestronia—Said to be derived from a Greek word for Daphne.

Neviusia—Named for the Rev. R. D. Nevius of Alabama, who discovered the shrub.

Oplopanax—From two Greek words meaning a weapon and all-healing.
Opuntia—Ancient Greek name of a plant growing near Opous in Boeotia.
Osmanthus—From two Greek words meaning odor and flower.

Pachystima—From two Greek words meaning thick and stigma.
Parthenocissus—From two Greek words meaning virgin and ivy.
Philadelphus—Named for King Ptolemy Philadelphus, King of Egypt in the 3rd century B.C.
Phoradendron—From two Greek words meaning a thief and tree, aluding to its parasitic habit.
Phyllodoce—Name of a sea-nymph mentioned by Virgil.
Physocarpus—From two Greek words meaning bellows and fruit, alluding to the inflated pods.
Pieris—Named for Pieris, a muse in Greek mythology.
Pinckneya—Named for Charles Coatesworth Pinckney, early South Carolina statesman, Revolutionary War general, and botanist.
Potentilla—From the Latin meaning powerful, alluding to supposed medicinal virtues.
Prunus—Ancient Latin name of the plum tree.
Ptelea—Ancient Greek name for the elm.
Pyrularia—A diminutive of *Pyrus,* a pear, alluding to the shape of the fruits.

Quercus—Classical Latin name of the oak tree.

Rhamnus—Ancient Greek name of the buckthorns.
Rhapidophyllum—From two Greek words meaning a needle and leaf.
Rhododendron—From two Greek words meaning rose and tree.
Rhus—From ancient Greek and Latin names for the sumacs.
Ribes—Ancient name of uncertain derivation but probably Arabic.
Robinia—Named for Jean Robin and his son Vespasian Robin, who first cultivated the locust tree in Europe.
Rosa—Ancient Latin name for a rose.
Rubus—Roman name for a bramble and meaning red.

Sabal—Name possibly of American Indian origin.
Sageretia—Named for Auguste Sageret, early French botanist.
Salix—Classical Latin name of the willows.
Sambucus—Ancient Latin name of the elders.
Sapindus—From two Latin words meaning soap and Indian.
Satureja—Ancient Latin name for savory.
Schisandra—From two Greek words meaning to cleave and anther.
Sebastiania—Possibly named for Don Sebastian, King of Portugal, 1554-1578.
Serenoa—Named for Sereno Watson, 19th-century American botanist.
Shepherdia—Named for John Shepherd, early English botanist.
Smilax—Ancient Greek name of an evergreen oak.

Spiraea—From the Greek *spira,* meaning a wreath.

Staphylea—From the Greek meaning a bunch of grapes.

Stewartia—Named for John Stuart, third Earl of Bute and patron of botany.

Stillingia—Named for Dr. Benjamin Stillingfleet, 18th-century English naturalist.

Styrax—Ancient Greek name of the tree producing storax.

Symphoricarpos—From two Greek words meaning to bear together and fruit.

Symplocos—From a Greek word meaning connected, alluding to the union of the stamens.

Taxus—Classical Greek name for the yew tree.

Trachelospermum—From two Greek words meaning a neck and seed.

Vaccinium—Classical Latin name of the Old World species called cowberry, alluding to the fondness of cattle for the fruit.

Viburnum—Classical Latin name of these plants.

Vitis—Classical Latin name of the grapes.

Wisteria—Named for Caspar Wister, distinguished Philadelphia anatomist who died in 1818.

Xanthorhiza—From two Greek words meaning yellow and root.

Yucca—A name of Haitian origin.

Zanthoxylum—From two Greek words meaning yellow and wood.

Zenobia—Named for Zenobia, a queen of Palmyra.

SPECIFIC NAMES

acerifolium—with maple-like leaves.

acicularis—with needle-like prickles.

acuminata—with a narrowly pointed tip.

aestivalis—flowering in summer.

alabamense
albamensis }—of Alabama.

alba—white.

albovestita—coated with white hairs.

alleghaniensis
allegheniensis }—of the Allegheny Mountains.

alnifolia
alnifolium }—with alder-like leaves.

aloifolia—with aloe-like leaves.

alpina
alpinum }—Alpine.

alternifolia—with alternate leaves.

altissima—very high.

ambigua—doubtful.

amelanchier—with leaves like a shadbush.

americana
americanum }—of America.
americanus

amomum—Latin name of some shrub.

amygdaloides—like the peach.

angustifolia }—with narrow leaves.
angustifolium

aquatica—aquatic, growing in water.

arborea
arborescens }—Treelike.
arboreum

arbutifolia—with leaves like arbutus.

argentifolia—with silvery leaves.

argutus—with sharp-toothed leaves.

argyrocarpa—with silvery fruits.

aromatica—with a fragrant or spicy odor.

ashei—named for William W. Ashe, American forester and botanist.

asperifolia—with rough leaves.

atlanticum—of the Atlantic Coast.

atrococcum—with black fruit.

atropurpureum }—dark purple.
atropurpureus

atrox—cruel; with formidable thorns or spines.

auriculata—with earlike lobes.

axillaris—with flowers in the axils of the leaves.

baccata—with berries.

baileyanus }—named for Liberty Hyde Bailey, American horticulturist
baileyi   and botanist.

barbara—of Barbary, the plant mistakenly thought to be African.

bartramiana—named for William Bartram, early Philadelphia botanist.

bebbiana—named for Michael S. Bebb, noted student of the willows.

benzoin—named for the official benzoin because of a similar odor.

betulifolia }—with leaves like a birch.
betulifolius

blanda—smooth; without thorns.

bona-nox—from the Spanish *buenas noches,* meaning good night.

borealis—northern.

boyntonii—named for Frank E. Boynton, American botanist.

brachycera—short-horned.

buckleyi—named for Samuel B. Buckley, American botanist.

buxifolium—with leaves like the box.

caespitosum—forming tufts.

calendulaceum—colored like Calendula, the marigold.

calyculata—with bracts simulating an outer calyx.

canadense ⎫
canadensis ⎭—of Canada.

candida—whitened or hoary.

canescens—grayish-downy or hoary.

capreolata—twining.

carolina ⎫
carolinensis ⎬—of the Carolinas.
caroliniana ⎭

cassine—older name for *Ilex vomitoria,* now applied to this species.

cassinoides—resembling *Ilex cassine.*

catawbiense—named from the Catawba River, North Carolina.

cerifera—bearing wax.

cirrhosa—having tendrils.

cisatlantica—on this side of the Atlantic.

cistifolium—with leaves like *Cistus,* the Old World rock-rose.

clava-herculis—Hercules' club.

coactilis—with feltlike hairs.

coccinea—scarlet.

communis—growing together; in a clump.

compressa—compressed or flattened.

conradii—named for Solomon W. Conrad, its discoverer.

copallina—exuding a copal-like gum.

cordata—heart-shaped.

coriacea—leathery.

cornuta—horned.

corymbosa ⎫
corymbosum ⎭—in flat-topped clusters, or corymbs.

crassifolium—with thick or leathery leaves.

crinitum—with long hairs.

crispa—crisped, from the wavy margin.

croceolanata—with yellowish wool.

crus-galli—meaning a cock's spur.

cumberlandense—of the Cumberland Plateau.

cuneata—wedge-shaped.

cuneifolius—with wedge-shaped leaf bases.

curvatum—curved or arched.

cynosbati—the dogberry.

decidua—deciduous, leaf-losing.

densiflorum—with flowers in dense clusters.

dentatum—dentate, with sharp outwardly pointed teeth.

depressa—lying down flat.

difforme—of two forms; with dissimilar leaves.

dioica—with stamen-bearing and pistil-bearing flowers on separate plants.

diptera—two winged.

discolor—partly colored; with two or more colors.

distichophylla—with leaves in two ranks.

dolabriforme—shaped like an ax.

drummondii—named for Thomas Drummond, early American botanist.

dumosa—bushy.

durior—tougher.

echinellum—prickly.

edule—edible.

elliottii—named for Stephen Elliott, early South Carolina botanist.

ericoides—heath-like.

eriocephala—cottony-headed.

erythrocarpum—with red fruits.

fasciculatum—in clusters; with clustered leaves.

filamentosa—bearing slender threads, referring to the leaves.

flagellaris—whip-like, referring to the stems.

flava—yellow.

flavescens—yellowish.

floribunda—full of flowers.

floridus—flowering.

fontanesiana—named for René Louiche Desfontaines, early French botanist.

frondosa
frondosum }—leafy; with leaflike sepals.
frondosus

fruticosa—shrubby.

gale—old generic name of the plant.

galioides—like Galium, the bedstraws.

gardeni—named for Alexander Garden, early Charleston, S. C., physician and correspondent of Linnaeus.

georgiana—of Georgia.

gigantea—very large.

glabra—without hairs.

glandulosa
glandulosum }—glandular, bearing glands.

glauca
glaucescens }—whitened with a bloom.

glaucophylla—with bluish-green leaves.

glomeruliflora—with clustered flowers or flower heads.

gloriosa—glorious.

gracilis—slender.

grandifolia—with large leaves.

gravesii—named for Charles Burr Graves, its discoverer.
groenlandicum—of Greenland.

halimifolia—with leaves resembling those of *Halimus.*
hartwegii—named for K. G. Hartwig, who discovered it among cultivated plants in Germany.
herbacea—herbaceous.
heterophylla—with variable leaves.
hirsuta
hirsutum —roughish, with stiff or bristly hairs.
hirsutus
hirtella
hirtellum —bristly.
hispida
hispidula —with stiff hairs or bristles.
hispidus
horizontalis—lying flat or horizonal.
horridus—very prickly.
humilis—low-growing.
hypericoides—like *Hypericum,* the St. John's-worts.
hypnoides—resembling *Hypnum,* a genus of mosses.
hypolasium—hairy beneath, refering to the leaves.
hystrix—a hedgehog, in reference to the needle-like spines.

idaeus—of Mt. Ida, ancient name of Mt. Psiloriti in Crete.
ilicifolia—with holly-like leaves.
imbricata—overlapping.
inodora
inodorus —without an odor.
inserta—inserted, referring to some mode of attachment.
interior
interius —inland, pertaining to the interior.
intermedia—intermediate.
intonsa—having hairs.
involucrata—with an involucre.

kalmianum—named for Peter Kalm, early Swedish botanist.
kelseyi—named for Harlan P. Kelsey, American horticulturist and nurseryman.

labrusca—old Latin name for the grape vine.
lacustre—of the lakes.
laevifolium—with smooth leaves.
laevigata
laevigatus —smooth.
laevis
lanceolata
lancifolia —with lance-shaped leaves.

60

lanuginosa—woolly.
lapponicum—of Lapland.
latifolia—with broad leaves.
laurifolia—with laurel-like leaves.
lentago—an old name for some shrub, meaning flexible.
leucoderme—with whitish skin or bark.
leurophylla—with smooth leaves.
ligustrina—resembling *Ligustrum,* the privets.
lincecumii—named for Gideon Lincecum, its discoverer.
lloydii—named for Dr. A. J. Lloyd, American botanist.
longipes—with a long stalk.
lonicera—resembling *Lonicera,* the honeysuckles.
lucida—lustrous or shining.
lucidulum—somewhat shining.
lycioides—resembling Lycium, the matrimony-vines.
lyoni—named for John Lyon, early English botanical explorer.

macrocarpon—large-fruited.
macrosperma—large-seeded.
macrostachya—large-spiked; with a large flower cluster.
maculata—spotted or variegated.
major—larger.
malachodendron—older generic name of the plant.
margaretta—named for Margaret H. Wilcox, later Mrs. W. W. Ashe.
marginatus—margined.
mariana—of Maryland.
maritima—bordering on the sea.
marshallii—named for Humphrey Marshall, early American botanist.
maximum—largest.
melanocarpa
melanocarpum }—with black or dark-colored fruits.
melissaefolium—with leaves like *Melissa.*
michauxii—named for André Michaux, early French botanist.
microphylla
microphyllus }—with small leaves.
minima—smallest.
minor
minus }—smaller.
missouriense—of Missouri.
molle
mollis }—soft; with soft hairs.
monophylla—one-leaved; with a simple leaf.
montana—of the mountains.
mucronata—tipped with a mucro or short point.
multiflora—with many flowers.
myrsinites—resembling a shrub of the myrtle family.

myrtifolia ⎱
myrtifolium ⎰ —with myrtle-like leaves.

myrtilioides—resembling *Vaccinium myrtillus,* the European whortle-
berry.

nana—dwarf.

nigra ⎱
nigrum ⎰ —black.

nitens ⎱
nitida ⎬ —shining.
nitidum ⎰

novae-angliae—of New England.

nudiflorum—naked-flowered; flowering before the leaves appear.

nudum—naked.

obliqua—oblique, uneven.

oblonga—oblong, longer than broad.

oblongifolia ⎱
oblongifolius ⎰ —with oblong leaves.

obovalis ⎱
obovatum ⎬ —inversely egg-shaped or obovate.
obovatus ⎰

occidentalis—of the western hemisphere.

odoratum ⎱
odoratus ⎰ —fragrant.

opulifolius—with leaves like *Viburnum opulus,* the snowball-bush.

ovalifolium—with oval leaves.

ovata ⎱
ovatus ⎰ —egg-shaped or ovate.

oxycanthoides—resembling *Crataegus oxycantha,* an Old World hawthorn.

oxycoccus—old generic name meaning a sour berry.

pallidum—pale.

palmata—with palmate leaves, with veins radiating from summit of leafstalk.

palustris—of swamps.

parviflora—with small flowers.

parvifolia—with small leaves.

pavia—named for Peter Paaw of Leyden.

pedicellaris ⎱
pedicellata ⎰ —having flower stalks or pedicels.

pellita—meaning clad in skins.

pensylvanica—of Pennsylvania

peregrina—foreign or strange.

perrostrata—very long-beaked, referring to the fruits.

62

phillyreifolia—with leaves like *Phillyrea,* an evergreen shrub of the Mediterranean region.

pilosa—having long, soft hairs.

planifolia—with flat leaves.

polifolia—with leaves like *Polium.*

prinoides—resembling *Quercus prinus,* the chestnut oak.

procumbens—lying flat on the ground.

prolifera—reproducing freely by vegetative means.

prostratum—lying flat.

prunifolia
prunifolium }—with leaves like a plum.

pubera
pubens }—downy; with short, soft hairs.
pubescens

pulverulenta—powdery; with very fine down.

pumila—dwarf.

punctata—dotted.

pusilla
pusillum }—very small.

pyrifolia—with leaves like the pear.

quercifolia—with leaves like an oak.

quinquefolia—five-leaved; a compound leaf with five leaflets.

racemiflora—with flowers in racemes.

racemosa—in racemes.

radiata—having rays or showy sterile flowers.

radicans—rooting.

rafinesquianum—named for C. S. Rafinesque-Schmaltz, early French botanist.

rankinii—named for H. A. Rankin, who originally discovered the plant.

recurva—recurved; bent backwards.

reductum—reduced; smaller.

repens—creeping and rooting.

rigida—stiff.

rigidiuscula—somewhat stiff.

riparia—pertaining to the banks of streams.

rivularis—of rills.

roseum—rosy.

rotundifolia
rotundifolium }—with round leaves.

rufidulum—reddish.

rugosa—wrinkled.

rupestris—of rocky places.

sanguinea—blood-red.

saxatilis—of rocks.

scandens—climbing.
schwerinii—apparently named for someone by the name of Schwerin.
sempervirens—evergreen.
sericea—silky.
serrissima—late-fruiting.
serrulata—finely saw-toothed.
sessilifolia—with stalkless or sessile leaves.
setigera—bearing bristles.
setosum—bristly.
simplicissima—simple or unbranched.
smallii—named for John Kunkle Small, **American botanist.**
spathulatum—shaped like a spatula.
speciosa }
speciosum }—showy.
spicata }
spicatum }—with flowers in spikes.
spinosa—with spines.
stamineum—with prominent stamens.
stans—standing upright.
stolonifera—with stolons or runners.
stragalum—forming a mat or carpet.
stricta—upright or straight.
strigosus—covered with bristles.
suffruticosum—very low and partly woody.
susquehanae—of the Susquehanna River.
sylvatica—of the woods.
syrticola—growing on sand dunes.

tenax—tough.
tenellum—slender.
tenuifolia—with slender leaves.
textoris—of the basket-maker.
tinctoria—used as a dye.
tomentosa—wooly; covered with matted hairs.
toxicodendron—an old name meaning poison tree.
tridentata—three-toothed.
trifolia }
trifoliata }—three-leaved; a compound leaf with three leaflets.
triloba }
trilobum }—three-lobed.
triste—dull-colored; gray.
trivialis—ordinary.
typhina—resembling *Typha,* the cattails.

uliginosum—growing in swamps.
umbellata—having flowers in umbels.
umbellula—with flowers in small umbels.

64

uniflora—one-flowered.
ursina—pertaining to a bear.
uva-ursi—an old generic name meaning bear's grape.

vacillans—vacillating; unsteady.
vaseyi—named for George R. Vasey, American botanist.
vernix—varnish.
verticillaris }
verticillatus } —whorled.
villosa—soft-hairy.
viorna—an old generic name.
virgata—wandlike.
virginiana }
virginica } —of Virginia.
viscosa }
viscosum } —sticky.
vitis-idea—name meaning grape of **Mt. Ida.**
vomitoria—inducing vomiting.
vulgaris—common.
vulpina—pertaining to a fox.

walteri—named for Thomas Walter, 18-century English botanist and author of *Flora Caroliniana.*

DESCRIPTIONS OF SHRUBS

Their field marks and ranges, with plates
illustrating their distinctive characteristics.

COMMON JUNIPER *Juniperus communis* L.

FIELD MARKS. An evergreen shrub or small tree; growing in exposed rocky or sandy places. *Leaves* awl-like, sharply-pointed, arranged in 3's, grooved and whitened above, ¼ to ¾ inch long. *Fruits* berry-like, roundish to egg-shaped, aromatic, about ¼ inch in diameter, bluish black and whitened with a bloom. The typical variety has an erect or columnar form. The following two varieties in our range are low, spreading, or mat-forming shrubs: var. *saxatilis* Pallas (Mountain Juniper) has relatively short, broad, curved leaves up to ⅛ inch long and is northern in distribution; var. *depressa* Pursh (Oldfield or Prostrate Juniper) has almost straight leaves ⅜ to ¾ inch long and is the most common and widespread variety.

RANGE. Newfoundland to Alberta; south to eastern Virginia, the region of the Great Lakes, and in the mountains to South Carolina and Georgia.

Sometimes used in ornamental planting. The fruits are used medicinally and are eaten by a number of species of wild birds.

CREEPING JUNIPER *Juniperus horizontalis* Moench

FIELD MARKS. A prostrate or creeping evergreen shrub, usually with long trailing branches and numerous short branchlets; growing on the sandy or rocky borders of swamps and bogs. *Leaves* bluish green, small and scalelike, with pointed tips; or awl-like on young specimens or vigorous growth. *Fruits* berry-like, light blue, ¼ to ⅜ inch in diameter, on backward curving stalks.

RANGE. Newfoundland to Alaska; south to northern portions of New England States, northwestern New York, and the region of the Great Lakes.

YEW FAMILY (Taxaceae)

AMERICAN YEW *Taxus canadensis* Marsh

FIELD MARKS. A sprawling evergreen shrub 1 to 3 feet high; growing in cool, moist, usually coniferous woods. *Leaves* narrow, flattened, rigid, abruptly pointed, lustrous dark green above, paler and yellowish green beneath, ⅜ to about 1 inch long; with short stalks running slightly down the branchlets. *Fruits* waxy-looking, orange red, fleshy, about ½ inch across, partly enclosing a large bony seed.

RANGE. Newfoundland to Manitoba; south to western Virginia, Kentucky, and Iowa. Also called Ground-hemlock.

PALM FAMILY (Palmae)

SAW-PALMETTO *Serenoa repens* (Bartr.) Small

FIELD MARKS. A dwarf palm with stout, creeping underground stems; growing in hammocks and sandy coastal plain pinelands. *Leaves* fan-shaped, nearly circular, deeply cleft into many radiating divisions, green or yellowish green, 1 to 3 feet broad; leafstalks slender, armed with numerous, small, very sharp spines. *Flowers* small, creamy white, in a large branched cluster; blooming May to July. *Fruits* oval-shaped, black, 1-seeded, ½ to about 1 inch long; ripening October or November.

RANGE. Southeastern South Carolina south to Florida, west to Louisiana. Fruits edible and used medicinally. Important as a honey plant.

BLUE-STEM PALMETTO *Sabal minor* (Jacq.) Pers.

FIELD MARKS. Similar to the preceding but leafstalks are smooth and fairly heavy, and leaves have a bluish-green cast. Fruits are smaller and roundish. Grows in low woods or swamps, often along streams, in the coastal plain from North Carolina south to Florida, west to Arkansas and Texas. (Not illustrated)

NEEDLE-PALM *Rhapidophyllum hystrix* (Pursh) W. & D.

FIELD MARKS. Distinguished by its short, thick, erect or reclining trunklike stems covered with loose fibers and numerous long black spines. Mature fruits are red. Grows in coastal plain hammocks and swamps from Florida west to Mississippi. (Not illustrated)

Common Juniper

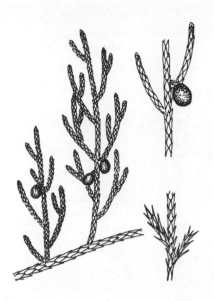

Creeping Juniper

American Yew

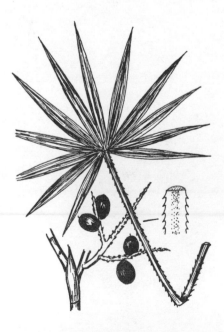

Saw-palmetto

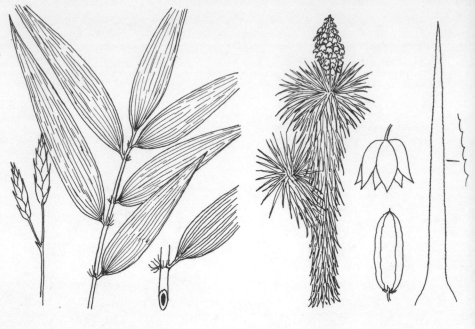

Cane

Spanish Bayonet

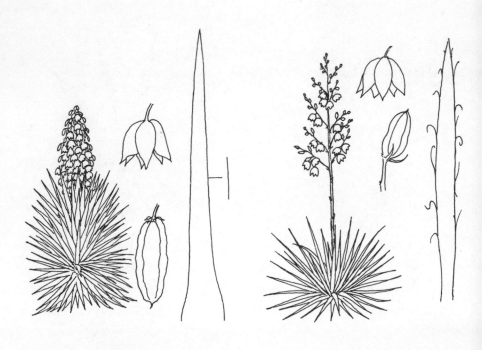

Spanish Dagger

Bear-grass

CANE   *Arundinaria gigantea* (Walt.) Muhl.

FIELD MARKS. A woody-stemmed, more or less evergreen, bamboo-like grass commonly 3 to 15 feet or higher; growing in low wet woods, stream bottoms, savannahs, and bogs. *Leaves* grasslike with flat blades 3 to 18 inches long and ⅜ to 1½ inches wide. *Flowers* small, greenish, in 5- to 15-flowered spikelets, either on short leafless basal shoots or on the leafy branches of the older stems; blooming irregularly in April or May.

RANGE. New Jersey and southern Delaware to southern Ohio, Illinois, Missouri, and Oklahoma; south to Florida and Texas.

In primitive America, canebreaks were extensive from Virginia and Missouri southward, with stems 3 or more inches in diameter. Stems used for fishing poles and other purposes. The starchy seeds were used as grain by the Indians and early settlers, and the young shoots as a potherb.

LILY FAMILY (Liliaceae)

YUCCAS (Yucca L.)

Yuccas are somewhat woody-stemmed, evergreen plants with alternate, crowded, swordlike or dagger-like leaves. The showy white or creamy-white flowers have a 6-parted, bell-shaped perianth and 6 stamens. They are pollinated by a small moth, the larvae of which feed upon the seeds. The fruits are elliptical, more or less 6-sided capsules containing a number of seeds. They were eaten to some extent by the Indians. Yuccas are popular ornamental plants.

SPANISH BAYONET   *Yucca aloifolia* L.

FIELD MARKS. A plant with a stem to about 15 feet high, commonly covered with downward-pointing old leaves, and with a dense cluster of spreading ones at the summit or ends of branches; growing in sandy woods and among coastal sand dunes. *Leaves* rigid, dagger-like, sharply pointed at tip, minutely saw-toothed on margin, 1½ to 2½ feet long. *Flowers* 1 to 2 inches long, white or creamy white, in a large and dense end cluster; blooming May or June. *Fruits* 2½ to 4 inches long, drooping, containing plump, marginless seeds.

RANGE. Coastal plain; North Carolina south to Florida, west to Alabama.

SPANISH DAGGER   *Yucca gloriosa* L.

FIELD MARKS. A plant usually with a simple stem 2 to 8 feet high, densely covered with spreading leaves except near the base; growing in sandy woods and among coastal sand dunes. *Leaves* rigid, dagger-like, sharply pointed at tip, smooth on margin, 1 to 2½ feet long. *Flowers* 2 to 4 inches long, white or creamy white, in a large and dense end cluster; blooming May or June. Fruits 2 to 3 inches long, drooping, prominently 6-ridged, containing flattened, thin-margined seeds.

RANGE. Coastal plain; North Carolina south to Florida.

BEAR-GRASS   *Yucca filamentosa* L.

FIELD MARKS. A plant with a short stem and cluster of spreading leaves close to the ground; growing in dry sandy open woods, clearings, and old fields. *Leaves* somewhat flexible, spine-pointed at tip, margin fraying into loose threads, 1 to 2 feet long. *Flowers* about 2 inches long, white or creamy white, in a large but rather open end cluster on a stalk 3 to 5 feet high; blooming May or June, or later northward. *Fruits* about 2 inches long, erect, containing elongate seeds.

RANGE. Southern New Jersey to West Virginia and Tennessee; south to Florida and Louisiana.

Also called Adam's-needle. Very popular as a garden plant.

(Key Appendix A)

Greenbriers are green-stemmed and often prickly vines which climb by means of paired tendrils on the bases of the leafstalks, these remaining after the leaves fall. The alternate leaves have from 3 to 7 prominent parallel veins and a network of smaller veins. The flowers are small, yellowish green, and borne in stalked umbels in the axils of the leaves. The fruits are small, usually roundish, 1- to 3-seeded berries.

The greenbriers often form impenetrable thickets. The starchy, tuberous roots of some species were used by the Indians as food. Rabbits and deer often eat the stems; the berries are eaten by many birds, including the ruffed grouse, wild turkey, and ring-necked pheasant. In the South, the greenbriers are popularly known as "bamboos."

COMMON GREENBRIER *Smilax rotundifolia* L.

FIELD MARKS. A scrambling or climbing leaf-losing vine with round or sometimes 4-angled stems and branchlets; armed with scattered, stout, broad-based prickles. *Leaves* egg-shaped to broadly egg-shaped or nearly round, often with a heart-shaped base, green and lustrous on both surfaces, 5-veined, 2 to 6 inches long. *Fruits* bluish black, coated with a whitish bloom, about ¼ inch in diameter; the cluster on a stalk hardly as long as the leafstalk.

RANGE. Nova Scotia to Minnesota, south to Florida and Texas.

Widely distributed in moist woods and thickets. The most common species of greenbrier northward as well as southward along the mountains. Also known as Horsebrier and Round-leaf Brier.

BRISTLY GREENBRIER *Smilax hispida* Muhl.

FIELD MARKS. A high-climbing, leaf-losing vine with stems thickly beset with weak bristly or needle-like blackish prickles (at least toward the base). *Leaves* thin, egg-shaped or broadly egg-shaped, lustrous green on both surfaces, 5- to 7-veined, 2 to 5 inches long, the margins roughish with minute bristle-tipped teeth. *Fruits* black, about ¼ inch in diameter, usually with a single shiny reddish-brown seed; the cluster on a stalk usually much longer than the leafstalk.

RANGE. New York to southern Ontario and Minnesota; south to Georgia and Mississippi.

A common greenbrier, especially in low moist thickets and woodlands and along the banks of streams.

GLAUCOUS GREENBRIER *Smilax glauca* Walt.

FIELD MARKS. A leaf-losing, or sometimes partly evergreen, scrambling or high-climbing vine; its round stems whitened with a bloom and usually armed with numerous stout prickles. *Leaves* egg-shaped to broadly egg-shaped, green above but conspicuously whitened and sometimes downy beneath, 3- to 5-veined, 2 to 5 inches long. *Fruits* bluish black, whitened with a bloom, about ¼ inch in diameter; the cluster on a stalk much longer than the leafstalk.

RANGE. Massachusetts to Illinois, south to Florida and Texas.

Also known as Catbrier and Sawbrier. Often common in dry to moist woods, thickets, and clearings, and spreading by underground runners.

CHINABRIER *Smilax bona-nox* L.

FIELD MARKS. A variable species which is sometimes high-climbing or partly evergreen; the 4-angled stems with usually some rigid prickles and starry-branched, scalelike hairs toward the base. *Leaves* more or less thick and leathery, commonly triangular or fiddle-shaped, the margins thickened and usually prickly, lustrous green on both surfaces or sometimes mottled with white, 5- to 7-veined, 2 to 5 inches long. *Fruits* bluish black, whitened with a bloom, about ¼ inch in diameter.

RANGE. Massachusetts to Illinois, south to Florida and Texas.

Also known as Bullbrier and Sawbrier. Often common southward in deciduous woods, old fields, and on sand dunes, but not present in the mountains.

Common Greenbrier

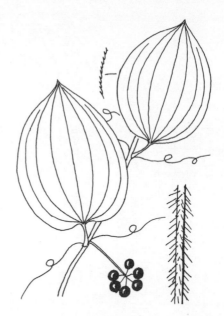

Bristly Greenbrier

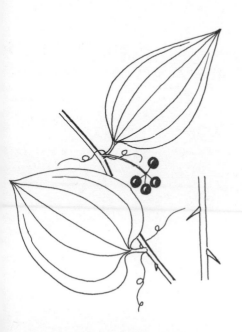

Glaucous Greenbrier

Chinabrier

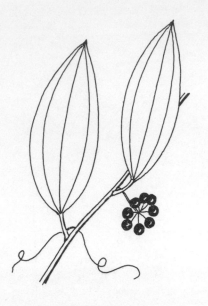

Laurel-leaf Greenbrier

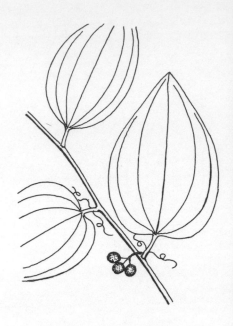

Red-berried Greenbrier

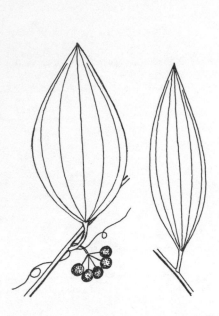

Lanceleaf Greenbrier

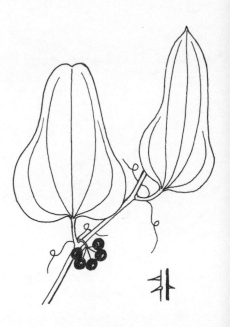

Wild Bamboo

LAUREL-LEAF GREENBRIER   *Smilax laurifolia* L.

FIELD MARKS. A high-climbing evergreen vine of low grounds and swamps; the round stems chiefly prickly toward the base and sometimes on the more vigorous shoots. *Leaves* thickish and leathery, pointed at both ends, dark green and lustrous above, paler and sometimes slightly whitened beneath, 3-veined, 2½ to 5 inches long. *Fruits* black, about ¼ inch in diameter.

RANGE. Coastal plain and piedmont; New Jersey south to Florida, west to Arkansas and Texas.

Unique among our greenbriers in having fruits which do not ripen until the second year; thus both ripe fruits and smaller green ones are commonly present. Also known as the Bamboo-vine or Blaspheme-vine.

RED-BERRIED GREENBRIER   *Smilax walteri* Pursh

FIELD MARKS. A slender-stemmed, leaf-losing vine with angled branchlets; usually scrambling over bushes about the borders of swamps and in low wet pinelands. The stems usually have scattered and slender prickles only toward the base. *Leaves* rather thin, egg-shaped to broadly egg-shaped, green on both surfaces, 5- to 7-veined, 2 to 4 inches long. *Fruits* bright coral red, about ¼ inch in diameter, persistent throughout the winter.

RANGE. Chiefly coastal plain; New Jersey south to Florida, west to Louisiana.

Easily recognized by its bright-red berries. Also known as the Coral Greenbrier.

LANCELEAF GREENBRIER   *Smilax smallii* Morong.

FIELD MARKS. A vigorous evergreen vine, the stems often whitened with a bloom and either unarmed or with a few stout prickles toward the base; growing in low wet woodlands, hammocks, and wayside thickets. *Leaves* rather thin but firm in texture, lance-shaped to egg-shaped, more or less pointed at the base and tapering gradually to the pointed tip, dark green and shiny above, pale green and dull or slightly whitened beneath, 5- to 7-veined, 2 to 4½ inches long. *Fruits* dull red, about ¼ inch in diameter.

RANGE. Chiefly coastal plain; North Carolina south to Florida, west to Texas and Arkansas.

Also known as Jacksonbrier. Often gathered and sold to florists where abundant.

WILD BAMBOO   *Smilax auriculata* Walt.

FIELD MARKS. A scrambling or sometimes high-climbing evergreen vine with more or less 4-angled stems and noticeably zigzag branchlets, sometimes armed with very small prickles. *Leaves* variable but commonly fiddle-shaped, margins thickened but not spiny, notched or abruptly pointed at the tip, 1 to 4½ inches long. *Fruits* black, often with a whitish bloom, ¼ to ½ inch in diameter.

RANGE. Outer coastal plain; North Carolina south to Florida, west to Mississippi.

Often grows among the coastal sand dunes.

WOOLLY GREENBRIER   *Smilax pumila* Walt.

FIELD MARKS. A low-climbing or often trailing evergreen vine which is easily recognized by its woolly and unarmed stems. *Leaves* broadly lance-shaped or egg-shaped, heart-shaped at the base, woolly on the lower surface, 3-veined, 2 to 4 inches long. *Fruits* red, egg-shaped, about ¼ inch long.

RANGE. Coastal plain; South Carolina south to Florida, west to Texas.

This greenbrier is unique in that it blooms in September or October and matures its berries the following spring. Also known as Sarsaparilla-vine.

CORKWOOD FAMILY (Leitneriaceae)

CORKWOOD   *Leitneria floridana* Chapm.

FIELD MARKS. A leaf-losing shrub or small tree which occurs rather rarely and locally in swamps along tidewater rivers. *Branchlets* rather stout, often with catkin-like flower buds clustered near the tip, and much smaller buds with 3 exposed scales. *Leaves* alternate, elliptic or lance-shaped, pointed at both ends, untoothed on the margin, bright green and smooth above, paler and downy beneath, 4 to 6 inches long. *Fruits* about ¾ inch long, dry, brown, wrinkled, 1-seeded.

RANGE. Coastal plain; southeastern Georgia and northern Florida west to Texas; also in portions of Arkansas and Missouri.

The wood is lighter than cork, weighing but 13 pounds per cubic foot, and is used locally to make floats for fishing nets. This is the only known member of its family.

BAYBERRY FAMILY (Myricaceae)

SWEETFERN   *Comptonia peregrina* (L.) Coult.

FIELD MARKS. An aromatic, much-branched, leaf-losing shrub from 1 to about 3 feet high; growing on dry rocky or sandy, and usually sterile, soils. *Branchlets* slender, downy, resin-dotted when young, fragrant when broken, often with clusters of catkins at the tips. *Leaves* alternate, fernlike, and deeply cut into numerous lobes, dark green above, paler and downy beneath, with numerous small resin dots on both surfaces, 1½ to 4 inches long, pleasantly fragrant when crushed. *Fruits* small olive-brown nutlets which are surrounded by pointed bracts and borne in little burrlike heads.

RANGE. Nova Scotia to Manitoba, south to interior North Carolina, and along the mountains to northern Georgia.

The leaves have astringent and tonic properties and were once used in home remedies and as a substitute for tea. Often heavily browsed by deer.

SWEETGALE   *Myrica gale* L.

FIELD MARKS. An aromatic leaf-losing shrub 1 to 4 feet high; growing in cool swamps and the boggy borders of streams and ponds. *Branchlets* often have large pointed flower buds toward the tips, and they are fragrant when broken. *Leaves* alternate, broadest toward the tip and tapering to the base, toothed above the middle, resin-dotted and sometimes with scattered hairs on the lower surface, 1 to 2 inches long, pleasantly fragrant when crushed. *Fruits* small, 2-winged, resin-dotted nutlets borne in conelike clusters.

RANGE. Newfoundland to Alaska; south to northern New Jersey, the region of the Great Lakes, Oregon, and in the Appalachians to western North Carolina.

The leaves have been used in clothes closets to repel moths, as a vermifuge, and as a substitute for tea.

76

Woolly Greenbrier

Corkwood

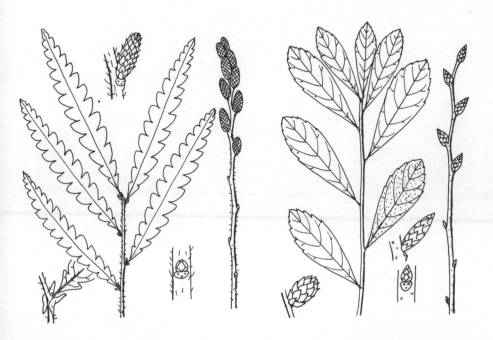

Sweetfern

Sweetgale

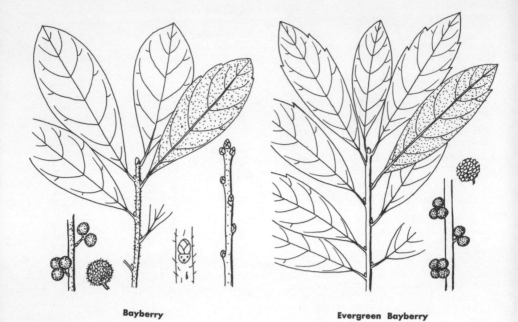

Bayberry

Evergreen Bayberry

Wax Myrtle

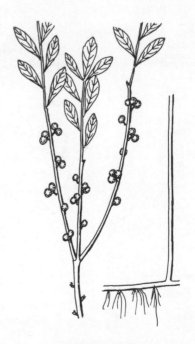

Dwarf Wax Myrtle

BAYBERRY *Myrica pensylvanica* Loisel.

FIELD MARKS. An aromatic leaf-losing shrub 3 to about 6 feet high; usually growing in dry sandy soils or on sand dunes. *Branchlets* grayish to ashy brown, often slightly hairy and resin-dotted, pleasantly fragrant when broken. *Leaves* alternate, elliptic or slightly broader above the middle, untoothed or sometimes with a few teeth toward the blunt tip, dull green and sometimes a little hairy above, paler and downy and resin-dotted beneath, 1½ to 3½ inches long, pleasantly fragrant when crushed. *Fruits* are bony nutlets which are minutely hairy and coated with whitish wax, about 3/16 inch in diameter.

RANGE. Coastal plain from Newfoundland south to North Carolina, inland near the Great Lakes to northern Ohio.

Wax of the fruits is used to make bayberry candles. The fruits are eaten by many wild birds. Leaves have been used as a substitute for bay leaves in seasoning. Rather attractive as an ornamental shrub and very useful in soil conservation.

EVERGREEN BAYBERRY *Myrica heterophylla* Raf.

FIELD MARKS. A large aromatic shrub which grows in wet woods and sandy bogs. *Branchlets* dark brown or blackish and sometimes hairy, pleasantly fragrant when broken. *Leaves* alternate, rather leathery, elliptic or broadest above the middle, usually with several distinct teeth, more or less sharply pointed at the tip, lustrous green above, paler and dull and resin-dotted beneath, 1½ to 3½ inches long, pleasantly fragrant when crushed. *Fruits* are bony nutlets which are wax-coated but not hairy, about ⅛ inch in diameter.

RANGE. Coastal plain; southern New Jersey south to Florida, west to Louisiana.

Wax of the fruits is used to make bayberry candles.

WAX MYRTLE *Myrica cerifera* L.

FIELD MARKS. An aromatic evergreen shrub or small tree which grows in wet sandy pinelands and bogs. *Branchlets* smooth or sparsely hairy, resin-dotted, pleasantly fragrant when broken. *Leaves* alternate, narrow, broadest toward the pointed tip and gradually tapered to the pointed base, untoothed or more often sharply toothed on the margin, resin-dotted on both surfaces, 2 to 4 inches long, pleasantly fragrant when crushed. *Fruits* are bony nutlets coated with whitish wax, about ⅛ inch in diameter.

RANGE. Coastal plain; southern New Jersey south to Florida, west to Texas, and northward to Arkansas and Oklahoma.

Wax of the fruits used to make bayberry candles. Fruits eaten by many birds, including the bobwhite quail and wild turkey. Makes a rather attractive ornamental shrub for wet places.

ODORLESS WAX MYRTLE *Myrica inodora* Bartr.

FIELD MARKS. A shrub similar to the Wax Myrtle, but the leaves are usually untoothed, 2 to 5 inches long, and not aromatic when crushed; and the wax-coated fruits are somewhat larger.

RANGE. Coastal plain; northern Florida west to Louisiana. (Not illustrated)

DWARF WAX MYRTLE *Myrica cerifera* var *pumila* Raf.

FIELD MARKS. An aromatic evergreen shrub 1 to (rarely) 3 feet high, forming colonies from its underground stems. *Leaves* similar to those of the Wax Myrtle but only ½ to 1½ inches long. It grows in low woods and sandy pinelands.

RANGE. Coastal plain; southern Delaware south to Florida, west to Texas and north to Arkansas.

Willows are leaf-losing shrubs or trees with bitter bark and usually slender branchlets. They have alternate simple leaves, and the buds are covered with a solitary hoodlike scale. The flowers are in catkins which appear either before or with the leaves, the stamen-bearing and pistil-bearing ones being on separate plants. Willow fruits are capsules which split down the middle at maturity, releasing the silky-hairy seeds. Many willows are useful in controlling the erosion of stream banks, or for ornamental planting. Twigs and bark are eaten by deer, moose, beaver, muskrats, and rabbits; the buds or young leaves are eaten by ptarmigan and grouse. The bark contains tannin and salicin which are used medicinally. Identification is often difficult and is complicated by the fact that hybrids often occur.

SLENDER WILLOW   *Salix gracilis* Anderss.

FIELD MARKS. A shrub 3 to 10 feet high; growing in low wet meadows and swales. *Branchlets* smooth or nearly so, often clustered at the ends of the branches. *Leaves* narrowly lance-shaped, long-pointed at tip, pointed at base, sharply toothed on margin but untoothed toward base, lustrous above, whitened and sometimes with silky hairs beneath, 2 to 4 inches long; leafstalks slender; stipules small and soon shed.

RANGE. Quebec to Manitoba; south to northern New Jersey, Pennsylvania, the region of the Great Lakes, Iowa, and Nebraska.

AUTUMN WILLOW   *Salix serissima* (Bailey) Fern.

FIELD MARKS. A shrub 3 to 12 feet high; growing in swamps or bogs, usually in marl or limestone regions. *Branchlets* smooth, lustrous, yellow brown to olive brown. *Leaves* narrowly elliptic or lance-shaped, pointed at tip, rounded to broadly pointed at base, finely and sharply toothed on margin, firm, lustrous above, smooth and pale or whitened beneath, 2 to 4 inches long; slender leafstalks usually have a pair of glands at the summit. *Flowers* blooming in June or July. *Fruits* maturing August or September.

RANGE. Newfoundland to Alberta; south to northern New Jersey, Pennsylvania, the region of the Great Lakes, North Dakota, and Colorado.

SILKY WILLOW   *Salix sericea* Marsh.

FIELD MARKS. A shrub 4 to 12 feet high; common and widely distributed along stream banks and other wet places. *Branchlets* brittle at base, purplish brown, smooth or minutely silky. *Leaves* lance-shaped, long-pointed at tip, pointed to rounded at base, margin finely and sharply toothed, smooth above, pale and with silvery-silky hairs beneath, 2 to 4 inches long; stipules small and soon shed.

RANGE. Nova Scotia to Wisconsin; south to Georgia, Tennessee, and Missouri.

SANDBAR WILLOW   *Salix interior* Rowlee

FIELD MARKS. A shrub 3 to 15 feet high; forming thickets on sand or gravel deposits along streams and places subject to frequent flooding. *Branchlets* reddish brown, smooth or nearly so. *Leaves narrowly* lance-shaped, pointed at both ends, margin with shallow and widely spaced teeth, green and smooth on both surfaces or sometimes silvery-silky, 2 to 5 inches long; leafstalks very short; stipules very small if present.

RANGE. New Brunswick to Quebec and Alaska; south to Maryland, Kentucky, Louisiana, and New Mexico.

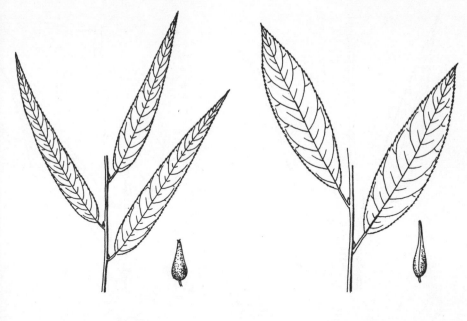

Slender Willow

Autumn Willow

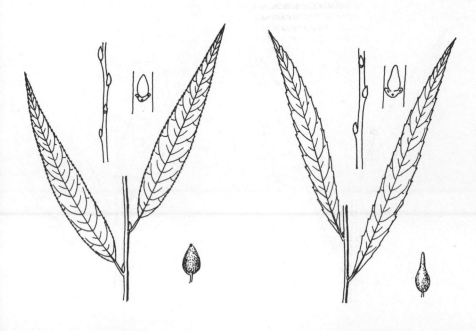

Silky Willow

Sandbar Willow

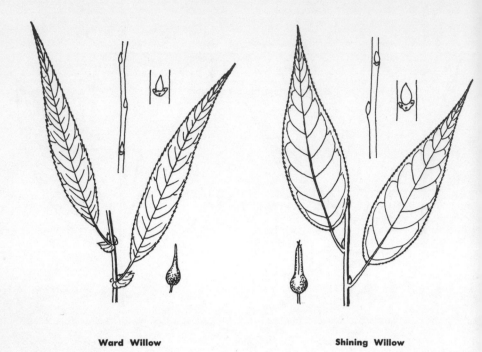

Ward Willow

Shining Willow

Missouri River Willow

Heartleaf Willow

WARD WILLOW *Salix caroliniana* Michx.

FIELD MARKS. A shrub or small tree of low moist places and stream banks. *Branchlets* smooth or somewhat downy, yellowish brown to reddish brown, sometimes brittle at base. *Leaves* narrowly lance-shaped, long-pointed at tip, pointed to rounded at base, finely and sharply toothed on margin, smooth or nearly so on both surfaces, dark green above, whitened beneath, 2½ to 6 inches long. Large stipules are often present at bases of the leafstalks.

RANGE. Maryland to southern Illinois and Missouri, south to Florida and Texas.

PEACHLEAF WILLOW *Salix amygdaloides* Anderss.

FIELD MARKS. A large shrub or small tree of stream banks, shores, and low wet places. *Branchlets* somewhat drooping, yellowish to orange brown, lustrous, flexible. *Leaves* lance-shaped or broadly lance-shaped, long-pointed at tip, pointed to rounded at base, finely and sharply toothed on margin, pale green and lustrous above, smooth and whitened beneath, 2 to 6 inches long. Stipules very small or absent.

RANGE. Vermont and southern Quebec to southeastern British Columbia; south to Massachusetts, New York, Michigan, Kentucky, Kansas, western Texas, and Arizona.
Also known as the Almondleaf Willow. (Not illustrated)

SHINING WILLOW *Salix lucida* Muhl.

FIELD MARKS. A shrub 4 to 10 feet high, or occasionally a small tree; growing in swampy places and along the banks of streams. *Branchlets* lustrous, smooth (or hairy in var. *intonsa* Fern.). *Leaves* broadly lance-shaped, long-pointed at tip, broadly pointed to rounded at base, finely and sharply toothed on margin, dark green and very lustrous above, slightly paler green and smooth (or hairy in var. *intonsa*) beneath, 2½ to 5 inches long. The leafstalks usually have large stipules at the base.

RANGE. Labrador to Manitoba; south to Delaware, Maryland, the region of the Great Lakes, and South Dakota.

MISSOURI RIVER WILLOW *Salix eriocephala* Michx.

FIELD MARKS. A shrub or small tree of lakeshores, borders of swamps, and stream banks. *Branchlets* smooth or somewhat downy, not brittle at base. *Leaves* lance-shaped to broadly lance-shaped, long-pointed at tip, pointed to rounded or heart-shaped at base, finely and sharply toothed on margin, dark green and smooth above, paler green or whitened to silvery-silky beneath, 2½ to 6 inches long. The leafstalks are slender, either smooth or downy, and usually have large stipules at the base.

RANGE. Newfoundland to Saskatchewan and Minnesota; south to Virginia, Kentucky, western Tennessee, Missouri, Kansas, and Nebraska.

HEARTLEAF WILLOW *Salix cordata* Michx.

FIELD MARKS. A shrub 1 to 5 feet high; growing on lakeshores, borders of swamps, and banks of streams. *Branchlets* densely gray-hairy. *Leaves* broadly lance-shaped to egg-shaped, pointed at tip, rounded to heart-shaped at base, finely and sharply toothed on margin, often gray-hairy on both surfaces, 1½ to 5 inches long. The leafstalks are hairy and usually have large and sometimes glandular-toothed stipules at the base.

RANGE. Labrador to Ontario; south to Massachusetts, northern New York, and northern Michigan.

PUSSY WILLOW *Salix discolor* Muhl.

FIELD MARKS. A large shrub usually 6 to 12 feet high, or occasionally a small tree; growing in swamps and other wet places. *Branchlets* dark purplish red, smooth or softly hairy. *Leaves* elliptic to lance-shaped, pointed at both ends, occasionally untoothed but usually with irregular and somewhat wavy teeth mostly above the middle, bright green and with a wrinkled-veiny appearance above, whitened and sometimes with rusty hairs beneath, 2 to 4 inches long. Large stipules are often present on vigorous shoots.

RANGE. Nova Scotia to Manitoba; south to Delaware, Maryland, West Virginia, Indiana, northeastern Missouri, and Nebraska.

The large furry catkins appear before the leaves and are a familiar harbinger of spring.

BEBB WILLOW *Salix bebbiana* Sarg.

FIELD MARKS. A large shrub usually 5 to 15 feet high, or occasionally a small tree; growing in either wet or dry places. *Branchlets* gray-downy. *Leaves* rather broad, elliptic or often broadest above the middle, pointed at tip, pointed to rounded at base, wavy-toothed or (more rarely) untoothed on the margin, thick and firm in texture; dull green, minutely downy, and wrinkled-veiny above; densely whitish- or grayish-woolly beneath; 1½ to 3 inches long. The slender, downy leafstalks are often reddish in color, and stipules are small or lacking.

RANGE. Newfoundland and Labrador to Alaska; south to New Jersey, Maryland, the region of the Great Lakes, Nebraska, New Mexico, and California.

Also known as the Beaked Willow.

PRAIRIE WILLOW *Salix humilis* Marsh.

FIELD MARKS. A shrub 2 to 10 feet high which is often common on dry and barren soils. *Branchlets* wandlike, erect, usually coated with a dirty-grayish down. *Leaves* narrowly elliptic, often broadest above the middle, pointed at both ends, margin slightly rolled, wavy, usually untoothed but sometimes sparingly toothed, bright green to dull grayish green and wrinkled-veiny above, pale and usually grayish-woolly beneath, 2 to 5 inches long. The leafstalks are stout and often have stipules at the base.

RANGE. Newfoundland and Labrador to Ontario and Minnesota; south to Florida and eastern Texas.

DWARF GRAY WILLOW *Salix humilis* var. *microphylla* (Anderss.) Fern.

FIELD MARKS. A tufted shrub 1 to (rarely) 3 feet high; growing in dry to moist sandy or stony soils. *Branchlets* usually grayish-downy. *Leaves* rather crowded, narrow, usually broadest near the tip, wedge-shaped at base, margin rolled and untoothed, dark green and often somewhat downy above, densely white-woolly beneath, ½ to 2 inches long. The leafstalks are very short.

RANGE. Southeastern Maine to southern Minnesota; south to Virginia, northwestern Florida, Louisiana, and Oklahoma.

Also known as the Dwarf Prairie Willow, Dwarf Pussy Willow, and Sage Willow.

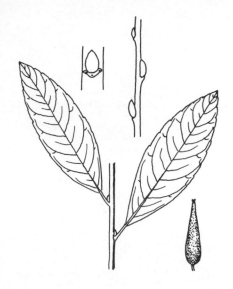

Pussy Willow

Bebb Willow

Prairie Willow

Dwarf Gray Willow

Blueleaf Willow

Balsam Willow

Furry Willow

Bog Willow

BLUELEAF WILLOW   *Salix glaucophylloides* Fern.

FIELD MARKS. A shrub 2 to 15 feet high, or (rarely) a small tree, of gravelly shores, beaches, and sand dunes. *Branchlets* smooth to densely white-woolly (in the variety *albovestita* (Ball) Fern.). *Leaves* egg-shaped to broadly lance-shaped, pointed at tip, rounded to somewhat heart-shaped at base, finely and sharply toothed on the margin, thickish and firm in texture, dark green and lustrous above, whitened and smooth beneath (leaves more or less white-woolly in var. *albovestita*), 2 to 4½ inches long. The stout leafstalks are smooth or downy.

RANGE. Newfoundland and northern Ontario to British Columbia; south to northern Maine and the region of the Great Lakes.

BALSAM WILLOW   *Salix pyrifolia* Anderss.

FIELD MARKS. A shrub 3 to 10 feet high, or (rarely) a small tree; growing in swamps, low thickets, and the borders of woods. *Branchlets* smooth, lustrous, reddish brown. *Leaves* with a pleasant balsamic or resinous odor when crushed, elliptic to egg-shaped, pointed at tip, broadly rounded to heart-shaped at base, slightly glandular-toothed on margin, thin in texture, dark green and smooth above, whitened and prominently veiny beneath, 1½ to 4 inches long. The leafstalks are smooth and slender.

RANGE. Newfoundland and Labrador to British Columbia; south to Maine, northern New York, Michigan, Minnesota, and Saskatchewan.

FURRY WILLOW   *Salix syrticola* Fern.

FIELD MARKS. A straggling shrub 3 to 10 feet high; growing on sand dunes and beaches. *Branchlets* densely woolly. *Leaves* egg-shaped to broadly lance-shaped, pointed at tip, broadly rounded to heart-shaped at base, finely toothed with gland-tipped teeth on margin, dark green and coated with lustrous silky hairs on both surfaces, 1½ to 4 inches long. The leafstalks are short, stout, and silky-hairy.

RANGE. Shores of the Great Lakes; western Ontario, Michigan, Indiana, northeastern Illinois, and eastern Wisconsin.

BOG WILLOW   *Salix pedicellaris* Pursh.

FIELD MARKS. A loosely branched and creeping shrub 1 to 3 feet high; growing in cold northern bogs. *Branchlets* long, rather erect, flexible, brown, and smooth. *Leaves* narrowly elliptic, often broadest well above the middle, bluntly pointed or rounded at tip, wedge-shaped at base, margin untoothed and rolled, more or less leathery in texture, smooth and green on both surfaces, ½ to 2 inches long. The leafstalks are smooth and slender.

RANGE. Labrador and Newfoundland to British Columbia; south to northern New Jersey, the region of the Great Lakes, northern Iowa, Idaho, and Oregon.

HOARY WILLOW   *Salix candida* Flugge

FIELD MARKS. A much-branched shrub 1 to (rarely) 5 feet high; growing in cold northern bogs. *Branchlets* densely coated with loose white wool. *Leaves* narrowly oblong or lance-shaped, bluntly pointed at tip, narrowed at the base, untoothed or with inconspicuous wavy teeth on the rolled margin, dull dark green above, densely coated with snow-white wool beneath, firm in texture, 1½ to 4 inches long. Leafstalks white-woolly. The narrow stipules are sometimes as long as the leafstalks.

RANGE. Labrador and Newfoundland to British Columbia; south to northern New Jersey, northeastern Pennsylvania, the region of the Great Lakes, northern Iowa, South Dakota, and Colorado.

SATINY WILLOW   *Salix pellita* Anderss.

FIELD MARKS. A shrub 3 to 8 feet high, or sometimes a small tree; growing along stream banks and in swampy places. *Branchlets* reddish brown to olive brown, smooth, usually coated with a whitish bloom. *Leaves* lance-shaped and often narrowly so, sometimes broadest above the middle, pointed at both ends, untoothed or obscurely toothed on the margin, thick and firm in texture, bright green and smooth above, pale or whitened and sometimes silky-haired or even velvety beneath, 1½ to 4½ inches long.

RANGE. Labrador and Newfoundland to northern Ontario; south to Maine, Vermont, and Michigan.

TEALEAF WILLOW   *Salix planifolia* Pursh

FIELD MARKS. A much-branched shrub 8 inches to 10 feet high; growing in swampy places and along stream banks. *Branchlets* smooth, often whitened with a bloom. *Leaves* elliptic to oblong, pointed or sometimes blunt at both ends, untoothed or nearly so on margin, dark green and lustrous above, smooth and whitened beneath, 1 to 3 inches long.

RANGE. Labrador to Alberta; south to Newfoundland, Quebec, and the higher mountains of northern New England.

SILVER WILLOW   *Salix argyrocarpa* Anderss.

FIELD MARKS. A shrub 8 inches to about 5 feet high; growing on tundras and southward in high mountain meadows or on wet rocks. *Branchlets* dark green, lustrous. *Leaves* narrowly elliptic to narrowly lance-shaped, often broadest well above the middle, pointed or bluntly pointed at tip, pointed at base, untoothed to obscurely wavy-toothed on the slightly rolled margin, bright green and smooth above, silvery-silky with minute hairs beneath, ¾ to 2½ inches long.

RANGE. Arctic Region south to Labrador, Quebec, and mountains of New Hampshire.

Hoary Willow

Satiny Willow

Tealeaf Willow

Silver Willow

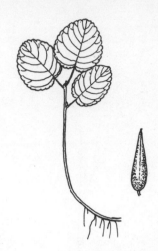

Bearberry Willow

Dwarf Willow

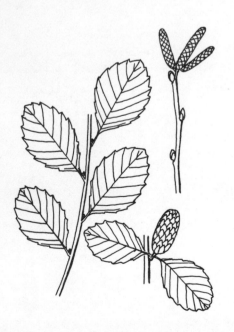

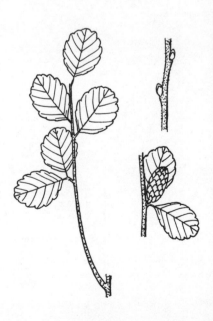

Low Birch

Dwarf Birch

BEARBERRY WILLOW   *Salix uva-ursi* Pursh

FIELD MARKS. A prostrate, trailing, mat-forming shrub of tundras and alpine mountain summits. *Branches* brown, 6 to 12 inches long, not rooting. *Leaves* elliptic or broadest above the middle, pointed to blunt at tip, wedge-shaped at base, margin finely and sharply toothed, firm, prominently veined, lustrous and smooth or (rarely) soft-hairy above, pale and usually smooth beneath, ¼ to 1 inch long; leafstalks very short.

RANGE. Greenland and Arctic Region south to Newfoundland, Nova Scotia, New England, northern New York, and Quebec.

DWARF WILLOW   *Salix herbacea* L.

FIELD MARKS. A creeping or mat-forming shrub of tundras and alpine mountain summits. *Branches* mostly below the surface and rooting at the nodes. *Branchlets* above ground 1 to 6 inches long, very slender, angled. *Leaves* roundish, heart-shaped at base, margin with blunt or rounded teeth, smooth and bright green and lustrous on both surfaces, ½ to 1¼ inches across; leafstalks slender.

RANGE. Arctic region south to Newfoundland, Quebec, northern portions of Maine, New Hampshire, and New York.

BIRCH FAMILY (Betulaceae)

LOW BIRCH   *Betula pumila* L.

FIELD MARKS. A leaf-losing, often low and mat-forming, shrub 1 to 6 feet high; growing in northern bogs and swamps. *Branchlets* smooth, hairy, or glandular-warty. *Leaves* oval to roundish or broadest above the middle, rounded or blunt at tip, rounded to pointed at base, margin coarsely toothed, dull above, pale or whitened and smooth to hairy or glandular-dotted beneath, ½ to 1½ inches long; leafstalks very short.

RANGE. Newfoundland and Labrador to British Columbia; south to northern New Jersey, New York, and the region of the Great Lakes.

Also known as Swamp Birch.

DWARF BIRCH   *Betula glandulosa* Michx.

FIELD MARKS. A leaf-losing shrub 1 to 6 feet high, often low and mat-forming; growing on tundras and south chiefly on alpine mountain summits. *Branchlets* thickly warty-dotted. *Leaves* oval, roundish, or broadest above the middle, rounded at tip, round to pointed at base, coarsely toothed on margin, leathery, green on both surfaces but glandular-dotted beneath, ¼ to 1 inch long; leafstalks short.

RANGE. Newfoundland to Alaska; south to Maine, New Hampshire, New York, Michigan, Minnesota, Colorado, and California.

DWARF WHITE BIRCH   *Betula minor* (Tuckerm.) Fern.

FIELD MARKS. Spreading or upright leaf-losing shrub 1 to 6 feet high. *Branchlets* warty-dotted. *Leaves* egg-shaped, double-toothed on margin, ½ to about 2 inches long.

RANGE. Labrador and Newfoundland to mountains of New England, northwestern New York, and Ontario. (Not illustrated)

NORTHERN BIRCH   *Betula borealis* Spach

FIELD MARKS. Spreading or erect leaf-losing shrub or small tree. *Branchlets* densely whitish-hairy. *Leaves* elliptic to broadly egg-shaped, double-toothed on margin, ½ to 2¼ inches long.

RANGE. Labrador and Ungava south to Newfoundland, Northern Maine and Vermont, and Quebec. (Not illustrated)

Alders are leaf-losing shrubs with alternate, simple leaves. The stamen-bearing flowers are in drooping catkins; the pistil-bearing ones are in much smaller catkins. Both are fully developed before the leaves are shed in the fall. The fruits are small, slightly winged nutlets, borne in the axils of woody scales of conelike structures which are peculiar to the alders. Alders are useful in controlling stream bank erosion. The bark and twigs are eaten by beavers, deer, and rabbits; many small birds feed on the seeds.

COMMON ALDER *Alnus serrulata* (Ait.) Willd.

FIELD MARKS. A thicket-forming shrub 5 to 15 feet high; growing along streams and in swampy places. *Bark* with scattered, small, dotlike lenticels. *Leaves* oval or broadest above the middle, broadly pointed to rounded at tip, pointed at base, margin finely toothed with simple teeth, smooth above, paler green and smooth or somewhat rusty-downy beneath, 1 to 6 inches long. *Flowers* blooming late February to April, the smaller catkins at branch tips and erect. *Buds* 2-scaled and noticeably stalked.

RANGE. Nova Scotia and Maine to the region of the Great Lakes, Missouri, and Oklahoma; south to northern Florida and Louisiana.

Also called Smooth Alder.

SPECKLED ALDER *Alnus rugosa* (Du Rois) Spreng.

FIELD MARKS. A shrub very much like the preceding. *Bark* with numerous whitish, horizontally elongated lenticels. *Leaves* oval or broadest above the middle, short-pointed at tip, rounded to slightly heart-shaped at base, margin double-toothed, smooth above, paler or more often whitened and sometimes pale- to rusty-downy beneath, 2 to 5 inches long. *Flowers* blooming March or April, the smaller catkins drooping and not at branch tips. *Buds* 2-scaled and noticeably stalked.

RANGE. Labrador to Saskatchewan; south to Maine, Maryland, West Virginia, the region of the Great Lakes, and northeastern Iowa.

Also called Hoary Alder.

GREEN ALDER *Alnus crispa* (Ait.) Pursh

FIELD MARKS. A northern shrub 2 to 10 feet high growing on rocky shores, slopes, and southward on mountain balds. *Leaves* roundish to egg-shaped or somewhat heart-shaped, finely and sharply but irregularly toothed on the often puckered margin, somewhat sticky, green and smooth on both sides or sometimes downy or velvety beneath, 1 to 3 inches long. *Flowers* blooming in May or June as the leaves expand. *Buds* have 3 or 4 visible scales and are not stalked.

RANGE. Newfoundland to Alaska; south to Massachusetts, northern New York, Michigan, and British Columbia; south in the high mountains to western North Carolina and eastern Tennessee.

Also called Mountain Alder.

SEASIDE ALDER *Alnus maritima* (Marsh.) Nutt.

FIELD MARKS. A shrub or small tree growing about ponds and on stream banks in the coastal plain of Delaware and Maryland. *Leaves* oval to egg-shaped or broadest above the middle, pointed at tip, wedge-shaped at base, margin with small but sharp and widely spaced teeth, lustrous above, paler green and smooth or nearly so beneath, 2 to 4 inches long. *Flowers* blooming in August or September. *Fruits* not maturing until the following year. *Buds* pointed, hairy, stalked, and several-scaled.

RANGE. Near coast; Delaware and Maryland.

Common Alder

Speckled Alder

Green Alder

Seaside Alder

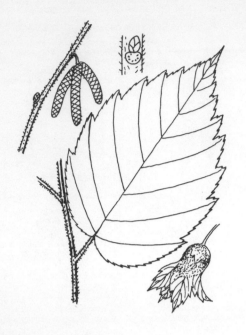

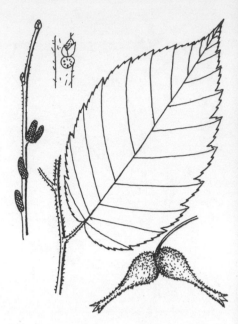

American Hazelnut

Beaked Hazelnut

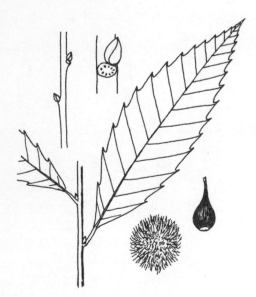

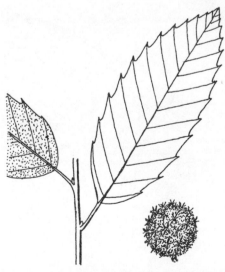

Common Chinquapin

Coastal Chinquapin

HAZELNUTS (Corylus L.)

Hazelnuts are leaf-losing shrubs with simple, alternate leaves. The branchlets are rather slender and somewhat zigzag. Along them are well-developed catkins of the stamen-bearing flowers. They bloom in early spring before the leaves appear; the catkins elongating and shedding their pollen while the bright-red stigmas of the pistil-bearing flowers protrude from buds along the branchlets. The fruits are light-brown, roundish nuts which are enclosed by pairs of leafy bracts.

The nuts are sweet and edible. They are eaten by deer, squirrels, chipmunks, blue jays, and a number of other kinds of wildlife.

AMERICAN HAZELNUT *Corylus americana* Walt.

FIELD MARKS. A shrub 3 to 10 feet high growing in moist to dry thickets, fence rows, roadsides, and borders of woods. *Branchlets* bristly-hairy; *catkins* stalked and often 1 inch long. *Leaves* egg-shaped to roundish, somewhat heart-shaped at base, abruptly pointed at tip, double-toothed on margin, smooth or nearly so above, downy on the veins beneath, 2½ to 6 inches long; leafstalks bristly-hairy. *Fruits* enclosed by a pair of ragged-edged leafy bracts.

RANGE. Maine to Saskatchewan; south to northern Florida, Missouri, and Oklahoma.

BEAKED HAZELNUT *Corylus cornuta* Marsh.

FIELD MARKS. A shrub quite similar to the American Hazelnut and found in similar situations. *Branchlets* sparingly if at all bristly-hairy; *catkins* stalkless and less than ½ inch long. *Fruits* enclosed by a pair of bracts which are united and form a prolonged, tubelike, bristly-hairy beak.

RANGE. Newfoundland to British Columbia; south principally in the mountains to Georgia, Missouri, and Colorado.

BEECH FAMILY (Fagaceae)

CHINQUAPINS (Castanea Hill)

Chinquapins are leaf-losing shrubs or small trees with alternate, simple leaves. They bloom in the late spring after the leaves are developed, and the flower clusters are quite showy. The stamen-bearing flowers are whitish and arranged in slender clusters. Those bearing the pistils are in small, prickly involucres at the base of the stamen-bearing clusters or in the axils of the leaves. The fruits are edible nuts which are enclosed in a prickly bur.

COMMON CHINQUAPIN *Castanea pumila* (L.) Mill.

FIELD MARKS. A shrub or small tree to about 30 feet high; growing in dry woods and thickets. *Leaves* narrowly elliptic, pointed at both ends or occasionally rounded at base, coarsely and sharply toothed on margin, smooth above, paler and whitish-downy beneath, 3 to 5 inches long. *Fruits* shiny brown, silky-hairy nuts ¼ to ½ inch across; usually solitary in a densely prickly bur.

RANGE. Massachusetts and New Jersey to Tennessee and Arkansas; south to Florida and eastern Texas.

COASTAL CHINQUAPIN *Castanea pumila* var. *ashei* Sudw.

FIELD MARKS. A shrub or small tree; growing in dry sandy soils of the coastal plain. *Leaves* somewhat shorter, broader, and of a firmer texture than those of the preceding, bluntly pointed or rounded at tip, and densely white-woolly beneath. *Fruits* similar but the burs with widely spaced clusters of spines.

RANGE. Virginia south to Florida, west to eastern Texas and Arkansas.

RUNNING CHINQUAPIN   *Castanea alnifolia* Nutt.

FIELD MARKS. A leaf-losing shrub 1 to (rarely) 3 feet high, with creeping underground stems; growing in dry sandy pinelands and sandhills. *Leaves* elliptic or broadest above the middle, rounded to somewhat pointed at the tip, usually pointed at the base, becoming nearly smooth beneath at maturity, 2 to 5 inches long. *Fruits* similar to those of the Coastal Chinquapin but with even more widely spaced clusters of spines.

RANGE. Coastal plain; North Carolina south to Florida, west to Louisiana.

FLORIDA CHINQUAPIN   *Castanea alnifolia* var. *floridana*

This variety has leaves and fruits similar to the Running Chinquapin, but it is an upright shrub or small tree. It grows in similar situations and is found in the same range. (Not illustrated)

OAKS (Quercus L.)

Oaks are trees, or sometimes shrubs, with simple, alternate leaves which tend to be more or less clustered toward the tips of the branchlets. The flowers appear in the spring along with the developing leaves; they are greenish, yellowish, or reddish. Stamen-bearing ones are in slender and drooping catkins. The pistil-bearing ones are small and inconspicuous, being in the axils of the new leaves. Oak fruits are called acorns. They are nuts which are seated in scaly-bracted cups.

The tree oaks are valuable shade and timber trees. Shrubby species are useful for the control of soil erosion. Acorns were a staple food of the American Indians. They are eaten by many kinds of wildlife, including deer, bears, squirrels, wild turkeys, wild ducks, blue jays, and some woodpeckers.

SCRUB OAK   *Quercus ilicifolia* Wang.

FIELD MARKS. A leaf-losing shrub or small tree 3 or more feet high; growing on dry and barren uplands and slopes. *Leaves* oblong-oval or often broadest above the middle, with 3 to 7 (usually 5) short, broadly triangular, bristle-tipped, and sparingly bristle-toothed lobes, dark green and lustrous above, whitish-downy beneath, 2 to 4 inches long. *Fruits* egg-shaped acorns about ⅜ inch long which are about half covered by a bowl-shaped cup.

RANGE. Maine to New York and western Pennsylvania; south to Virginia, West Virginia, and western North Carolina.

Also known as the Bear Oak.

DWARF CHESTNUT OAK   *Quercus prinoides* Willd.

FIELD MARKS. A leaf-losing shrub or small tree 2 to 12 feet high; growing on dry and barren uplands and slopes. *Leaves* oblong or broadest above the middle, blunt-pointed at tip, pointed at base, margin with 3 to 7 pairs of bluntish or pointed teeth, bright green and smooth above, grayish-downy beneath, 3 to 5 inches long. *Fruits* lustrous egg-shaped acorns ½ to ¾ inch long, about half covered by a bowl-shaped cup.

RANGE. Maine to Minnesota and Nebraska; south to Virginia, western North Carolina, northern Alabama, and Texas.

Also known as Scrub Chestnut Oak and Chinquapin Oak.

SAND POST OAK   *Quercus margaretta* Ashe

FIELD MARKS. A leaf-losing shrub or small tree of dry sandy pinelands and sandhills. *Leaves* broadest and with usually 3 (seldom 5) short and irregularly rounded lobes above the middle, pointed at base, smooth or nearly so above, somewhat downy to nearly smooth beneath, 2 to 4 inches long. *Fruits* egg-shaped or oval acorns about ½ inch long, about half covered by a deeply bowl-shaped cup.

RANGE. Coastal plain; southeastern Virginia south to Florida, west to Texas, and north to Missouri and Oklahoma.

Also known as Dwarf Post Oak and Scrub Post Oak.

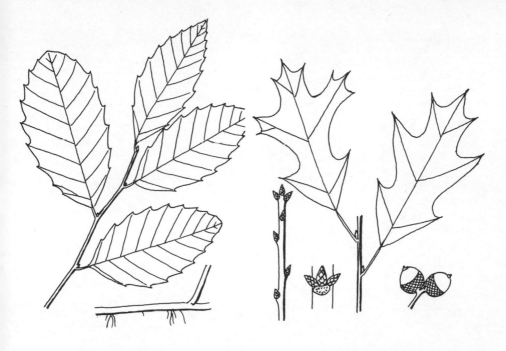

Running Chinquapin

Scrub Oak

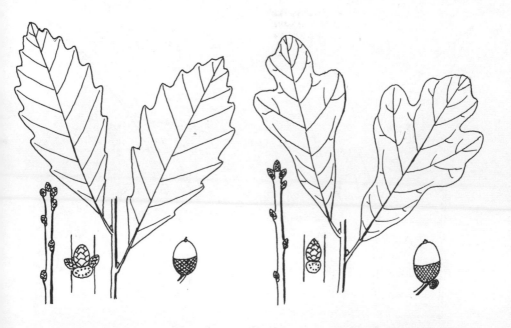

Dwarf Chestnut Oak

Sand Post Oak

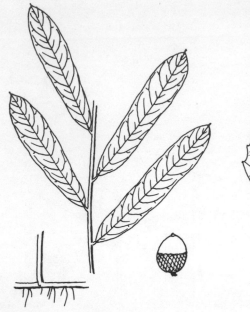

Running Oak

Creeping Live Oak

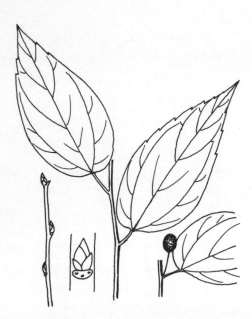

Dwarf Hackberry

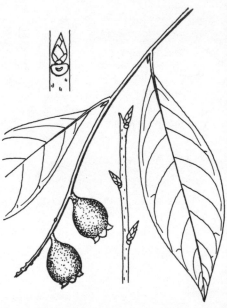

Buffalonut

RUNNING OAK *Quercus pumila* Walt.

FIELD MARKS. A tardily leaf-losing shrub with running underground stems and erect branches 1 to 3 feet high; growing in flat and sandy pinelands. *Leaves* narrowly elliptic, lance-shaped or broadest near the tip, rounded to broadly pointed at both ends but with a bristle-point at tip, margin wavy but untoothed, bright green and smooth above, paler and downy beneath, leathery, 1½ to 3 inches long; leafstalks very short. *Fruits* egg-shaped acorns about ½ inch long, about half covered by a deep bowl-like cup.

RANGE. Coastal plain; North Carolina south to Florida, west to Mississippi.

CREEPING LIVE OAK *Quercus virginiana* var. *minima* Sarg.

FIELD MARKS. An evergreen shrub with running underground stems and erect branches 1 to 3 feet high; growing on sandhills and in dry sandy pinelands. *Leaves* thick and leathery, elliptic to narrowly elliptic or often broadest above the middle, usually wavy-toothed on margin, smooth above, smooth or downy beneath, 1¼ to 4 inches long. *Fruits* narrowly egg-shaped acorns about ⅝ inch long, about half covered by deep bowl-like cups.

RANGE. Coastal plain; Georgia, Florida, and southern Alabama.

ELM FAMILY (Ulmaceae)

DWARF HACKBERRY *Celtis tenuifolia* Nutt.

FIELD MARKS. A straggling, leaf-losing shrub or small tree 3 to about 20 feet high; growing on dry uplands and slopes. *Leaves* have 3 prominent veins from near the base, egg-shaped, unevenly rounded or heart-shaped at base, pointed at tip, untoothed or sparingly toothed on margin, thin, often roughish above, 1 to 3 inches long. *Flowers* small, greenish, blooming in April or May. *Fruits* roundish, orange brown to purplish, 1-seeded, flesh thin and sweet, about ¼ inch in diameter.

RANGE. Pennsylvania to Indiana and Missouri; south to northern Florida and Louisiana.

SANDALWOOD FAMILY (Santalaceae)

BUFFALONUT *Pyrularia pubera* Michx.

FIELD MARKS. An upright, but often straggling, leaf-losing shrub 3 to about 12 feet high; growing on moist, often rocky, wooded slopes. *Leaves* alternate, elliptic or broadest above the middle, pointed at both ends, margin untoothed, soft and very veiny in appearance, smooth or nearly so at maturity, with minute clear dots which are visible when the leaf is held up to light, 2 to about 6 inches long. *Flowers* small, pale green, in short clusters; blooming in April or May. *Fruits* more or less pear-shaped, leathery, yellowish green, about 1 inch long; containing a solitary large oily seed; maturing July to October.

RANGE. Chiefly mountains; Pennsylvania south to Georgia and Alabama.

A root parasite of other shrubs and trees. All parts of the plant, but particularly the seeds, contain a bitterly pungent and poisonous oil. Also known as Oilnut.

NESTRONIA *Nestronia umbellula* Raf.

FIELD MARKS. A leaf-losing and often colonial shrub 1 to (rarely) 3 feet high; growing in dry woodlands. *Branchlets* slender, dark purplish brown. *Leaves* opposite, oval to egg-shaped or often broadest above the middle, usually pointed at both ends, margin untoothed, bright yellowish green and smooth or nearly so, 1 to 2½ inches long; leaf-stalks short. *Flowers* small, greenish, the stamen-bearing ones in long-stalked clusters in the leaf axils, the pistil-bearing ones on separate plants; blooming in April or May. *Fruits* berry-like, egg-shaped, 1-seeded, yellowish green, almost ½ inch across; ripening in July.

RANGE. Western Virginia south to northern Georgia and Alabama.

A rather rare shrub of local occurrence, parasitic on the roots of various broad-leaved trees and shrubs.

BUCKLEYA *Buckleya distichophylla* (Nutt.) Torr.

FIELD MARKS. A leaf-losing shrub 6 to 12 feet high; growing on cliffs or bluffs along streams in the southern Appalachians. *Branchlets* green or grayish green, slender, with prominent pale lenticels. *Leaves* opposite or nearly so, lance-shaped to narrowly egg-shaped, taper-pointed at tip, roundish or broadly pointed at base, margin untoothed, smooth or nearly so and bright green on both surfaces, 1 to 3 inches long; stalkless or short-stalked. *Flowers* small, greenish, the stamen-bearing ones clustered, the pistil-bearing ones solitary at the tips of branches; blooming in April or May. *Fruits* berry-like, ellipsoid, 1-seeded, yellowish green to dull orange, about ½ inch long; ripening in August.

RANGE. Western Virginia south to western North Carolina and eastern Tennessee.

A rare shrub of local occurrence, parasitic on the roots of hemlock and possibly other trees.

MISTLETOE FAMILY (Loranthaceae)

AMERICAN MISTLETOE *Phoradendron flavescens* (Pursh) Nutt.

FIELD MARKS. An evergreen, yellowish-green, much-branched shrubby plant, parasitic on the branches of oaks and other broad-leaved trees. *Branchlets* jointed, brittle at base. *Leaves* opposite, oblong or narrowly oblong and often broadest above the middle, rounded at tip, pointed at base, untoothed on margin, thickish and leathery in texture, smooth on both sides, ¾ to 2 inches long. *Flowers* small and inconspicuous, yellowish green; blooming in October or November. *Fruits* maturing the following fall, berry-like, round, waxy white, 1-seeded, about ⅛ inch across, with a sticky-gummy pulp.

RANGE. New Jersey to southern Illinois and southeastern Kansas, south to Florida and Texas.

Well known as a Christmas decoration. The fruits are eaten by birds, and the seeds are placed on tree branches when birds wipe the sticky pulp from their bills.

BIRTHWORT FAMILY (Aristolochiaceae)

DUTCHMAN'S-PIPE *Aristolochia durior* Hill

FIELD MARKS. A twining and high-climbing, leaf-losing, woody vine; growing in rich woods and along streams. *Leaves* alternate, heart-shaped, untoothed on margin, thin in texture, dark green and smooth above, paler and smooth or nearly so beneath, 3 to 8 inches wide. *Flowers* with a yellowish-green, U-shaped and pipelike calyx tube, spreading at summit into a 3-lobed and brownish-purple border; blooming in May and June. *Fruits* cylindrical, 6-ribbed capsules, 2 to 3 inches long, and containing many seeds.

RANGE. Appalachian region; western Pennsylvania and West Virginia south to Georgia and Alabama.

Cultivated and grown on trellises and porches; often listed in nursery catalogs as *Aristolochia sipho*.

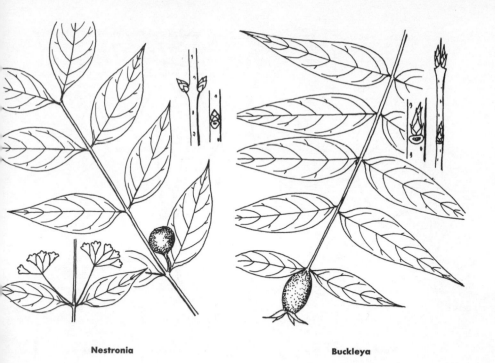

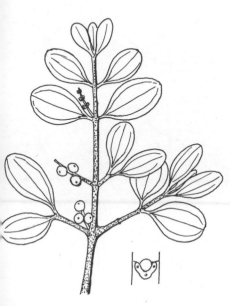

Nestronia

Buckleya

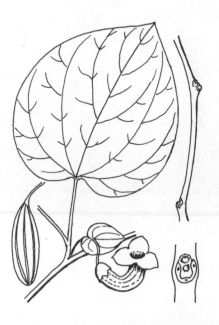

American Mistletoe

Dutchman's-Pipe

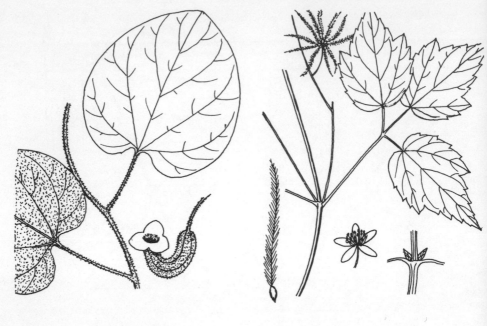

Woolly Pipevine

Common Virgin's-bower

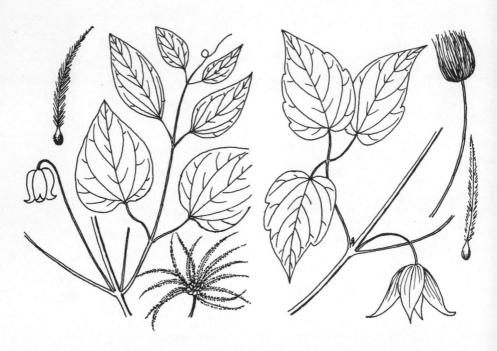

Leatherflower

Purple Virgin's-bower

WOOLLY PIPEVINE   *Aristolochia tomentosa* Sims

FIELD MARKS. A twining, leaf-losing vine usually found in bottomlands or along the banks of streams. *Branchlets* densely white-woolly. *Leaves* alternate, roundish heart-shaped, untoothed on margin, smooth or nearly so above, densely white-woolly beneath, 3 to 6 inches broad; leafstalks white-woolly beneath, 3 to 6 inches broad; leafstalks white-woolly. *Flowers* similar to those of the Dutchman's Pipe but the yellowish calyx tube downy. *Fruits* similar to those of Dutchman's Pipe but more or less woolly.

RANGE. North Carolina to southwestern Indiana, southern Illinois, Missouri, and Kansas; south to Florida and eastern Texas.

CROWFOOT FAMILY (Ranunculaceae)

VIRGIN'S-BOWERS (Clematis L.)

Virgin's-bowers are more or less soft-woody climbing vines or sometimes erect plants. They have opposite, compound leaves which sometimes end in a tendril. The leafstalks of the climbing species bend and twine about supporting objects. Their flowers are usually showy and have 4 petal-like parts which are really sepals. The fruits are achenes on which the style remains as a long, silky or plumelike tail; and they are grouped in fluffy and showy clusters.

COMMON VIRGIN'S-BOWER   *Clematis virginiana* L.

FIELD MARKS. A climbing, leaf-losing vine with stems to 20 feet long; growing over bushes along streams, borders of swamps and woods, and in wayside thickets. *Branchlets* furrowed, downy. *Leaves* usually with 3 leaflets which are egg-shaped, pointed at tip, rounded to somewhat heart-shaped at base, coarsely toothed on margin, smooth or nearly so on both surfaces, 1½ to 4 inches long. *Flowers* white, about ¾ inch across, in leafy-bracted clusters on stalks from the axils of leaves; blooming in June and July. *Fruits* silver gray, in dense clusters about 2 inches across.

RANGE. Nova Scotia to Manitoba; south to Georgia, Louisiana, and eastern Kansas.

LEATHERFLOWER   *Clematis viorna* L.

FIELD MARKS. A slightly woody, leaf-losing vine with slender stems 8 to 12 feet long; growing in thickets on rich soils. *Branchlets* furrowed, finely downy. *Leaves* with 3 to 7 leaflets which are egg-shaped, pointed at tip, bluntly pointed to rounded or heart-shaped at base, untoothed on margin, firm in texture, smooth or nearly so on both surfaces, 1¼ to 3 inches long. *Flowers* solitary on a long stalk from leaf axils, bell-shaped, nodding, with thick, leathery, reddish-purple sepals; blooming between May and August. *Fruits* with brownish plumelike tails 1½ or more inches long.

RANGE. Southern Pennsylvania to southern Illinois and southeastern Iowa, south to Georgia and Texas.

PURPLE VIRGIN'S-BOWER   *Clematis verticillaris* DC.

FIELD MARKS. A climbing, woody, leaf-losing vine with smooth, 6-sided, brown stems to 15 feet long; growing in rich, rocky woods. *Leaves* with 3 leaflets which are egg-shaped to heart-shaped, untoothed or sparingly toothed on margin, thin, smooth or nearly so on both surfaces, 1¼ to 3 inches long. *Flowers* solitary on long stems from the leaf axils, purple or bluish purple, 2 to 3 inches across; blooming in May or June. *Fruits* with grayish to brownish plumelike tails about 2 inches long.

RANGE. Eastern Quebec to Manitoba; south to Delaware, Maryland, West Virginia, Ohio, Illinois, and northeastern Iowa.

SHRUB YELLOWROOT *Xanthorhiza simplicissima* **Marsh.**

FIELD MARKS. A sparingly-branched, leaf-losing shrub 8 inches to 2 feet high; growing in cool, moist woods and along the banks of streams. *Wood* of both stems and roots is very bright yellow. *Leaves* alternate, more or less clustered toward the summits of the short branchlets, usually divided into 5 leaflets which are deeply cut-toothed and often cleft, thin, bright green and lustrous on both surfaces. *Flowers* small, brownish purple, in drooping clusters; blooming in April or May and occasionally in the fall. *Fruits* small, light yellow, inflated, 1-seeded capsules, 4 to 8 grouped together.

RANGE. Southwestern New York southward, chiefly in the mountains, to Alabama and northwestern Florida.

Roots are used medicinally and to make a yellow dye.

MOONSEED FAMILY (Menispermaceae)

COMMON MOONSEED *Menispermum canadanse* **L.**

FIELD MARKS. A soft-wooded, leaf-losing vine with slender, faintly grooved, twining stems; growing in woods and along streams. *Leaves* alternate, broadly egg-shaped or roundish, untoothed but usually 3- to 7-lobed or angled, dark green and smooth above, paler and often slightly downy beneath, attached to the long leafstalks a little within the margin of the leaf blades, 3 to 8 inches wide. *Flowers* small, greenish white, blooming in June and July. *Fruits* roundish, bluish black with a whitish bloom, about ⅜ inch in diameter; resembling small grapes but with a single flattened and crescent-shaped seed.

RANGE. Western New England and Quebec to Manitoba; south to Georgia, Alabama, Arkansas, and Oklahoma.

Roots have been used medicinally. The fruits are said to be poisonous.

RED-BERRIED MOONSEED *Cocculus carolinus* **(L.) DC.**

FIELD MARKS. A scrambling, leaf-losing vine with slender and usually downy stems; growing in rich woods and thickets, usually along streams. *Leaves* alternate, heart-shaped, egg-shaped, or triangular, margin untoothed but sometimes lobed, smooth or nearly so above, downy beneath, 2 to 4 inches long; leafstalks slender, ¾ to 1½ inches long. *Flowers* small, greenish; blooming June to August. *Fruits* roundish, red, about ¼ inch in diameter, with a single flattened, crescent-shaped seed; ripe from August to October.

RANGE. Southeastern Virginia to Kentucky, southern Illinois, Missouri, and southeastern Kansas; south to Florida and Louisiana.

Also called Carolina Moonseed.

CUPSEED *Calycocarpum lyoni* **(Pursh) Gray**

FIELD MARKS. A rather smooth, high-climbing, leaf-losing vine of rich, usually bottom-land woods. *Leaves* alternate, heart-shaped with 3 to 5 rather long lobes which are pointed at the tips and sometimes have a few coarse wavy teeth, thin in texture, smooth above, often somewhat downy beneath, 5 to 8 inches long; leafstalks 2 to 6 inches long. *Flowers* small, greenish, blooming in May or June. *Fruits* roundish to oval, black, nearly 1 inch long, with a single flattened and dish-shaped seed; ripe from August to October.

RANGE. Kentucky to southern Illinois, Missouri, and eastern Kansas; south to Florida and Louisiana.

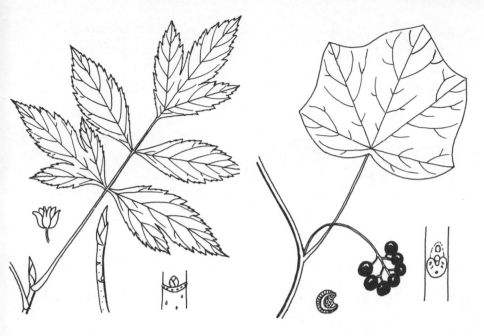

Shrub Yellowroot

Common Moonseed

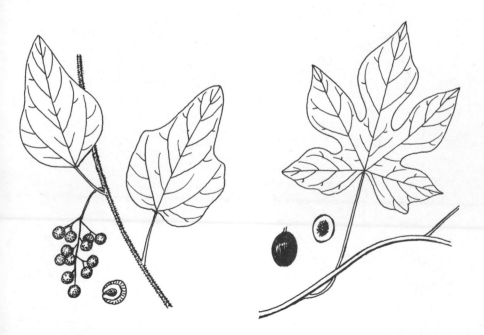

Red-berried Moonseed

Cupseed

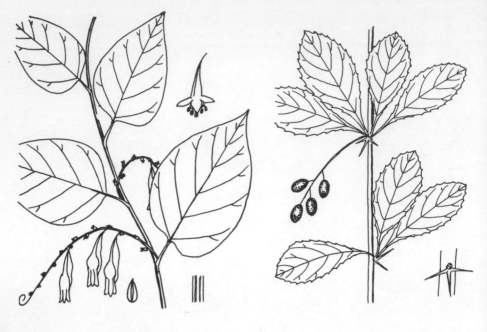

Brunnichia

American Barberry

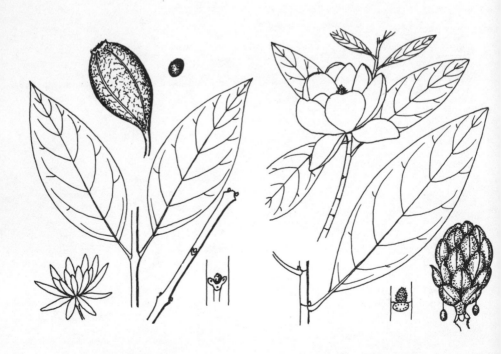

Strawberry-shrub

Sweetbay Magnolia

BUCKWHEAT FAMILY (Polygonaceae)

BRUNNICHIA   *Brunnichia cirrhosa* Banks x Gaertn.

FIELD MARKS. A leaf-losing vine with grooved stems, climbing by means of tendrils at tips of branches; growing in swamps and along banks of streams. *Leaves* alternate, egg-shaped, pointed at tip, sometimes heart-shaped at the broad base, untoothed on margin, often slightly downy beneath, 1 to 6 inches long. *Flowers* greenish, 2 to 5 in a cluster. *Fruits* dry, 1-seeded, 3-angled, brown, enclosed by a persistent calyx which develops a broad wing.

RANGE. Chiefly coastal plain; South Carolina south to Florida, west to Texas; north in Mississippi Valley to southern Illinois and southeastern Missouri.

BARBERRY FAMILY (Berberidaceae)

AMERICAN BARBERRY   *Berberis canadensis* Mill.

FIELD MARKS. A leaf-losing shrub 3 to 6 feet high, armed with 3-pronged spines at nodes; growing chiefly in woods of the southern Appalachians. *Branchlets* slender, dark brown, minutely warty, yellow within. *Leaves* alternate or in lateral clusters, broadest near or above the middle, usually rounded at tip, wedge-shaped at base, sharply toothed on margin, smooth or nearly so, ¾ to 2 inches long. *Flowers* yellow, in 5- to 15-flowered clusters; blooming May or June. *Fruits* oval-shaped, bright-red berries about ⅜ inch long, in drooping clusters; ripening September or October.

RANGE. South-central Pennsylvania south to Georgia; also in Missouri.

Serves as an alternate host of black stem rust of wheat.

CALYCANTHUS FAMILY (Calycanthaceae)

STRAWBERRY-SHRUB   *Calycanthus floridus* L.

FIELD MARKS. A leaf-losing, aromatic shrub 3 to 9 feet high; growing in rich woods and along streams. *Branchlets* dark brown, somewhat enlarged and flattened at nodes, spicy-aromatic when bruised. *Leaves* opposite, elliptic or egg-shaped, pointed at tip, pointed to roundish at base, untoothed on margin, often roughish or rather lustrous above, smooth to somewhat downy beneath, 2 to 6 inches long, spicy-aromatic when crushed (or in var. *laevigatus* (Willd.) T. & G. lustrous green and smooth or whitened beneath). *Flowers* greenish brown to dark reddish brown or maroon, 1 to 2 inches across, almost odorless or with a decided strawberry-like fragrance; blooming April to August. *Fruits* urn-shaped capsules 2 to 2½ inches long; containing many large hard-coated seeds.

RANGE. South-central Pennsylvania and southern Ohio south, chiefly in mountains and upper piedmont, to Florida and Mississippi.

Also called Sweetshrub or Carolina-allspice. Commonly cultivated.

MAGNOLIA FAMILY (Magnoliaceae)

SWEETBAY MAGNOLIA   *Magnolia virginiana* L.

FIELD MARKS. A large shrub to medium-sized tree, leaf-losing or evergreen southward; growing in swampy places and along streams. *Branchlets* green, ringed at the nodes with stipule scars, spicy-fragrant when bruised. *Leaves* alternate, oval to narrowly elliptic, usually pointed at both ends, untoothed on margin, lustrous above, whitened beneath, 3 to 5 inches long, spicy-aromatic when crushed. *Flowers* cup-shaped, creamy white, 2 to 3 inches across, very fragrant; blooming April to June. *Fruits* borne in conelike clusters; the individual fruits podlike, splitting down the outside and releasing the scarlet-coated seeds on silklike threads; ripening July to October.

RANGE. Chiefly coastal plain; southeastern Massachusetts and southern Pennsylvania south to Florida, west to Texas, north in Mississippi Valley to eastern Tennessee and southern Arkansas.

107

PURPLE-ANISE *Illicium floridanum* Ellis.

FIELD MARKS. An aromatic evergreen shrub 6 to 18 feet high; growing in stream bottoms, swamps, or low hammocks. *Leaves* alternate, more or less crowded toward tips of the branchlets, elliptic, pointed at both ends, margin untoothed, smooth, dark green above, paler beneath, leathery, veins except the midrib not prominent, with an anise-like odor when crushed, 2½ to 6 inches long. *Flowers* dark red, ill-scented, about 1½ inches across, with many strap-shaped petals. *Fruits* 1-seeded greenish capsules in a wheel-shaped cluster about 1¼ inches across.

RANGE. Coastal plain; northern Florida west to Louisiana.

Also called Anise-tree, Starbush, and Stinkbush.

WILD-SARSAPARILLA *Schisandra glabra* (Brickell) Rehd.

FIELD MARKS. A leaf-losing, aromatic, twining, woody vine; growing in low, rich woods. *Leaves* alternate, sometimes clustered on short lateral spurs, elliptic to oval or egg-shaped, pointed at both ends, sometimes with a few marginal teeth, bright green and smooth on both surfaces, 1½ to 5 inches long; leafstalks long and slender. *Flowers* crimson, about ½ inch across, 5- or 6-petalled; blooming May or June. *Fruits* berry-like, bright red, about ⅜ inch long, arranged along a drooping stem.

RANGE. Coastal plain; North Carolina south to Florida, west to Louisiana; north in Mississippi Valley to western Tennessee.

Also called Star-vine. The stamens and pistils are in separate flowers.

CUSTARD-APPLE FAMILY (Annonaceae)

PAWPAWS (Asimina Adans)

Pawpaws are leaf-losing shrubs or small trees with alternate, simple leaves. The flowers have 3 sepals, 3 petals, numerous stamens in a globe-shaped cluster, and several pistils. The fruits are rather large, cylindrical berries which have several big seeds and a soft, pulpy, edible flesh.

DWARF PAWPAW *Asimina parviflora* (Michx.) Dunal.

FIELD MARKS. A shrub 2 to 5 feet high, growing in dry oak and pine woods. *Branchlets* slender, densely rusty-hairy, ill-scented when bruised. *Leaves* broadest above the middle, blunt, short-pointed, or notched at tip, wedge-shaped at base, margin untoothed, thickish in texture, smooth or nearly so above, rusty-hairy beneath, 2 to 5 inches long. *Flowers* reddish brown to purplish brown, about ¾ inch across; blooming April or May, before the leaves appear. *Fruits* greenish yellow becoming brown, 1 to 2 inches long, with oval-shaped and slightly flattened seeds; ripening July to September.

RANGE. Southeastern Virginia to northwestern South Carolina, south to Florida and Louisiana.

Also called Possum-simmon.

COMMON PAWPAW *Asimina triloba* (L.) Dunal.

FIELD MARKS. A shrub or small tree (rarely) to 40 feet high; growing in low woods and along streams. *Branchlets* slender, rusty-hairy to smooth, ill-scented when bruised. *Leaves* broadest toward tip and tapering to a wedge-shaped base, abruptly short-pointed at tip, margin untoothed, thin and veiny in appearance, smooth or nearly so at maturity, paler beneath, 6 to 12 inches long. *Flowers* purplish brown to greenish brown, 1 to 1½ inches across; blooming March to May, before the leaves appear. *Fruits* greenish yellow becoming brown, 2½ to 5 inches long, with elongate and slightly flattened seeds; ripening August to October.

RANGE. New Jersey to Michigan, south to Florida and Texas.

The tropical appearance of the foliage makes this plant a handsome ornamental.

Purple-Anise

Wild-sarsaparilla

Dwarf Pawpaw

Common Pawpaw

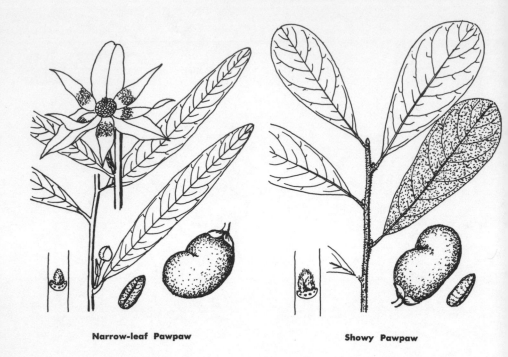

Narrow-leaf Pawpaw

Showy Pawpaw

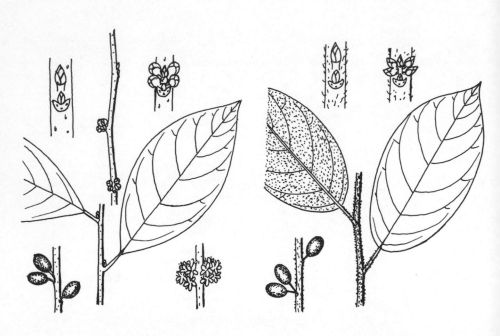

Common Spicebush

Hairy Spicebush

NARROW-LEAF PAWPAW *Asimina angustifolia* Gray

FIELD MARKS. A shrub 2 to 4 feet high; growing in dry sandy pinelands. *Branchlets* minutely downy to smooth, ill-scented when bruised. *Leaves* narrow, blunt or somewhat pointed at tip, pointed at base, untoothed on margin, somewhat leathery in texture, smooth and rather lustrous above, paler and often tawny-downy beneath, 2½ to about 4 inches long, ½ to ¾ inch wide. *Flowers* creamy white, the inner petals often reddish purple at the base, 2 to 3 inches across, borne in the axils of the new leaves; blooming April or May. *Fruits* greenish yellow becoming brown, usually more or less lopsided, 1½ to 2½ inches long, the seeds elongate.

RANGE. Coastal plain; southern Georgia, northern Florida, and southeastern Alabama.

SHOWY PAWPAW *Asimina speciosa* Nash

FIELD MARKS. A shrub 2 to about 4 feet high; growing in sandy pinelands. *Branchlets* densely tawny-woolly, ill-scented when bruised. *Leaves* narrowly top-shaped, broadest toward the rounded tip and gradually narrowed to the base, untoothed on margin, somewhat leathery in texture, smooth or nearly so above, velvety with tawny wool beneath, 1½ to about 3 inches long, often 1½ inches wide. *Flowers* white or creamy white, 3 to 4 inches across, developing from buds formed the previous season; blooming April or May. Fruits greenish yellow becoming brown, somewhat lopsided, 1½ to 2½ inches long, the seeds elongate.

RANGE. Coastal plain; southeastern Georgia and northeastern Florida.

This and the preceding species are often called Flag Pawpaw or Dog-apple.

LAUREL FAMILY (Lauraceae)

COMMON SPICEBUSH *Lindera benzoin* (L.) Blume

FIELD MARKS. A leaf-losing, aromatic shrub 3 to 15 feet high; growing in moist woods and along streams. *Branchlets* slender, smooth, brittle, greenish brown to olive brown, spicy-fragrant when broken. *Leaves* alternate, elliptic or broadest above the middle, pointed at both ends, untoothed on margin, smooth on both sides or sparingly downy beneath, bright green above, paler beneath, spicy-fragrant when crushed, 2 to 6 inches long. *Flowers* small, honey-yellow, fragrant, clustered at the nodes; blooming in March or April, before the leaves appear. *Fruits* oval-shaped, bright red, 1-seeded, about ⅜ inch long, very spicy-aromatic when crushed; ripening July to September.

RANGE. Southeastern Maine to southern Ontario, southern Michigan, Iowa, and southeastern Kansas; south to Florida and Texas.

Also called Benjamin-bush and Wild-allspice. The leaves have been used to make a tea, and the dried powdered fruits are used as a substitute for allspice. The fruits are eaten by many wild birds, and the twigs are often eaten by deer and rabbits.

HAIRY SPICEBUSH *Lindera melissaefolium* (Walt.) Blume

FIELD MARKS. A leaf-losing, aromatic shrub 2 to about 6 feet high; growing in swamps and about the borders of ponds. *Branchlets* slender, downy, spicy-fragrant when broken. *Leaves* alternate, lance-shaped to elliptic, pointed at tip, rounded to slightly heart-shaped at base, smooth or nearly so above, densely downy beneath, spicy-fragrant when crushed, 2 to 6 inches long. *Flowers* similar to those of preceding species; blooming March or April. *Fruits* similar to those of the preceding species but often larger and inversely egg-shaped; ripening August or September.

RANGE. Chiefly coastal plain; North Carolina south to Florida, west to Alabama; north in Mississippi Valley to southern Missouri and southern Illinois.

Uncommon and local in distribution. Also known as Jove's-fruit.

111

PONDSPICE   *Litsea aestivalis* (L.) Fern.

FIELD MARKS. A leaf-losing, aromatic shrub 6 to 10 feet high; growing in low wet woods and pond and swamp margins. *Branchlets* slender, zigzag, frequently forked, spicy-aromatic when broken. *Leaves* alternate, elliptic, pointed at both ends, untoothed on margin, smooth, somewhat leathery in texture, dark green above, paler beneath, spicy-aromatic when crushed, ¾ to 2 inches long. *Flowers* small, honey yellow, in clusters of 2 to 4; blooming February to April, before the leaves. *Fruits* roundish, red, 1-seeded, spicy-aromatic, about ¼ inch in diameter; ripening in May or June.

RANGE. Coastal plain; North Carolina south to Florida.

Rare and local in occurrence.

SASSAFRAS   *Sassafras albidum* (Nutt.) Nees

FIELD MARKS. A leaf-losing, aromatic shrub or tree, sometimes 20 to 40 feet high; growing in borders of woods, old fields, and along fence rows. *Branchlets* yellowish green to reddish, brittle, smooth or finely downy, with a spicy-aromatic odor when broken. *Leaves* alternate, oval or elliptic and often with 1 or 2 lobes, bluntly pointed at tip, pointed at base, smooth or nearly so above but sometimes slightly downy beneath, spicy-aromatic when crushed, 3 to 6 inches long. *Flowers* greenish yellow; blooming March to May, before the leaves. *Fruits* oval-shaped, dark blue, 1-seeded, borne on club-shaped red stalks; ripening June to October.

RANGE. Southwestern Maine to Michigan and southeastern Iowa, south to Florida and Texas.

The bark of the roots is used to make sassafras tea and is the source of an oil used as a flavoring in candies and medicines and to perfume soaps. The fruits are eaten by many kinds of wild birds, including the bobwhite quail and wild turkey, and the twigs are eaten by deer and rabbits.

SAXIFRAGE FAMILY (Saxifragaceae)

MOCK-ORANGES (Philadelphus L.)

The mock-oranges are leaf-losing shrubs with simple, opposite leaves. The leaves have 3 to 5 prominent veins from near the base, and the leafstalks are short. They have showy flowers with 4 white petals and numerous stamens. The fruits are cup-shaped capsules on which the 4 calyx lobes persist at the summit, and they contain numerous minute seeds. The branchlets are often somewhat 6-sided or lined and have a large white pith. Excellent for ornamental planting.

COMMON MOCK-ORANGE   *Philadelphus inodorus* L.

FIELD MARKS. A shrub 3 to 10 feet high, growing on rocky slopes and along streams. *Branchlets* smooth, with reddish-brown bark that is soon shed in thin papery flakes; the buds concealed by the leaf scars. *Leaves* egg-shaped, sharply pointed at tip, somewhat pointed or rounded at base, margin usually with some widely spaced but sharply pointed teeth, usually smooth on both surfaces but sometimes roughish above or sparingly hairy beneath, 2 to 4 inches long. *Flowers* 1 to 4 at tips of short branchlets, 1½ to 2 inches across, odorless or nearly so, with distinctly separate stigmas; blooming in May or June. *Fruits* usually smooth and with ascending calyx lobes.

RANGE. Virginia and Tennessee south to Florida and Alabama.

HAIRY MOCK-ORANGE   *Philadelphus hirsutus* Nutt.

FIELD MARKS. A shrub 2 to 5 feet high; growing on rocky slopes and along the banks of streams. *Branchlets* appressed-hairy, the brown bark soon shed in thin papery flakes; buds not hidden by the leaf scars. *Leaves* egg-shaped, pointed at tip, pointed to rounded at base, sharply toothed on margin, smooth or nearly so above, densely grayish-downy beneath, 1½ to 3 inches long. *Flowers* usually in clusters of 3 at the tips of short branchlets, about 1 inch across, odorless, with united stigmas; blooming in May or June. *Fruits* hairy, the calyx lobes spreading.

RANGE. North Carolina and Kentucky south to Georgia and Alabama.

112

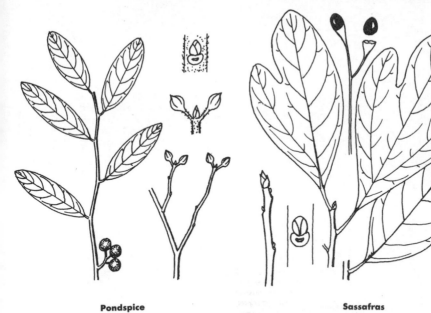

Pondspice   **Sassafras**

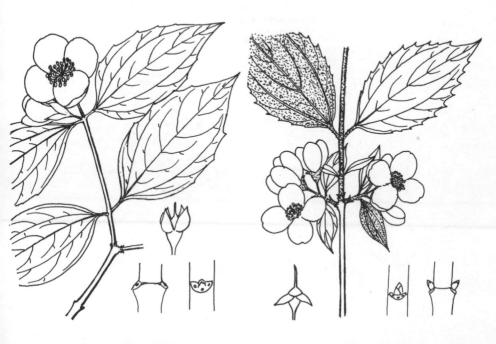

Common Mock-orange   **Hairy Mock-orange**

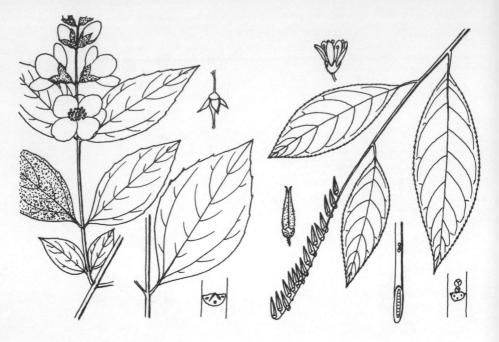

Downy Mock-orange

Virginia Willow

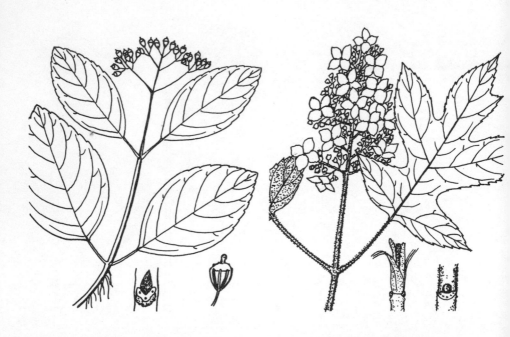

Climbing-Hydrangea

Oakleaf Hydrangea

DOWNY MOCK-ORANGE   *Philadelphus pubescens* Loisel.

FIELD MARKS. A shrub 3 to 10 feet high; growing on rocky bluffs and the banks of streams. *Branchlets* gray or sometimes straw-colored, the bark not freely peeling; buds hidden by the leaf scars. *Leaves* egg-shaped or elliptic, sharply pointed at tip, broadly pointed or rounded at base, usually with some sharp teeth on margin, dark green and smooth or nearly so above, densely grayish-downy beneath, 1½ to 4 inches long. *Flowers* in end clusters of 5 to 9, 1 to 1½ inches across, odorless or nearly so; blooming in May or June. *Fruits* downy, the calyx lobes spreading or reflexed.

RANGE. Tennessee to southern Illinois, south to Alabama and Arkansas.

VIRGINIA WILLOW   *Itea virginica* L.

FIELD MARKS. A leaf-losing shrub 3 to 8 feet high with slender and wandlike branches; growing in swamps and along streams. *Branchlets* slender, green or reddish-tinged, often minutely downy, the white pith showing interruptions when cut lengthwise. *Leaves* alternate, elliptic or sometimes broadest above the middle, pointed at both ends, finely and sharply toothed on margin, smooth on both surfaces or sparingly hairy beneath, 2 to 4 inches long. *Flowers* rather small, 5-petalled, white, in narrow upright end clusters 3 to 5 inches long; blooming April to June. *Fruits* narrowly cone-shaped, 2-grooved, downy capsules about ¼ inch long; containing numerous small flattened seeds.

RANGE. New Jersey and southeastern Pennsylvania south to Florida; southern Illinois, Kentucky, and Missouri south to Louisiana and Texas.

Also called Sweet-spires and Tassel-white.

CLIMBING-HYDRANGEA   *Decumaria barbara* L.

FIELD MARKS. A semi-evergreen vine climbing trunks of trees by means of aerial rootlets on its stems; growing in rich, moist woods and swamps. *Leaves* opposite, egg-shaped or elliptic, broadly pointed to roundish at base, usually somewhat pointed at tip, margin usually with low teeth above the middle, bright green and lustrous above, paler and sometimes slightly downy beneath, thickish in texture, 1½ to 4 inches long. *Flowers* small, white, fragrant, in stalked flat-topped clusters at ends of branchlets; blooming April to June. *Fruits* small, urn-shaped, prominently ribbed capsules containing numerous small seeds.

RANGE. Southeastern Virginia to northwestern South Carolina and Tennessee, south to Florida and Texas.

HYDRANGEAS (Hydrangea L.)

Hydrangeas are leaf-losing shrubs with opposite, long-stalked, simple leaves; soft-wooded, mostly rather stout branchlets with a large whitish pith. The flowers are in dense and usually flat-topped clusters and are of two types: small ones which have stamens and pistils and produce fruits and seeds; and much larger, showy, but sterile ones which usually have 4 petal-like rays. The fruits are small urn-shaped capsules which contain a large number of very small seeds.

OAKLEAF HYDRANGEA   *Hydrangea quercifolia* Bartr.

FIELD MARKS. A shrub 3 to 7 feet high; growing on bluffs and stream banks. *Branchlets* rusty-woolly. *Leaves* egg-shaped to roundish, deeply 3- to 7-lobed and also sharply toothed on margin, thickish and somewhat leathery in texture, dark green and smooth above, whitish- to tawny-woolly beneath, 3 to 8 inches long; leafstalks rusty-woolly. *Flowers* in cone-shaped clusters 4 to 12 inches long, the numerous sterile ones about 1 inch across and turning purple.

RANGE. Chiefly coastal plain and adjacent piedmont; Georgia to northern Florida and west to Louisiana.

Often cultivated as an ornamental and sometimes escaping.

WILD HYDRANGEA   *Hydrangea arborescens* L.

FIELD MARKS. A loosely branched shrub 3 to 6 feet high; growing on shaded banks and along streams. *Branchlets* pale brown, smooth or nearly so. *Leaves* roundish to egg-shaped, elliptic, or broadly lance-shaped, round to heart-shaped or broadly pointed at base, sharply pointed at tip, sharply toothed on margin, smooth or nearly so on both surfaces, dark green above, paler green beneath, 3 to 6 inches long. *Flowers* in flat-topped end clusters, creamy white, usually with several sterile flowers about ⅝ inch across; blooming May to July.

RANGE. New York to Illinois, Missouri, and Oklahoma; south to Florida and Louisiana.

The cultivated Hills-of-snow Hydrangea is a form with only sterile flowers.

ASHY HYDRANGEA   *Hydrangea arborescens* ssp. *discolor* (Seringe) McClintock

Differs from the preceding in having leaves which are grayish beneath. West Virginia to Indiana, Illinois, and Missouri; south to Georgia and Alabama. (Not illustrated)

SNOWY HYDRANGEA   *Hydrangea arborescens* ssp. *radiata* (Walt.) McClintock

Leaves are snowy white with felted down on the lower surfaces. Grows in rocky woods from western North Carolina and eastern Tennessee to northern Georgia. (Not illustrated)

CURRANTS AND GOOSEBERRIES (Ribes L.)

(Key Appendix C)

Currants and gooseberries are leaf-losing shrubs with alternate leaves and leaves clustered on short lateral spurs. The flowers are small, bell-shaped, and borne singly or in small clusters. The fruits are pulpy berries tipped with the remains of the calyx. These shrubs are alternate hosts of the blister rust which affects white pine trees. The fruits of most species are edible and used to make jelly, preserves, or pies.

FLORIDA GOOSEBERRY   *Ribes echinellum* (Cov.) Rehd.

FIELD MARKS. A shrub 1½ to 3 feet high; growing in rich woods. *Branchlets grayish,* armed with slender nodal spines. *Leaves* roundish or broader than long, somewhat pointed to rather square at base, with 3 to 5 coarsely toothed lobes, smooth above, sparingly hairy beneath, ½ to 1 inch wide; leafstalks slender. *Flowers* whitish; blooming March or April. *Fruits* about ½ inch in diameter, greenish, densely covered with slender gland-tipped spines; ripening June to September.

RANGE. South-central South Carolina and north-central Florida.

ROUNDLEAF GOOSEBERRY   *Ribes rotundifolium* Michx.

FIELD MARKS. A shrub 2 to 3 feet high; growing in cool rocky mountain woods. *Branchlets* pale brown or grayish, unarmed or with short nodal spines. *Leaves* roundish, often heart-shaped at base, usually with 3 bluntly toothed lobes, smooth or minutely downy above, sometimes sparingly hairy beneath, ¾ to 3 inches wide. *Flowers* greenish purple, solitary or 2 or 3 in a cluster; blooming April to July. *Fruits* smooth, purplish, ¼ to ⅜ inch in diameter, sweet; ripening June to September.

RANGE. Massachusetts to New York and Kentucky; south to western North Carolina and eastern Tennessee.

Also called Mountain Gooseberry.

PRICKLY GOOSEBERRY   *Ribes cynosbati* L.

FIELD MARKS. A shrub 1½ to 4 feet high; growing in rocky woods and clearings. *Branchlets* pale brown or grayish, with slender nodal spines and often scattered prickles. *Leaves* roundish, often heart-shaped at base, 3- to 5-lobed and bluntly toothed, soft-hairy on both surfaces or nearly smooth, 1½ to 2½ inches wide. *Flowers* greenish, solitary or 2 or 3 in a cluster; blooming April to June. *Fruits* prickly, reddish purple, ⅓ to ½ inch in diameter, sweet; ripening July to September.

RANGE. New Brunswick to Manitoba; south to Georgia, Alabama, and Missouri.

Also called Pasture Gooseberry and Dogberry.

Wild Hydrangea

Florida Gooseberry

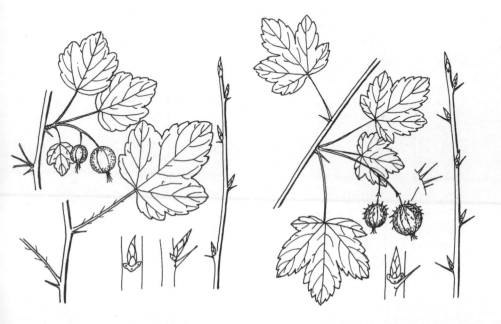

Roundleaf Gooseberry

Prickly Gooseberry

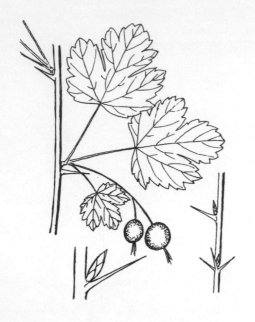

Missouri Gooseberry

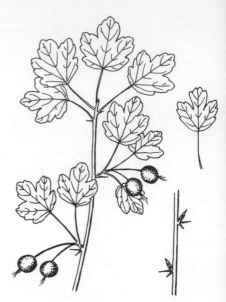

Granite Gooseberry

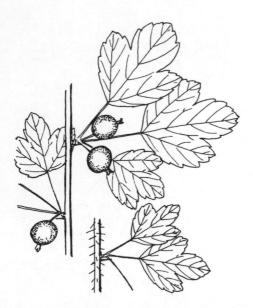

Northern Gooseberry

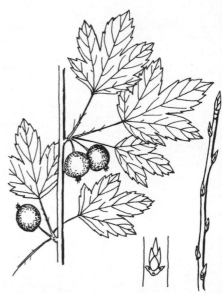

Smooth Gooseberry

MISSOURI GOOSEBERRY *Ribes missouriense* Nutt.

FIELD MARKS. An erect shrub 3 to 6 feet high; growing in dry woods, ravines, and on stream banks. *Branchlets* whitish or gray, with stout red nodal spines to ⅝ inch long and often with scattered prickles. *Leaves* flattened to rounded, or heart-shaped at base, 3- to 5-lobed and toothed on margin, smooth or nearly so above, somewhat hairy beneath, ¾ to 1½ inches wide. *Flowers* white or greenish white, solitary or 2 to 3 on a slender stalk longer than the leafstalks; blooming April and May. *Fruits* smooth, purplish, about ½ inch in diameter, sweet; ripening July to September.

RANGE. Connecticut to Michigan, Minnesota, and South Dakota; south to Tennessee, Arkansas, and Kansas. Rare eastward.

GRANITE GOOSEBERRY *Ribes curvatum* Small

FIELD MARKS. A diffusely branched shrub 2 to 4 feet high, with recurving or drooping branches; growing in rocky woods and slopes. *Branchlets* reddish brown to purplish brown with short, slender, red nodal spines. *Leaves* roundish, broadly pointed to somewhat heart-shaped at base, 3- or sometimes 5-lobed and with few bluntish teeth on margin, sparingly hairy or nearly smooth, ⅜ to 1 inch wide. *Flowers* white, solitary or 2 to 5 on a slender stalk; blooming April or May. *Fruits* greenish, ¼ to ⅜ inch in diameter; ripening June to August.

RANGE. Northern Georgia and Alabama and southeastern Tennessee.

NORTHERN GOOSEBERRY *Ribes oxyacanthoides* L.

FIELD MARKS. A shrub 1½ to 3 feet high; growing in cool, moist, northern woods. *Branchlets* with short nodal spines and often bristly between. *Leaves* roundish, flattened to somewhat heart-shaped at base, 3- to 5-lobed and bluntly toothed on margin, somewhat hairy and also glandular beneath, ¾ to 1½ inches wide. *Flowers* greenish white or purplish, 1 or 2 on a stalk shorter than the leafstalks; blooming May to July. *Fruits* smooth, reddish purple, about ⅜ inch in diameter, sweet; ripening July and August.

RANGE. Northern Ontario to Yukon; south to Michigan, Minnesota, South Dakota, and Montana.

SMOOTH GOOSEBERRY *Ribes hirtellum* Michx.

FIELD MARKS. An erect shrub 1 to 3 feet high; growing in swamps and cool, moist, rocky woods. *Branchlets* grayish, unarmed or with very small nodal spines, sometimes bristly between. *Leaves* roundish, usually more or less pointed but sometimes roundish to heart-shaped at base, deeply 3- to 5-lobed and sharply toothed on margin, smooth or nearly so on both surfaces, ¾ to 2½ inches wide. *Flowers* greenish or purplish, 1 to 3 on a stalk shorter than the leafstalks; blooming April to July. *Fruits* smooth, purplish to black, about ⅜ inch in diameter, sweet; ripening June to September.

RANGE. Southern Labrador to eastern Manitoba; south to Maryland, West Virginia, and the region of the Great Lakes.

BRISTLY GOOSEBERRY *Ribes setosum* Lindl.

FIELD MARKS. An erect or spreading shrub 2 to 3 feet high; growing on rocky slopes and lakeshores. *Branchlets* reddish brown, unarmed or with nodal spines up to ¾ inch long and usually bristly. *Leaves* roundish, deeply 3- to 5-lobed and sharply toothed, usually somewhat hairy on both surfaces, ½ to 1½ inches wide. *Flowers* greenish white, 1 to 4 on a stalk; blooming in May. *Fruits* red or black, smooth or sparingly bristly; ripening July and August.

RANGE. North-central Ontario to Manitoba; south to northern Michigan, Wisconsin, and Nebraska. (Not illustrated)

119

WILD BLACK CURRANT *Ribes americanum* L'Her.

FIELD MARKS. An erect unarmed shrub 1½ to 4 feet high, with spreading branches; growing in rich, moist, often rocky woods. *Branchlets* dotted with small yellow resin-glands. *Leaves* roundish, squarish to somewhat heart-shaped at base, sharply 3- to 5-lobed and double-toothed on margin, smooth or nearly so above, more or less downy and dotted with yellow resin-glands beneath, 1½ to 3 inches wide. *Flowers* rather large, yellow and whitish, several in a drooping cluster; blooming April to June. *Fruits* smooth, black, about 5/16 inch in diameter; ripening July to September.

RANGE. Nova Scotia to Alberta; south to Delaware, West Virginia, the region of the Great Lakes, Missouri, and Oklahoma.

SWAMP BLACK CURRANT *Ribes lacustre* (Pers.) Poir.

FIELD MARKS. An erect shrub 1 to 3 feet high, with prickly and bristly stems; growing in cool, moist woods and swamps. *Branchlets* with 1 to 3 long nodal spines and prickly bristles between. *Leaves* roundish, heart-shaped at base, deeply 3- to 5-lobed and toothed on margin, smooth or nearly so on both surfaces, 1 to 3 inches wide. *Flowers* greenish or purplish, several in a drooping cluster; blooming May to July. *Fruits* glandular-bristly, purplish black, about 5/16 inch in diameter, unpleasant to the taste; ripening July to September.

RANGE. Newfoundland to Alaska; south to western Massachusetts, New York, southwestern Pennsylvania, the region of the Great Lakes, Colorado, Utah, and California.

SKUNK CURRANT *Ribes glandulosum* Grauer

FIELD MARKS. A low, prostrate, sprawling or reclining unarmed shrub, all parts giving off a skunklike odor when crushed; growing in cold, damp, rocky woods. *Leaves* broader than long, deeply 5- to 7-lobed and doubly toothed on margin, heart-shaped at base, smooth above, sometimes slightly downy beneath, 1½ to 3 inches wide. *Flowers* yellowish green or purplish, several in a slender-stalked cluster; blooming May or June. *Fruits* glandular-bristly, coral red, unpleasant to the taste; ripening July to September.

RANGE. Newfoundland to British Columbia; south to New England, New York, northern Ohio, Michigan, Minnesota, and in the Appalachian Mountains to western North Carolina and northwestern South Carolina.

SWAMP RED CURRANT *Ribes triste* Pall.

FIELD MARKS. A low sprawling or reclining unarmed shrub, with stems often rooting; growing in cold mossy woods and boggy places. It does not have a skunklike or other disagreeable odor when crushed. *Leaves* roundish or somewhat broader than long, flattened to somewhat heart-shaped at base, 3- to 5-lobed and irregularly toothed on margin, light green and smooth above, paler and somewhat white-woolly beneath, 2 to 4 inches wide. *Flowers* brownish or purplish, several in a drooping cluster; blooming May to July. *Fruits* smooth, bright red, about ¼ inch in diameter; ripening July to September.

RANGE. Labrador to Alaska; south to northern New Jersey, West Virginia, Michigan, South Dakota, and Oregon.

120

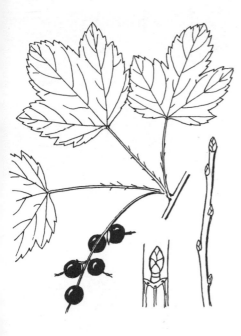

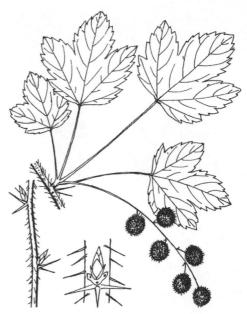

Wild Black Currant

Swamp Black Currant

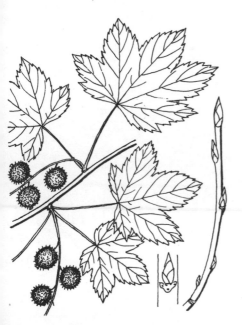

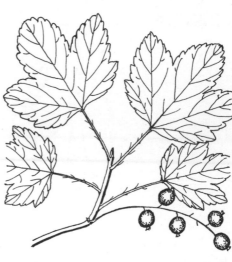

Skunk Currant

Swamp Red Currant

Buffalo Currant

Witch-Hazel

Mountain Witch-alder

Dwarf Witch-alder

BUFFALO CURRANT   *Ribes odoratum* Wendl.

FIELD MARKS. An unarmed shrub 4 to 6 feet high; growing on rocky bluffs, slopes, and along streams. *Branchlets* more or less minutely grayish-downy. *Leaves* roundish, deeply 3- to 5-lobed and usually coarsely toothed, broadly pointed to rather flat at base, smooth or nearly so above, sometimes more or less downy beneath, 1 to 3 inches long; the slender leafstalks usually somewhat hairy. *Flowers* bright yellow, spicy-fragrant, 5 to 10 in nodding and leafy-bracted axillary clusters; blooming April to June. *Fruits* black or (rarely) yellow, smooth, about ⅜ inch in diameter; ripening June to August.

RANGE. Minnesota and South Dakota south to Missouri, Arkansas, and Texas. Commonly cultivated and often escaping eastward.

Also called Golden or Missouri Currant.

WITCH-HAZEL FAMILY (Hamamelidaceae)

WITCH-HAZEL   *Hamamelis virginiana* L.

FIELD MARKS. A leaf-losing shrub or small tree 5 to 20 feet high; growing in rich woods, thickets, and clearings. *Branchlets* with stalked, naked buds; both roughish with tawny or rusty hairs. *Leaves* alternate, oval or broadest above the middle, unevenly rounded or heart-shaped at base, pointed or rounded at tip, irregularly wavy-toothed on margin, smooth above, paler and smooth or nearly so beneath, 2½ to 6 inches long (or in the variety *parvifolia* Nutt. with somewhat leathery leaves 1½ to 4 inches long, whitened and rather densely rusty-hairy beneath). *Flowers* bright yellow, with 4 ribbon-like petals; blooming September to November or later, usually after the leaves have fallen. *Fruits* urn-shaped, grayish-downy, woody capsules containing 2 shiny black seeds which are forcibly ejected in October or November.

RANGE. Nova Scotia to southern Ontario, central Michigan, and southeastern Minnesota; south to Florida and Texas.

The plant has astringent properties, and commercial witch-hazel is distilled from the bark. Twigs or bark eaten by deer and rabbits; seeds by ruffed grouse and bobwhite quail.

MOUNTAIN WITCH-ALDER   *Fothergilla major* (Sims) Lodd.

FIELD MARKS. A leaf-losing shrub 3 to 10 feet high; growing in woods of the southern Appalachians. *Branchlets* and buds downy. *Leaves* oval to roundish and often broadest above the middle, heart-shaped to broadly pointed at base, coarsely wavy-toothed on margin above the middle, smooth or nearly so above, paler or whitened and more or less hairy beneath, 2 to 4½ inches long. *Flowers* without petals but with numerous creamy-white stamens, in dense end clusters 1 to 2 inches long; blooming April or May. *Fruits* egg-shaped, downy, woody, 2-beaked capsules about ½ inch long, containing two lustrous brown seeds; maturing September or October and forcibly ejecting the seeds.

RANGE. Western North Carolina to northern Georgia and Alabama.

A handsome shrub suitable for ornamental planting.

DWARF WITCH-ALDER   *Fothergilla gardeni* Murr.

FIELD MARKS. A leaf-losing shrub 1 to 3 feet high, sometimes with creeping underground stems; growing in sandy coastal plain bogs and savannahs. *Branchlets* and buds densely downy. *Leaves* elliptic to oval or oblong and often broadest above the middle, pointed to roundish or heart-shaped at base, margin usually with some wavy teeth above the middle, usually with scattered starry-branched hairs above, paler and more densely coated with such hairs beneath, ¾ to 2¼ inches long. *Flowers* white, similar to those of preceding species, in dense clusters ¾ to 1¼ inches long; blooming April or May. *Fruits* similar to those of the preceding species but somewhat smaller.

RANGE. Virginia south to Florida, west to Mississippi; north in Mississippi Valley to western Tennessee.

COMMON NINEBARK *Physocarpus opulifolius* (L.) Maxim.

FIELD MARKS. A leaf-losing shrub 3 to 10 feet high, with arching branches and bark peeling off in thin papery layers; growing on rocky slopes, cliffs, and along streams. *Branchlets* with prominent ridges below the leaves or leaf scars, smooth to densely hairy with starry-branched hairs. *Leaves* alternate, roundish to egg-shaped, heart-shaped to roundish or broadly pointed at base, pointed to roundish at tip, commonly more or less 3-lobed and double-toothed on margin, smooth or nearly so above, smooth to downy or coated with starry-branched hairs beneath, ¾ to about 3 inches long. *Flowers* small, white or pinkish, 5-petalled, in often dense umbrella-shaped end clusters; blooming May to July. *Fruits* small, papery, red or purplish, smooth or hairy, inflated pods, 3 to 5 grouped on each stalk in the cluster; maturing July to September and persisting.

RANGE. Quebec and northern Ontario to Minnesota; south to Georgia, Tennessee, and Arkansas.

The hairy southern forms have been described as distinct species by some botanists but are not considered valid by others.

ALABAMA SNOW-WREATH *Neviusia alabamensis* Gray

FIELD MARKS. A leaf-losing shrub 4 to 6 feet high, with recurving branches; growing on shady cliffs and bluffs in a limited area of northwestern Alabama. *Branchlets* yellowish brown, downy, with ridges below the leaves or leaf scars. *Leaves* alternate, egg-shaped to somewhat rhombic, roundish to somewhat pointed at base, pointed to blunt at tip, sharply and doubly toothed on margin, smooth or nearly so on both surfaces, ¾ to 2½ inches long. *Flowers* white, petals none, sepals 5 (pale green or whitish and toothed), stamens white and numerous in a tassel-like cluster; blooming March to May. *Fruits* somewhat fleshy-coated achenes about 3/16 inch long, 2 to 4 in a group.

A very attractive ornamental shrub deserving much wider use in ornamental planting; hardy as far north as Massachusetts.

SPIRAEAS (Spiraea L.)

The spiraeas are rather low, leaf-losing shrubs with alternate, simple, short-stalked leaves and slender, often wandlike branches. They have small 5-petalled white or pink flowers in rather dense, narrow or flat-topped clusters. The fruits are small dry pods, usually in groups of 5, and they persist for some time after maturing.

NARROW-LEAF MEADOWSWEET *Spiraea alba* DuRoi

FIELD MARKS. An erect shrub 2 to 5 feet high; growing in wet open places, swamp thickets, and along streams. *Branchlets* yellowish brown, more or less angled, often slightly downy. *Leaves* numerous, crowded, narrowly elliptic or broadest above the middle, pointed at both ends, finely and sharply toothed on margin, smooth on both surfaces or slightly downy beneath, 2 to 3 inches long. *Flowers* white, in a narrow and somewhat downy end cluster from 2 to 5 inches in length; blooming June to September.

RANGE. Northwestern Vermont to southwestern Quebec and Saskatchewan; south to Delaware, Ohio, Illinois, Missouri, North Dakota, and in the Appalachian Mountains to North Carolina.

BROADLEAF MEADOWSWEET *Spiraea latifolia* (Ait.) Borkh.

FIELD MARKS. An erect shrub 2 to 4 feet high; growing in wet open places, swamp thickets, and along streams. *Branchlets* reddish brown to purplish brown, more or less angled, smooth or nearly so. *Leaves* numerous, crowded, broadly elliptic or sometimes broadest above the middle, blunt or broadly pointed at tip, pointed to roundish at base, rather coarsely and sharply toothed on margin, smooth or nearly so on both surfaces, 1 to 2½ inches long. *Flowers* white or pale pink, in a fairly broad or pyramidal end cluster from 3 to 8 inches in length; blooming June to September.

RANGE. Newfoundland to northern Quebec and Michigan; south to New York and the mountains of western North Carolina.

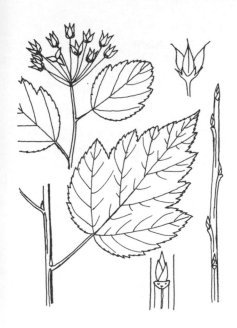

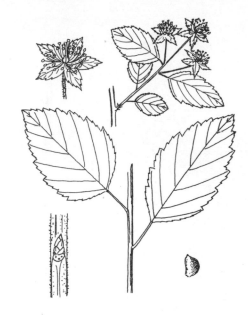

Common Ninebark

Alabama Snow-wreath

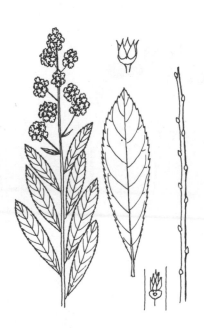

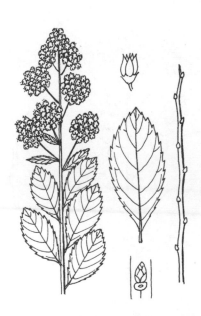

Narrow-leaf Meadowsweet

Broadleaf Meadowsweet

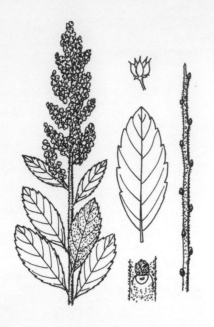

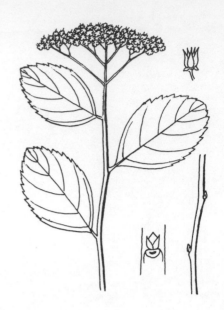

Hardhack

Dwarf Spiraea

Virginia Spiraea

Black Chokeberry

HARDHACK   *Spiraea tomentosa* L.

FIELD MARKS. A simple or sparingly branched shrub 1 to (rarely) 4 feet high; growing in wet meadows and bogs. *Stems* angular, purplish brown, at first densely coated with tawny or rusty wool. *Leaves* numerous, egg-shaped to elliptic, pointed at base, pointed to blunt at tip, sharply toothed on margin, bright green and smooth above, densely tawny- to rusty-woolly beneath, 1 to 3 inches long. *Flowers* pink or rose-colored (rarely white), in a dense spirelike end cluster 4 to 7 inches long; blooming June to September.

RANGE. Nova Scotia to Manitoba; south to Virginia, northern Georgia, Tennessee, and Arkansas.

Also known as Steeplebush.

DWARF SPIRAEA   *Spiraea betulifolia* Pall.

FIELD MARKS. A simple or sparingly branched shrub 1 to (rarely) 3 feet high; growing on rocky slopes or stream banks in the Appalachian Region. *Stems* round, purplish brown to reddish brown, smooth. *Leaves* oval to broadly egg-shaped, rounded to broadly pointed at base, rounded or bluntly pointed at tip, margin coarsely and usually doubly toothed above the middle, firm in texture, smooth or nearly so on both surfaces, paler beneath, 1 to 3 inches long. *Flowers* white, in a flat-topped and finely downy end cluster 2 to 4 inches broad; blooming May to July.

RANGE. New Jersey, Pennsylvania, and Kentucky; south to northern Georgia.

VIRGINIA SPIRAEA   *Spiraea virginiana* Britt.

FIELD MARKS. A slender, branching shrub 2 to 5 feet high; growing on damp rocky banks and slopes of the Appalachian Region. *Branchlets* at first downy but becoming smooth. *Leaves* narrowly oblong or broadest toward the tip, usually pointed at both ends and bristle-tipped, margin untoothed or with a few low teeth above the middle, thin, smooth above, whitened and sometimes finely downy beneath, 1 to 2 inches long. *Flowers* white, in downy flat-topped end clusters 1¾ to 2 inches across; blooming June or July.

RANGE. West Virginia south to western North Carolina and eastern Tennessee.

CHOKEBERRIES (Aronia Medic.)

The chokeberries are leaf-losing shrubs with alternate, simple leaves which have small, dark-colored glands along the midrib on the upper side. They have white or purplish-tinged 5-petalled flowers in flat-topped clusters, blooming in spring when the new leaves appear. The fruits are small, round, and apple-like; they ripen in the fall.

BLACK CHOKEBERRY   *Aronia melanocarpa* (Michx.) Ell.

FIELD MARKS. A shrub 2 to 6 feet high, growing in swamps and moist to fairly dry thickets and woods. *Branchlets* smooth. *Leaves* elliptic or more often broadest above the middle, pointed at base, pointed to blunt at tip, finely and sharply toothed on margin, smooth on both surfaces, paler beneath, 1 to 3 inches long. *Flowers* blooming in June. *Fruits* black, about ¼ inch in diameter; ripening September or October.

RANGE. Newfoundland to northwestern Ontario and Minnesota, south to Pennsylvania and along the mountains to northern Georgia.

RED CHOKEBERRY *Aronia arbutifolia* (L.) Ell.

FIELD MARKS. A shrub 3 to 8 feet high; growing in wet or boggy places. *Branchlets* more or less woolly. *Leaves* elliptic or broadest above the middle, wedge-shaped to broadly pointed at base, pointed at tip, finely toothed on margin, smooth above, grayish-woolly beneath, 1½ to 4 inches long. *Flowers* white or purplish-tinged; blooming March to June. *Fruits* red, about ¼ inch in diameter; ripening August to November and persisting.

RANGE. Nova Scotia to Ontario, Michigan, and Missouri; south to Florida and Texas.

PURPLE CHOKEBERRY *Aronia prunifolia* (Marsh.) Rehd.

FIELD MARKS. A shrub with characteristics intermediate between the two preceding species. *Branchlets* at first woolly but becoming smooth. *Leaves* downy beneath or becoming smooth. *Fruits* deep reddish purple to blackish purple.

RANGE. Newfoundland to Ontario; south to North Carolina, Ohio, and Illinois. (Not illustrated)

JUNEBERRIES (Amelanchier Medic.)

(Key Appendix D)

The Juneberries are leaf-losing shrubs or small trees with alternate, simple leaves. They have showy white 5-petalled flowers, usually in narrow clusters and blooming in early spring. The small apple-like fruits are usually soft, sweet, and juicy. They are edible and can be made into jelly, preserves, or pies; they are eaten by many wild birds and mammals, including deer, bears, raccoons, wild turkeys, and ruffed grouse. The Juneberries are also known as serviceberries, sarvisberries, and shadbushes. Although readily recognizable as a group, the species are often difficult to identify.

LOW JUNEBERRY *Amelanchier humilis* Wieg.

FIELD MARKS. A shrub 1 to 3 feet high, with creeping underground stems and colony-forming; growing in dry rocky or sandy places. Leaves oval to oblong, rounded to heart-shaped at base, round or bluntly pointed at tip, margin with rather large teeth to slightly below the middle, smooth or nearly so on both surfaces, 1 to 2 inches long. *Fruits* black but with a whitish bloom, sweet and juicy; ripening July or August.

RANGE. Quebec and Ontario; south to Vermont, West Virginia, the region of the Great Lakes, and South Dakota.

ROUNDLEAF JUNEBERRY *Amelanchier sanguinea* (Pursh) DC.

FIELD MARKS. A somewhat straggling shrub 3 to 8 feet high, with a solitary stem or a few stems in a clump; growing in dry, upland, rocky woods. *Leaves* roundish to oblong oval, blunt or rounded at tip, often heart-shaped at base, margin coarsely and sharply toothed nearly to the base, 1 to 2½ inches long. *Fruits* purplish black with a whitish bloom, sweet and juicy; ripening July or August.

RANGE. Quebec and Ontario; south to New York, western North Carolina, Michigan, Wisconsin, and Iowa.

RUNNING JUNEBERRY *Amelanchier spicata* (Lam.) K. Koch

FIELD MARKS. A shrub 1 to 4 feet high, with creeping underground stems and thicket-forming; growing in sandy or rocky woodlands. *Leaves* oval or roundish, rounded at base, bluntly pointed to roundish at tip, margin finely and sharply toothed to a little below the middle, smooth above, sometimes slightly downy beneath, ¾ to 2 inches long. *Fruits* purplish black, sweet and juicy; ripening July or August.

RANGE. Newfoundland to Ontario; south to South Carolina, Michigan, and Minnesota.

128

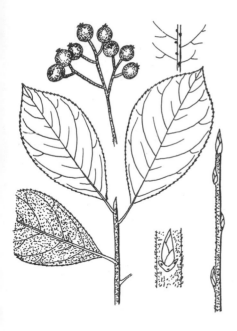

Red Chokeberry

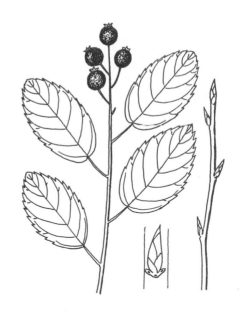

Low Juneberry

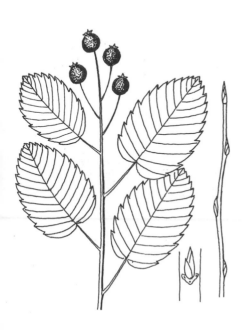

Roundleaf Juneberry

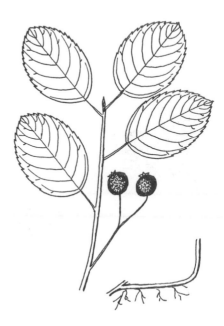

Running Juneberry

Oblong-leaf Juneberry

Swamp Juneberry

Coastal Juneberry

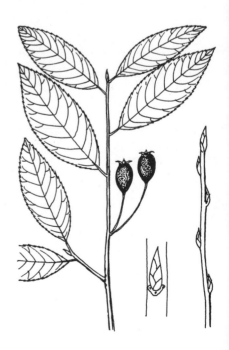

Oblong-fruited Juneberry

OBLONG-LEAF JUNEBERRY *Amelanchier canadensis* (L.) Medic.

FIELD MARKS. A shrub 5 to about 20 feet high with several slender stems in a clump; growing in low, moist places and swamps. *Leaves* oblong to oblong-elliptic, usually rounded at both ends, margin finely and sharply toothed nearly to the base, smooth above and smooth or nearly so beneath, 1 to 2½ inches long. *Fruits* blackish, about ¼ inch in diameter, sweet and juicy; ripening June and July.

RANGE. Maine to New York and southwestern Quebec, south to Georgia.

SWAMP JUNEBERRY *Amelanchier intermedia* Spach

FIELD MARKS. A shrub 5 to about 20 feet high with several slender stems in a clump; growing in swamps and bogs. *Leaves* oblong-elliptic or sometimes broadest above the middle, rounded to heart-shaped at base, pointed at tip, margin finely and sharply toothed nearly to the base, smooth or nearly so on both surfaces or sometimes slightly hairy beneath, 1 to 2½ inches long. *Fruits* dark purplish, sweet and juicy; ripening July and August.

RANGE. Newfoundland to northern Minnesota; south to western Virginia, Michigan, and southern Minnesota.

Also known as the Swamp Sugar-pear.

COASTAL JUNEBERRY *Amelanchier obovalis* (Michx.) Ashe

FIELD MARKS. A slender thicket-forming shrub 1 to 4 feet high, spreading by creeping underground stems; growing in low, moist, sandy woods and pinelands. *Leaves* oblong-elliptic, egg-shaped, or more often broadest above the middle, rounded at base, blunt or pointed at tip, margin finely and sharply toothed nearly to the base, thin in texture, dull pale green and smooth above, usually somewhat downy beneath, ¾ to 2 inches long. *Fruits* purplish black, sweet and juicy; ripening May or June.

RANGE. Chiefly coastal plain; southern New Jersey, eastern Maryland, and southeastern Pennsylvania; south to central Virginia and the interior of South Carolina.

OBLONG-FRUITED JUNEBERRY *Amelanchier bartramiana* (Tausch) Roemer

FIELD MARKS. A shrub 1½ to about 8 feet high, usually with several stems in a clump; growing in cold, wet, rocky woods or swamps and bogs. *Leaves* elliptic or narrowly so, more or less pointed at both ends, finely and sharply toothed on margin to below the middle, thin in texture, smooth on both surfaces, bright green above, paler and often somewhat whitened beneath, 1 to 2½ inches long; leafstalks short. *Flowers* 1 to 3 clustered together in the axils of the leaves; blooming May to August. *Fruits* oval or pear-shaped, about ½ inch long, dark purplish with a whitish bloom, sweet and juicy; ripening July to September.

RANGE. Labrador to western Ontario; south to northeastern Pennsylvania, West Virginia, northern Michigan, northern Wisconsin, and Minnesota.

131

AMERICAN MOUNTAIN-ASH *Sorbus americana* Marsh.

FIELD MARKS. A tall shrub or small tree to 20 or 25 feet; growing in cold swamps or bogs and on rocky ridges at high elevations. *Branchlets* rather stout and with large gummy buds. *Leaves* alternate, compound, 6 to 10 inches long; leaflets 11 to 17, lance-shaped, rounded to pointed at base, long-pointed at tip, sharply toothed on margin, smooth on both surfaces, 2 to 3 inches long. *Flowers* small, white, 5-petalled, many in a broad flat-topped end cluster; blooming May or June. *Fruits* apple-like, bright orange red, shiny, about ¼ inch in diameter; ripening August to October.

RANGE. Newfoundland to Manitoba; south to New Jersey, northern Illinois, and along the mountains to northern Georgia.

The fruits are eaten by the ruffed grouse and many other wild birds; the twigs are browsed by deer.

AMERICAN CRAB APPLE *Malus coronaria* (L.) Mill.

FIELD MARKS. A bushy shrub or small tree to about 15 or 20 feet; often forming thickets along fence rows, roadsides, and abandoned fields. *Branchlets* smooth, often spurlike and ending in a sharp point. *Leaves* alternate, egg-shaped to oval (or lance-shaped in var. *lancifolia* [Rehd.] Fern.), rounded to pointed at base, pointed at tip, sharply and irregularly toothed on margin, thin-textured, smooth on both surfaces, 2 to 4 inches long. *Flowers* white to pink, 5-petalled, almost 1 inch across, very fragrant, 5 or 6 in clusters; blooming March to May. *Fruits* yellowish green, waxy or greasy, fragrant apples about 1 inch in diameter; ripening October or November.

RANGE. Western New York to Indiana and Missouri, south in the uplands to northern Georgia.

The fruits can be used to make jelly and vinegar.

SOUTHERN CRAB APPLE *Malus angustifolia* (Ait.) Michx.

FIELD MARKS. A shrub or small tree similar to the preceding. *Leaves* elliptic, pointed at base, rounded or blunt at tip, sparingly or bluntly toothed on margin, thick-textured, smooth on both surfaces, 1 to 2½ inches long. *Flowers* similar to those of preceding species. *Fruits* also similar but somewhat more flattened, 1 to 1½ inches in diameter.

RANGE. Chiefly coastal plain; Maryland to northern Florida, west to Louisiana and north in Mississippi Valley to southern Illinois.

Also known as Narrow-leaf Crab apple.

HAWTHORNS (Crataegus L.)

Hawthorns (also called haws or thorns) are shrubs or small trees with alternate, simple leaves; branches armed with large unbranched thorns or spines. They have showy 5-petalled white flowers about ½ inch across, which are usually in small, flat, end clusters. The *fruits* resemble small apples. They are tipped with the conspicuous remains of the calyx and have from 1 to 5 large, bony seeds.

As a group the hawthorns are quite distinctive, but the identity of the various species is extremely difficult even for trained botanists. Only a few species are presented here, either because they are usually easily recognized or because they are common. Most of us will be content if we recognize them as hawthorns.

MAY HAW *Crataegus astivalis* (Walt.) Torrey & Gray

FIELD MARKS. A rather distinctive shrub or small tree; growing on wet soils, chiefly in coastal regions. *Leaves* broadest above the middle, wedge-shaped at base, rounded to pointed at tip, margin sharply toothed to or below the middle, sometimes 3-lobed, smooth or nearly so on both surfaces or somewhat rusty-hairy beneath, 1 to 2½ inches long; leafstalks short. *Fruits* red, dotted, about ½ inch in diameter, with 3 to 5 bony seeds; ripening in May.

RANGE. North Carolina south to Florida and west to Texas.

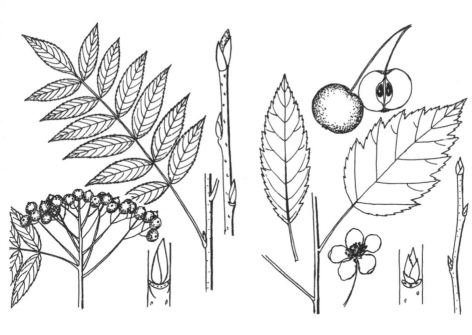

American Mountain-ash

American Crab Apple

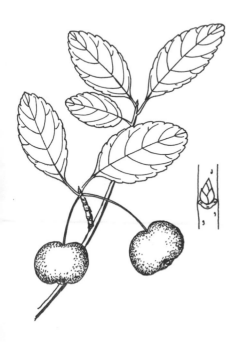

Southern Crab Apple

May Haw

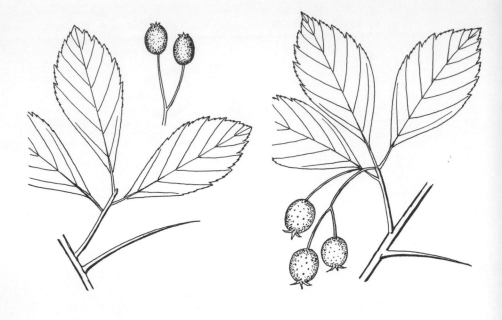

Cockspur Thorn   Dotted Hawthorn

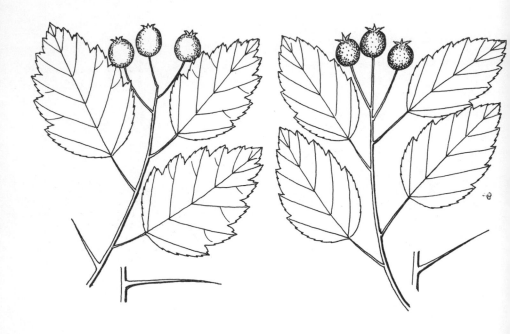

Variable Thorn   Waxy-fruited Thorn

COCKSPUR THORN *Crataegus crus-galli* L.

FIELD MARKS. A bushy shrub or small tree; growing in old pastures, borders of woods, thickets, etc. *Branches* with many slender, straight or slightly curved thorns 2 to 4 inches long. *Leaves* broadest above the middle, wedge-shaped at base, rounded to pointed at tip, margin sharply and irregularly toothed above the middle, thickish and somewhat leathery in texture, dark green and lustrous above, paler and smooth or nearly so beneath, 2 to 4 inches long. *Flowers* blooming April to June. *Fruits* greenish to dull red, hard, about ⅜ inch in diameter, usually 2-seeded; ripening September or October.

RANGE. Quebec to Ontario and Minnesota; south to Georgia, Kansas, and eastern Texas.

DOTTED HAWTHORN *Crataegus punctata* Jacq.

FIELD MARKS. A rather flat-topped shrub or small tree; growing in stream bottoms and on adjoining slopes. *Branches* with rather scattered, stout, mostly straight thorns 2 to 3 inches long. *Leaves* broadest above the middle, wedge-shaped at base, pointed to rounded at tip, margin sharply and doubly toothed above the middle, firm in texture, dull grayish green and smooth but with sunken veins above, paler and often somewhat downy beneath, 2 to 3 inches long. *Flowers* blooming April to June. *Fruits* yellow to red, dark-dotted, ½ to ¾ inch in diameter, 3- to 5-seeded; ripening September or October.

RANGE. Quebec and Ontario south to North Carolina and Kentucky. Also known as the Large-fruited Thorn.

VARIABLE THORN *Crataegus macrosperma* Ashe

FIELD MARKS. A bushy shrub or small tree of stony woods and thickets. *Branches* with many slender thorns 1¼ to 2½ inches long. *Leaves* egg-shaped or broadly egg-shaped, rounded to broadly pointed or flattened at base, pointed at tip, margin with about 5 pairs of broadly triangular and sharply toothed lobes, thin in texture, dark yellowish green above, slightly paler beneath, smooth or nearly so on both surfaces, 1 to 3 inches long. *Flowers* blooming April or May. *Fruits* bright red, about ½ inch in diameter, 3- to 5-seeded; ripening August or September.

RANGE. Southeastern Canada and New England to northern Illinois and Wisconsin; south in the mountains to northern Georgia.

WAXY-FRUITED THORN *Crataegus pruniosa* (Wend.) K. Koch

FIELD MARKS. A bushy shrub or small tree growing in stony woods and thickets. *Branches* with many slender thorns 1¼ to 2½ inches long. *Leaves* egg-shaped or broadly egg-shaped, rounded to pointed at base, pointed at tip, margin with 3 or 4 pairs of broad and shallow lobes and sharply and irregularly toothed, firm in texture, dark green or yellowish green above, paler beneath, smooth on both surfaces, 1 to 2½ inches long. *Flowers* blooming April or May. *Fruits* greenish to dull red or purplish, dark-dotted, waxy-coated, about ½ inch in diameter; ripening October or November.

RANGE. Newfoundland and southeastern Canada to Michigan and Wisconsin; south to North Carolina, Kentucky, and Arkansas.

PARSLEY HAWTHORN *Crataegus marshallii* Egglest.

FIELD MARKS. A rather distinctive shrub or small tree; growing along streams, the borders of swamps, and on slopes. *Branches* unarmed or with occasional short thorns. *Leaves* broadly egg-shaped to roundish, deeply cleft between the 5 to 7 lobes, which are sharply and irregularly toothed, bright green and lustrous above, paler beneath, smooth or nearly so on both surfaces, 1½ to 2½ inches long. *Flowers* blooming April or May. *Fruits* bright red, about ⅓ inch long, 1- to 3-seeded; ripening about October.

RANGE. Virginia, Missouri, and Oklahoma south to Florida and Texas.

DWARF THORN *Crataegus uniflora* Muenchh.

FIELD MARKS. An irregularly branched and sprawling shrub 2 to 5 feet high; growing on sandy soils or rocky banks. *Branches* long, slender, often quite flexible, with thorns ½ to 1 inch long. *Leaves* elliptic or broadest above the middle, wedge-shaped at base, rounded or bluntly pointed at tip, margin bluntly toothed and sometimes obscurely lobed above the middle, thick-textured, dark green and lustrous but sometimes roughish-hairy above and with sunken veins, paler and more or less downy beneath, ½ to 1½ inches long; leafstalks short. *Flowers* usually solitary, blooming April or May. *Fruits* greenish yellow to dull red, 3- to 5-seeded; ripening in October.

RANGE. Southeastern New York and southeastern Pennsylvania south to Florida, west to Texas, and north in Mississippi Valley to southern Missouri.

SHRUBBY CINQUEFOIL *Potentilla fruticosa* L.

FIELD MARKS. A leaf-losing shrub 1 to 3 feet high, with erect or ascending branches and shreddy bark; growing in cold, moist, rocky places or in northern bogs. *Leaves* alternate, compound, with prominent pointed stipules at the bases of the leafstalks; leaflets usually 5 (rarely 3 or 7), stalkless, lance-shaped, pointed at both ends, margin untoothed but often slightly rolled, silvery-silky on both surfaces, ½ to about 1 inch long. *Flowers* bright yellow, 5-petaled, about ¾ inch across; blooming June to September. *Fruits* greenish becoming brown, small, dry, densely hairy, borne in heads.

RANGE. Newfoundland and southern Labrador to Alaska; south to northern New Jersey, northeastern Pennsylvania, the region of the Great Lakes, northern Iowa, South Dakota, New Mexico, and California.

Found in the northern portions of Europe and Asia, as well as North America, and cultivated in many varieties as an ornamental shrub.

THREE-TOOTHED CINQUEFOIL *Potentilla tridentata* Ait.

FIELD MARKS. A small evergreen tufted and creeping plant 1½ to (rarely) 10 inches high, woody at the base; growing on dry, open, rocky or peaty soils, southward only at high elevations in the mountains. *Leaves* alternate, compound, long-stalked; leaflets 3, broadest at the 3-toothed tip and tapering to the base, stalkless, leathery-textured, dark green and lustrous above, paler beneath, smooth on both surfaces or somewhat hairy beneath, ½ to 2 inches long. *Flowers* white, 5-petaled, about ⅜ inch across, 1 to 6 in an end cluster; blooming late May to September. *Fruits* greenish becoming brown, small, dry, densely hairy, borne in heads.

RANGE. Labrador to Manitoba; south to New England, New York, southern Ontario, Michigan, Wisconsin, northeastern Iowa, North Dakota, and along the Appalachians to northern Georgia.

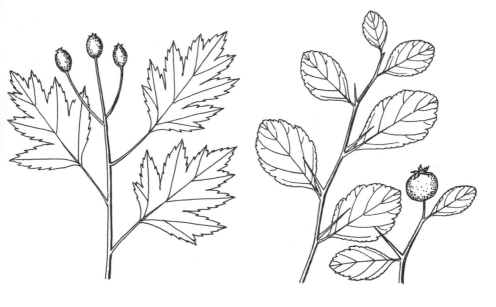

Parsley Hawthorn

Dwarf Thorn

Shrubby Cinquefoil

Three-toothed Cinquefoil

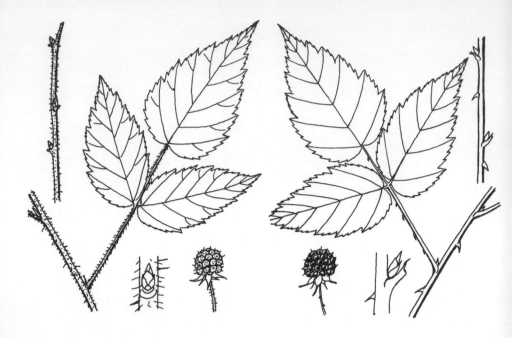

Red Raspberry

Black Raspberry

Purple-flowering Raspberry

Swamp Dewberry

BLACKBERRIES AND RASPBERRIES (Rubus L.)

These are soft-wooded, short-lived, leaf-losing or (rarely) half-evergreen plants which are usually bristly or prickly. They have simple stems called "canes," which produce flowers and fruits the second year and then die. The leaves are alternate, long-stalked, and usually compound. The flowers are perfect, 5-petalled, and usually showy. The fruits are not true berries but compact clusters of small 1-seeded drupelets. Those of the raspberries separate readily from the receptacle and appear hollow inside when picked. Those of blackberries are firmly attached to the receptacle which is picked along with the cluster of drupelets.

As a group these plants are commonly called "briers" or "brambles." They are common and well known, but the various species are very difficult to identify. Only a few of the more common or distinctive ones are included here. The plants provide food and cover for wildlife; the fruits are often gathered to be eaten raw or made into pies, jelly, preserves, or wine.

RED RASPBERRY *Rubus idaeus* var. *strigosus* (Michx.) Maxim.

FIELD MARKS. A shrub with arching, round canes 2 to 6 feet high, sometimes slightly whitened when young and usually bristly but with few or no prickles; growing on rocky slopes and in clearings. *Leaves* with 3 to 5 leaflets which are egg-shaped, rounded to somewhat heart-shaped at base, pointed at tip, double-toothed on margin, whitened and downy beneath, 2 to 3 inches long; leafstalks bristly. *Flowers* white, petals small; blooming May to July. *Fruits* red, in half-round clusters; ripening July to September.

RANGE. Newfoundland to British Columbia; south to western North Carolina, Ohio, Indiana, Nebraska, and Wyoming.

BLACK RASPBERRY *Rubus occidentalis* L.

FIELD MARKS. Different from the preceding in having strongly whitened canes with scattered, hooked prickles and leafstalks with smaller but similar prickles. *Fruits* purplish black, in half-round clusters; ripening June or July.

RANGE. New Brunswick to Minnesota, south to Georgia and Colorado.

PURPLE-FLOWERING RASPBERRY *Rubus odoratus* L.

FIELD MARKS. A straggling, unarmed shrub 2 to 5 feet high; growing in moist rocky woods and ravines. *Branchlets,* leafstalks, and flower stalks are covered with sticky, reddish, bristly hairs; the bark peels freely off the canes. *Leaves* maple-like, 3- to 5-lobed and sharply toothed on margin, bright green and more or less downy on both surfaces, 4 to 7 inches wide. *Flowers* 1½ to 2 inches across, roselike, rose purple; blooming June to August. *Fruits* dull red, rather insipid, in somewhat flattened dome-shaped clusters ½ to ¾ inch across; ripening July to September.

RANGE. Nova Scotia and southern Ontario to southern Michigan; south to New York, northern Georgia, and Tennessee.

SWAMP DEWBERRY *Rubus hispidus* L.

FIELD MARKS. A semi-evergreen plant with slender, trailing, bristly-hairy stems; growing in cool moist woods and bogs. *Leaves* usually with 3 leaflets which are elliptic to roundish or broadest above the middle, rounded to pointed at both ends, sharply toothed on margin, dark green and lustrous above, paler and often slightly downy beneath, ¾ to 2 inches long. *Flowers* small, white; blooming June to September. *Fruits* small, purplish to black, few in a cluster; ripening August to October.

RANGE. Nova Scotia to Wisconsin; south to Maryland, the region of the Great Lakes, and in the mountains to northern Georgia.

139

NORTHERN DEWBERRY *Rubus flagellaris* Willd.

FIELD MARKS. A leaf-losing plant with long, trailing stems which are armed with scattered, broad-based, often slightly curved prickles; growing in dry open places, often in poor soils. *Leaves* with 3 or sometimes 5 leaflets which are oval to egg-shaped or roundish, rounded to broadly pointed at base and tip, sharply and doubly toothed on margin, thin in texture, smooth or nearly so above, slightly paler and sometimes slightly downy beneath, 1½ to 4 inches long. *Flowers* white, often 1 inch across; blooming April to June. *Fruits* black, in roundish or somewhat elongate clusters; ripening May to August.

RANGE. Maine to Minnesota, south to northern Georgia and Missouri.

SOUTHERN DEWBERRY *Rubus trivialis* Michx.

FIELD MARKS. A somewhat evergreen plant with long trailing stems which are bristly and armed with rather small prickles; growing in open places. *Leaves* with 3 or sometimes 5 leaflets which are elliptic or lance-shaped, pointed to rounded at base, pointed or blunt at tip, sharply and doubly toothed on margin, rather leathery in texture, lustrous above, paler beneath, smooth on both surfaces, 1 to 4 inches long. *Flowers* usually solitary, white or pinkish, often 1¼ inches across; blooming March to May. *Fruits* black, in roundish or elongate clusters; ripening late April to June.

RANGE. Coastal plain and lower piedmont; Maryland south to Florida, west to Texas, north to Missouri and Oklahoma.

HIGHBUSH BLACKBERRY *Rubus allegheniensis* Porter

FIELD MARKS. A shrub with erect or arching, often stout, angled, purplish-red canes 3 to 6 feet high; well armed with stout, straight, broad-based prickles; growing in woods borders, clearings, and wayside thickets. *Leaves* with prickly leafstalks and 3 or 5 leaflets which are egg-shaped, rounded to somewhat heart-shaped at base, pointed at tip, sharply and doubly toothed on margin, smooth or nearly so above, densely downy beneath, 2 to 4½ inches long. *Flowers* white, about 1 inch across, clustered; blooming April to June. The younger branchlets and the flower stalks are quite densely covered with gland-tipped hairs. *Fruits* black, in roundish to thimble-shaped clusters; ripening July or August.

RANGE. New Brunswick to Minnesota; south to Maryland, Missouri, and in the Appalachians to nothern Georgia.

TALL BLACKBERRY *Rubus argutus* Link

FIELD MARKS. Similar to the Highbush Blackberry, from which it can best be distinguished by the absence of gland-tipped hairs on the young growth and flower stalks.

RANGE. Massachusetts to southern Illinois, south to Florida and Mississippi. (Not illustrated)

BLACKBERRY *Rubus betulifolius* Small

FIELD MARKS. Differs from the Highbush and Tall blackberries in that the leaflets are smooth or nearly so beneath; and from the Highbush Blackberry in that the young growth and flower stalks lack gland-tipped hairs. Common in southern lowlands and often in swamps.

RANGE. North Carolina south to Florida and Mississippi. (Not illustrated)

MOUNTAIN BLACKBERRY *Rubus canadensis* L.

FIELD MARKS. Similar to Highbush Blackberry but stems unarmed or with only an occasional weak prickle. *Leaves* smooth and green on both surfaces. Young growth and flower stalks smooth.

RANGE. Newfoundland to Ontario and Minnesota, south along the higher Appalachians to northern Georgia.

140

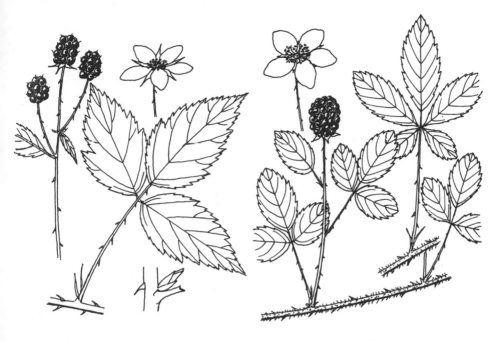

Northern Dewberry

Southern Dewberry

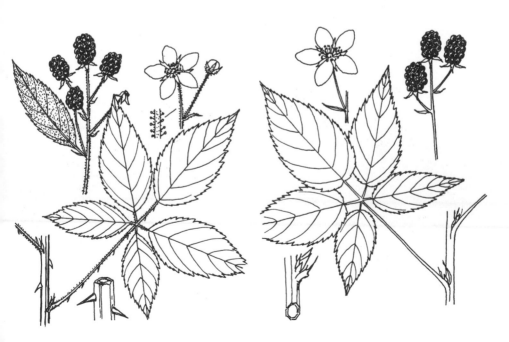

Highbush Blackberry

Mountain Blackberry

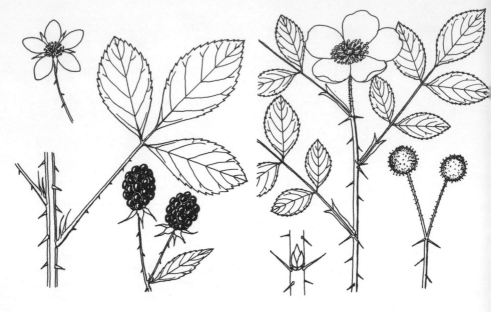

Sand Blackberry

Pasture Rose

Swamp Rose

Shining Rose

SAND BLACKBERRY *Rubus cuneifolius* Pursh

FIELD MARKS. A shrub with erect or slightly arching, angled, and densely prickly canes 1 to 3 feet high. *Leaves* with usually 3 (sometimes 5) leaflets which are broadest above the middle, tapered to the base, rounded or broadly pointed at tip, sharply toothed on margin to or slightly below the middle, thickish, smooth or nearly so above, densely white-woolly beneath, ¾ to 2½ inches long. *Flowers* white or (rarely) pink, about 1 inch across, clustered; blooming April to June. *Fruits* black, in short cylindrical clusters ½ to 1 inch long; ripening June or July.

RANGE. Chiefly coastal plain; Connecticut to southeastern Pennsylvania, south to Florida.

ROSES (Rosa L.)

(Key Appendix E)

Roses are usually prickly leaf-losing shrubs with alternate and pinnately compound leaves. A pair of stipules is united with the base of the leafstalk, often for half or more of the length of the leafstalk. The showy flowers have 5 sepals, 5 petals, numerous stamens, and several pistils within the calyx cup. The fruits are called "hips" and consist of the cuplike or urn-shaped receptacle on which the sepals sometimes persist; but within the fleshy receptacle are the small, hard, dry true fruits which are achenes.

The native roses are not always easy to identify, for numerous hybrids occur. Thus in many cases the amateur is justified in simply calling them "wild roses." Besides the native species described here, there are several introduced species which are now widely naturalized.

PASTURE ROSE *Rosa carolina* L.

FIELD MARKS. An erect shrub ½ to 2½ feet high, the stems armed with needle-like prickles; growing in dry open woods, thickets, and pastures. *Leaves* with usually 5 leaflets which are elliptic or egg-shaped, pointed to rounded at base, pointed at tip, sharply toothed on margin, usually dull above, paler and sometimes slightly downy beneath, ¾ to 1¼ inches long; the stipules narrow, flat, and untoothed. *Flowers* usually solitary, pink, about 2 inches broad; blooming May to July. *Fruits* roundish, red, about ½ inch in diameter, and with gland-tipped hairs.

RANGE. Nova Scotia to Minnesota and Nebraska, south to Florida and Texas. Also called Low or Carolina Rose.

SWAMP ROSE *Rosa palustris* Marsh.

FIELD MARKS. An erect shrub 2½ to 6 feet high, the stems armed with broad-based and commonly hooked prickles; growing in swamps and other wet places. *Leaves* with 5 to 9 (usually 7) leaflets which are oval or elliptic, usually pointed at both ends, sharply toothed on margin, smooth above, paler and smooth or slightly downy beneath, ¾ to 2 inches long; the stipules often broadened upward or with slightly rolled margins. *Flowers* solitary or few in a cluster, pink, 2 to 2½ inches broad; blooming May to August. *Fruits* roundish, red, about ½ inch in diameter, smooth to rather densely glandular-bristly.

RANGE. Newfoundland and Nova Scotia to Ontario and Minnesota; south to Florida, Tennessee, and Arkansas.

SHINING ROSE *Rosa nitida* Willd.

FIELD MARKS. An erect shrub 8 inches to 2 feet high, the stems densely bristly and prickly; growing in bogs and wet thickets. *Leaves* usually with 7 or 9 leaflets which are narrowly elliptic or oblong, pointed at both ends, finely and sharply toothed on margin, lustrous above, paler and usually smooth beneath, ½ to (rarely) 2 inches long; the stipules broadened upward. *Flowers* solitary or few in a cluster, pink, 1½ to 2¼ inches broad; blooming June to September. *Fruits* roundish, red, bristly-hairy, about ⅜ inch in diameter, the erect sepals soon shed.

RANGE. Newfoundland to Quebec, south to Massachusetts and Connecticut.

SMOOTH ROSE *Rosa blanda* Ait.

FIELD MARKS. An erect shrub 2 to 5 feet high, unarmed or with a few weak or bristly prickles; growing in moist rocky places, along streams, or on lakeshores. *Leaves* with 5 or 7 leaflets which are elliptic or broadest above the middle, blunt or pointed at tip, pointed at base, sharply toothed on margin, smooth and dull above, sometimes downy beneath, ½ to 1½ inches long; stipules somewhat broadened upward. *Flowers* solitary or few, pink or white, 2 to 2½ inches broad; blooming June to August. *Fruits* roundish, red, smooth, about ½ inch in diameter, with persistent sepals.

RANGE. Newfoundland to Manitoba; south to New England, Pennsylvania, the region of the Great Lakes, Missouri, and Nebraska.

PRICKLY WILD ROSE *Rosa acicularis* Lindl.

FIELD MARKS. Shrub 1 to 3 feet high, the stems densely covered with needle-like prickles; growing in thickets and on rocky slopes. *Leaves* with 3 to 7 leaflets which are blunt at tip, roundish at base, often hairy-resinous, 1 to 2 inches long; leafstalks glandular-hairy. *Flowers* solitary, pink, 1 to 2 inches broad; blooming June or July. *Fruits* roundish or egg-shaped, ⅝ to 1 inch long, usually smooth, sepals persistent.

RANGE. New England and Quebec to Yukon and British Columbia; south to Michigan, Wisconsin, South Dakota, and Colorado. (Not illustrated)

PRAIRIE ROSE *Rosa setigera* Michx.

FIELD MARKS. Stems 5 to 15 feet long, trailing, arching, or climbing; armed with scattered, broad-based, often hooked prickles; growing in open woods, clearings, or along streams. *Leaves* with 3 (rarely 5) egg-shaped leaflets which are pointed at tip, rounded at base, sharply toothed, usually lustrous above, often downy beneath, 1 to 3 inches long. *Flowers* in small clusters, usually pink, 2 to 3 inches broad; blooming May to August. *Fruits* roundish, red, usually bristly-hairy, about ⅜ inch in diameter.

RANGE. New York to Ontario, Missouri, and Nebraska; south to Florida and Texas.

DEER-PLUM *Chrysobalanus oblongifolius* Michx.

FIELD MARKS. An evergreen shrub ½ to 2 feet high, with creeping underground stems; growing in dry sandy woods or on sandhills. *Branchlets* smooth, dark purplish brown. *Leaves* alternate, narrowly elliptic or broadest above the middle, wedge-shaped at base, blunt to indented or sometimes with a minute bristle at tip, margin indistinctly toothed, veiny and lustrous above, slightly paler beneath, smooth, 1¼ to 4½ inches long. *Flowers* small, yellowish white to greenish white, in end clusters; blooming May or June. *Fruits* ivory white tinged with red or purple, oval-shaped, about 1 inch long, not edible; ripening September or October.

RANGE. Coastal plain; South Carolina south to Florida, west to Mississippi.

Also called Gopher-apple or Ground-oak.

PLUMS AND CHERRIES (Prunus L.)

These are shrubs or trees with alternate, simple leaves; often with glands at the summits of the leakstalks or with narrow stipules at the base. Bark of the younger stems and branches usually marked with horizontally elongated lenticels. The flowers are 5-petalled, often showy; the fruits are drupes with a bony pit enclosing the seed.

BEACH PLUM *Prunus maritima* Marsh.

FIELD MARKS. A straggling, unarmed, leaf-losing shrub 1 to 6 feet high; growing on dunes and sands along the coast. *Branchlets* velvety, gradually becoming smooth. *Leaves* elliptic to egg-shaped or broadest above the middle, rounded or broadly pointed at base, pointed or blunt at tip, finely and sharply toothed on margin, smooth or nearly so above, downy beneath, 1¼ to 2¼ inches long. *Flowers* white; blooming April to June. *Fruits* roundish, purple with a white bloom, ½ to 1 inch in diameter; ripening August to October.

RANGE. Coastal plain; Maine south to Delaware and southeastern Pennsylvania.

Smooth Rose　　　　　　　　　　**Prairie Rose**

Deer-Plum　　　　　　　　　　**Beach Plum**

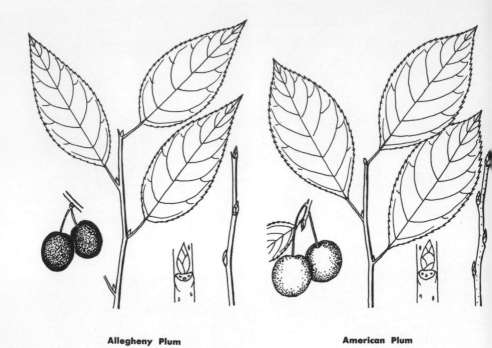

Allegheny Plum

American Plum

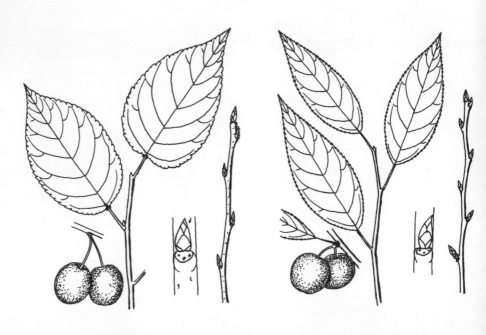

Canada Plum

Chickasaw Plum

ALLEGHENY PLUM *Prunus alleghaniensis* Porter

FIELD MARKS. A straggling, leaf-losing shrub or small tree 3 to 15 feet high, sometimes with spiny-tipped branches; growing on mountain slopes or ridges and often thicket-forming. *Leaves* lance-shaped to egg-shaped, pointed at base, often long-pointed at tip, finely and sharply toothed on margin, smooth or nearly so above, paler and often somewhat downy beneath, 2 to 3½ inches long. *Flowers* white, ½ inch across; blooming April or May. *Fruits* roundish or oval, dark purple with whitish bloom, ½ inch in diameter; ripening August or September.

RANGE. Connecticut and Pennsylvania south to western Virginia. Also called Porter Plum or Sloe.

AMERICAN PLUM *Prunus americana* Marsh

FIELD MARKS. A leaf-losing shrub or small tree with spine-tipped branches; often forming thickets in woods borders, or along fence rows and streams. *Leaves* oval or broadest above the middle, mostly broadly pointed at base and abruptly pointed at tip, finely and often doubly toothed on margin, smooth or nearly so on both surfaces, 2 to 4 inches long; leafstalks usually without glands. *Flowers* white, ¾ inch across, 2 to 5 in a cluster; blooming April to June. *Fruits* roundish, yellow or red, ¾ to 1 inch in diameter; ripening August to October.

RANGE. Massachusetts to Manitoba; south to Florida, Louisiana, and New Mexico.

CANADA PLUM *Prunus nigra* Ait.

FIELD MARKS. A shrub or small tree similar to the preceding. Leaves usually egg-shaped, rounded or somewhat heart-shaped at base, margin with more bluntish teeth; leafstalks with glands at summit. The flowers and fruits are similar to those of the American Plum.

RANGE. New Brunswick to southern Manitoba; south to New England, New York, Ohio, northern Illinois, and Iowa.

CHICKASAW PLUM *Prunus angustifolia* Marsh.

FIELD MARKS. A leaf-losing shrub or small tree with spiny-tipped branches; often forming thickets along fence rows, abandoned fields, and woods borders. *Leaves* lance-shaped, pointed at base, long-pointed at tip, finely toothed on margin, smooth, 1 to 2½ inches long; leafstalks with glands at summit. *Flowers* white, about ⅓ inch across, 2 to 4 in a cluster; blooming March or April. *Fruits* roundish, red or yellow with a whitish bloom, ¾ to 1 inch in diameter; ripening June or July and often quite sweet.

RANGE. New Jersey to southern Illinois and Nebraska; south to Florida and Texas.

FLATWOODS PLUM *Prunus umbellata* Ell.

FIELD MARKS. A leaf-losing shrub or small tree with spiny-tipped branches; growing in dry sandy woods or along stream banks. *Leaves* elliptic, pointed at tip, very finely toothed on margin, smooth or sometimes slightly downy beneath, 1 to 2½ inches long. *Flowers* white, about ⅜ inch across, 2 to 4 in a cluster; blooming late February to April. *Fruits* roundish, reddish purple, ½ inch or less in diameter, sour or bitter; ripening June or July.

RANGE. Southeastern North Carolina south to Florida, west to Texas, north in Mississippi Valley to Arkansas.

Also called Hog Plum or Black Sloe. (Not illustrated)

GRAVES PLUM *Prunus gravesii* Small

FIELD MARKS. A shrub similar to the Beach Plum but smaller, with roundish leaves, blunt or abruptly short-pointed at tip, ¾ to 1½ inches long. *Flowers* often 1 inch across. *Fruits* almost black, about ½ inch in diameter.

RANGE. Southeastern Connecticut. (Not illustrated)

SAND CHERRY *Prunus pumila* L.

FIELD MARKS. An erect leaf-losing shrub 1 to about 6 feet high; growing on sandy soils, dunes, and rocky shores. *Leaves* narrowly elliptic or broadest above the middle, wedge-shaped at base, pointed at tip, margin toothed with low and bluntish teeth above the middle, somewhat leathery in texture, dark green and lustrous above, paler and smooth beneath, 1½ to 3 inches long. *Flowers* white, about ½ inch across, few in a cluster; blooming May or June. *Fruits* roundish, purplish black, about ⅜ inch in diameter; ripening July to September.

RANGE. Ontario south to St. Lawrence Basin and the Great Lakes region from New York to Minnesota.

APPALACHIAN CHERRY *Prunus susquehanae* Willd.

FIELD MARKS. An erect leaf-losing shrub 2 to about 8 feet high; growing in sandy or rocky woods, thickets, and clearings. *Leaves* elliptic or sometimes broadest above the middle, wedge-shaped at base, blunt or broadly pointed at tip, margin toothed with low and bluntish teeth above the middle, thin but firm in texture, light green above, paler beneath, smooth on both surfaces, 1¼ to 2½ inches long. *Flowers* white, about ⅜ inch across, 2 to 4 in a cluster; blooming May or June. *Fruits* roundish, purplish black, about ⅜ inch in diameter; ripening July to September.

RANGE. Southwestern Maine and Quebec to southeastern Minnesota; south to Long Island, Virginia, central and western North Carolina, Ohio, Illinois, and Minnesota.

PROSTRATE SAND CHERRY *Prunus depressa* Pursh

FIELD MARKS. A prostrate, spreading, leaf-losing shrub with more or less upright branchlets 8 inches to 2 feet high; growing on sandy or gravelly shores or along streams. *Leaves* narrowly elliptic or rather narrow but broader toward the tip, wedge-shaped at base, pointed or blunt at tip, margin toothed with low and bluntish teeth above the middle, light green above, pale or somewhat whitened beneath, smooth on both surfaces, 1½ to 4 inches long. *Flowers* white, about ½ inch across, 2 to 4 in a cluster; blooming May to July. *Fruits* roundish, reddish purple or blackish purple, about ⅜ inch in diameter; ripening July to September.

RANGE. Quebec to Ontario; south to western Massachusetts, New York, Pennsylvania, and Wisconsin.

CHOKECHERRY *Prunus virginiana* L.

FIELD MARKS. A large leaf-losing shrub or small tree; growing along woods borders, fence rows, and wayside thickets. *Branchlets* have a very disagreeable odor when bruised or broken. *Leaves* oval or broadest above the middle, rounded to broadly pointed at base, abruptly pointed at tip, finely and sharply toothed on margin, dull green above, paler beneath, smooth on both surfaces, 2 to 4 inches long; leafstalks with glands at summit. *Flowers* white, about ⅜ inch across, strong-scented, numerous, and in a dense and elongate cluster; blooming April to June. *Fruits* roundish, dark red to purplish black, about ⅜ inch in diameter, very astringent; ripening July to September.

RANGE. Newfoundland to British Columbia; south to Maryland, northern Georgia, eastern Kentucky, Illinois, Kansas, New Mexico and California.

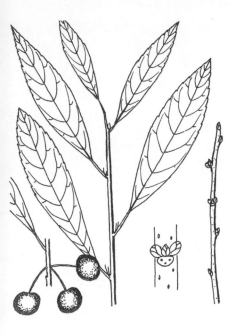

Sand Cherry

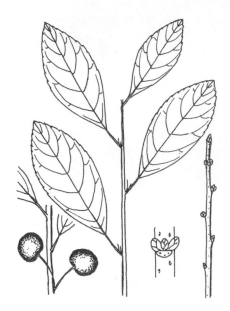

Appalachian Cherry

Prostrate Sand Cherry

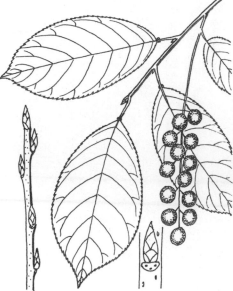

Chokecherry

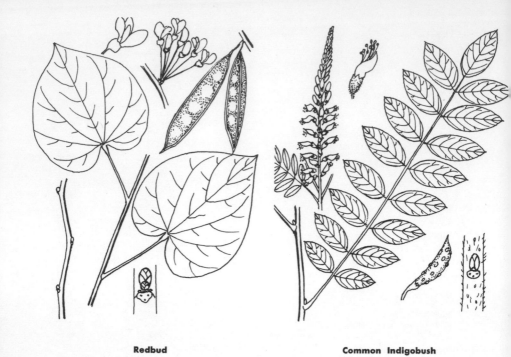

Redbud

Common Indigobush

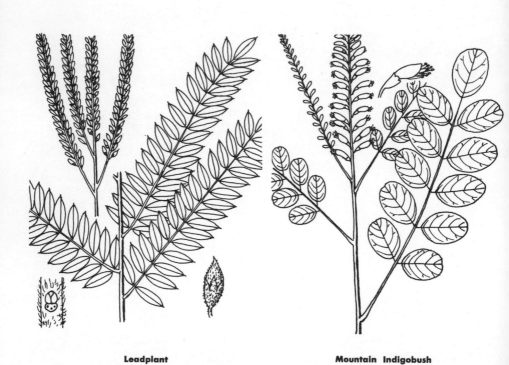

Leadplant

Mountain Indigobush

REDBUD   *Cercis canadensis* L.

FIELD MARKS. A leaf-losing shrub or small tree to 30 feet high; growing in rocky woods, ravines, or along streams. *Leaves* alternate, heart-shaped, untoothed, smooth or nearly so, 2 to 4 inches wide; leafstalks swollen at summit. *Flowers* somewhat pealike, rose purple or pink; blooming late March to May, before the leaves appear. *Fruits* light brown, flattened pods, 2 to 3 inches long; maturing July or August and persisting.

RANGE. Connecticut to southern Ontario, Wisconsin, and Nebraska; south to Florida and western Texas.

Very popular as an ornamental. Also called Judas-tree.

THE INDIGOBUSHES (Amorpha L.)

(Key Appendix F)

The indigobushes are leaf-losing shrubs with alternate, pinnately compound leaves; the numerous leaflets have untoothed margins. The small flowers have only a standard petal and are borne in long, dense, narrow end clusters. They are followed by small, usually 1-seeded pods, which are usually glandular-dotted.

COMON INDIGOBUSH   *Amorpha fruticosa* L.

FIELD MARKS. A shrub 4 to about 10 feet high; growing in open woods, along streams, or borders of swamps. *Leaves* 6 to 12 inches long; the 11 to 35 oval or elliptic leaflets ½ to 2 inches long, dull green, minutely glandular-dotted, usually with some short grayish hairs (but with long tawny hairs in the variety *croceolanata* [P. W. Wats.] Schneid.), usually rounded at both ends but with an abrupt little point at tip. *Flowers* violet purple, ¼ to ⅜ inch long, usually in several clusters 3 to 6 inches long; blooming April to June. *Fruits* curved, about ⅜ inch long, dotted with large raised glands; maturing June to August.

RANGE. Southern Pennsylvania to southern Michigan, Wisconsin, and Kansas; south to Florida and Texas.

LEADPLANT   *Amorpha canescens* Pursh

FIELD MARKS. A shrub 1 to 3 feet high; growing on dry hillsides and prairies. *Branchlets* densely grayish-hairy. *Leaves* short-stalked, 2 to 5 inches long; the 21 to 51 leaflets elliptic or lance-shaped, abruptly short-pointed at tip, sometimes slightly hairy above, densely grayish-hairy beneath, ¼ to about ½ inch long. *Flowers* purplish blue, in several end clusters 2 to 6 inches long; blooming June to August. *Fruits* about 3/16 inch long, densely hairy; maturing August or September.

RANGE. Southern Michigan to Saskatchewan; south to northern Indiana, Arkansas, Texas, and New Mexico.

MOUNTAIN INDIGOBUSH   *Amorpha glabra* Poir.

FIELD MARKS. A shrub 3 to 6 feet high; growing on wooded slopes of the southern Applachians. *Leaves* long-stalked, 3 to 6 inches long; the 9 to 19 leaflets quite broadly egg-shaped or oval, rounded or notched at tip, smooth on both sides, ¾ to 2 inches long. *Flowers* deep purple, about ⅜ inch long, usually in several end clusters 2½ to 6 inches long; blooming April to June. *Fruits* about 5/16 inch long, sparingly glandular-dotted; maturing July or August.

RANGE. North Carolina and Tennessee south to Georgia and Alabama.

MOUNTAIN INDIGOBUSH   *Amorpha vigata* Small

FIELD MARKS. A shrub similar to the preceding; growing in dry woods. *Leaflets* 9 to 19, ¾ to 2 inches long, elliptic or egg-shaped, somewhat leathery, lustrous above, somewhat hairy beneath. *Fruits* dotted with small glands.

RANGE. Western Florida and Alabama north to Tennessee. (Not illustrated)

151

PLUME-LOCUST *Amorpha herbacea* Walt.

FIELD MARKS. A shrub 1 to 3 feet high; growing in open sandy woods and pinelands. *Leaves* very short-stalked; the 11 to 37 downy leaflets elliptic to oblong or egg-shaped, rounded at both ends but with an abrupt little bristle-point at tip, ⅜ to 1 inch long. *Flowers* violet purple to white, the calyx with amber-colored dotlike glands, usually in several downy end clusters 4 to 12 inches long; blooming May to July. *Fruits* about 3/16 inch long, downy and glandular-dotted.
RANGE. Chiefly coastal plain; North Carolina south to Florida.

GEORGIA INDIGOBUSH *Amorpha georgiana* Wilbur

FIELD MARKS. A shrub 1 to about 3 feet high, with creeping underground stems and few branches; growing in sandy open woods or woods borders. *Leaves* very short-stalked; the 11 to 25 leaflets oval-shaped, rounded at both ends but with an abrupt little point at tip, smooth or nearly so but conspicuously glandular-dotted on the lower surface, ⅜ to about 1 inch long. *Flowers* blue, the calyx smooth or nearly so, usually in a solitary end cluster 2 to 6 inches long; blooming June and July. *Fruits* about 3/16 inch long, smooth or nearly so.
RANGE. Coastal plain; North Carolina south to Georgia.

SCHWERIN INDIGOBUSH *Amorpha schwerinii* C. K. Schneid.

FIELD MARKS. A shrub 3 to 6 feet; growing in rocky woods or on river bluffs. *Branchlets* brownish-hairy. *Leaves* rather long-stalked; the 11 to 23 leaflets elliptic or narrowly egg-shaped, broadly pointed and often with a small bristle at tip, rounded at base, quite densely brownish-hairy beneath, ⅜ to 1¼ inches long. *Flowers* purplish, about ⅜ inch long, in 1 or 2 hairy end clusters 1½ to 3 inches long; blooming April to June. *Fruits* about 3/16 inch long, hairy.
RANGE. Chiefly piedmont: North Carolina south to Georgia.

SHINING INDIGOBUSH *Amorpha nitens* F. E. Boynt.

FIELD MARKS. A smooth shrub 3 to about 9 feet; growing in swamps or along streams. Both the branchlets and the upper surfaces of the 9 to 19 oblong egg-shaped leaflets are lustrous. The leaves are long-stalked, and the purple flowers are usually in a solitary end cluster 4½ to 10 inches long. Fruit pods are curved and quite smooth.
RANGE. Southern Illinois south to Arkansas and Georgia. (Not illustrated)

THE LOCUSTS (Robinia L.)

(Key Appendix G)

The locusts are leaf-losing trees or shrubs with alternate, pinnately compound leaves. The branchlets usually have pairs of nodal spines which are modified stipules; the leaflets are untoothed. Locusts have large, showy, pealike white or pink flowers in slender-stalked, usually drooping, axillary clusters. The fruits are flattened pealike pods with several hard seeds.

CLAMMY LOCUST *Robinia viscosa* Vent.

FIELD MARKS. A shrub or small tree to 20 or more feet high; growing in open woods or on wooded slopes in the southern Appalachians. *Branchlets* have small nodal thorns and are densely covered with sticky stalkless or short-stalked glands. *Leaves* 6 to 12 inches long; the 11 to 25 leaflets elliptic to egg-shaped, broadly pointed to rounded at base, usually rounded but with an abrupt bristle-point at tip, 1 to 2 inches long; leafstalks glandular-sticky. *Flowers* pink or lavender pink, not fragrant, the calyx and stalks of the flower cluster sticky-glandular; blooming May or June. *Fruits* 2 to 3 inches long, at first sticky-glandular, later dry.
RANGE. Western Virginia south to northern Georgia and Alabama. Often found as an escape from cultivation northward.

Plume-locust

Georgia Indigobush

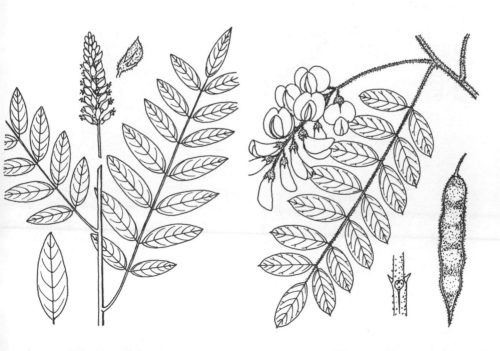

Schwerin Indigobush

Clammy Locust

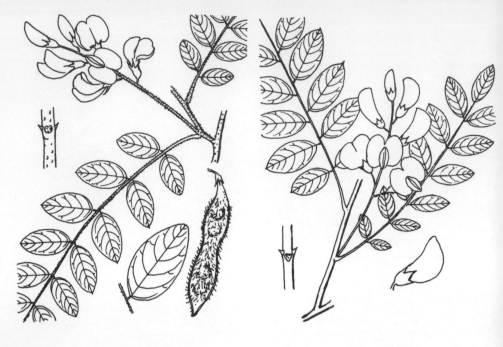

Hartweg Locust

Elliott Locust

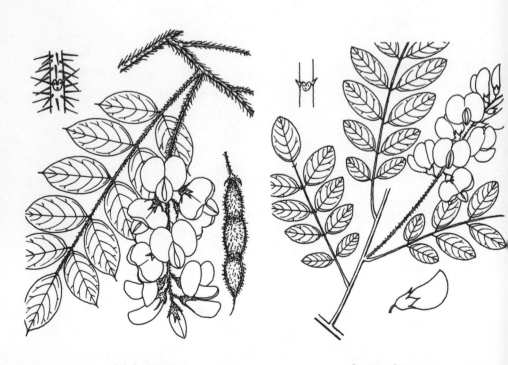

Bristly Locust

Boynton Locust

HARTWEG LOCUST *Robinia hartwegii* Koehne

FIELD MARKS. A shrub 3 to about 6 feet high; growing on wooded slopes and ridges in the southern Appalachians. *Branchlets* downy and covered with stout but short-stalked glands; unarmed or with very small nodal spines. *Leaves* with 13 to 23 leaflets which are elliptic to oval or egg-shaped, bluntish but often with a small bristle-point at tip, roundish at base, smooth or nearly so above, more or less downy beneath, ¾ to about 2 inches long. *Flowers* pale pink to rose purple, 10 to 20 in a downy and glandular-dotted axillary cluster; blooming June or July. *Fruits* downy and glandular-bristly, 2 to 3½ inches long; maturing August or September.

RANGE. Western North Carolina and eastern Tennessee south to northern Georgia and Alabama.

ELLIOTT LOCUST *Robinia elliottii* (Chapm.) Ashe

FIELD MARKS. A shrub 2 to about 5 feet high, chiefly branching above; growing in sandy woods or on sandhills. *Branchlets* densely grayish-downy when young; usually armed with short but stout nodal spines. *Leaves* with 9 to 15 leaflets which are oval or elliptic, blunt or somewhat pointed at both ends, more or less downy beneath, ¾ to 2 inches long. *Flowers* rose pink or purplish, 5 to 10 in a downy-stalked axillary cluster; the calyx teeth triangular and narrowly pointed; blooming April and May. *Fruits* narrow, bristly-hairy; maturing July to September.

RANGE. Chiefly coastal plain; North Carolina south to Georgia, west to Alabama.

BRISTLY LOCUST *Robinia hispida* L.

FIELD MARKS. A shrub 2½ to about 10 feet high with stems, branchlets, leafstalks and stalks of the flower clusters densely covered with reddish-brown bristles; growing in open woods and on slopes and ridges. *Leaves* 4 to 8 inches long, with 9 to 15 leaflets which are egg-shaped, rounded at base, prominently bristle-pointed at tip, ¾ to about 2 inches long. *Flowers* large, rose pink, in clusters of 3 to 8; blooming May and June. *Fruits* at first sticky-glandular, later dry and bristly, 1½ to 2½ inches long.

RANGE. Virginia, West Virginia, and Kentucky south to North Carolina; and northern Georgia and Alabama.

Also called Rose-acacia. Often planted as an ornamental and escaping north of its natural range.

BOYNTON LOCUST *Robinia boyntonii* Ashe

FIELD MARKS. A shrub 3 to about 6 feet high; growing on wooded slopes and ridges in the southern Appalachians. *Branchlets* smooth or nearly so; unarmed or with very short nodal spines. *Leaves* with 7 to 13 leaflets which are elliptic or narrowly egg-shaped, roundish to pointed at base, blunt but often with a minute bristle at tip, smooth on both surfaces, ¾ to 1½ inches long. *Flowers* pink or rose purple, 8 to 10 on a sparingly glandular-bristly stalk from the leaf axils; blooming April to June. *Fruits* seldom present.

RANGE. Western North Carolina and eastern Tennessee south to northern Georgia and Alabama.

KELSEY LOCUST *Robinia kelseyi* Hutchins

FIELD MARKS. A shrub 3 to about 10 feet high; growing on wooded slopes and ridges in the southern Appalachians. *Branchlets* smooth; armed with slender nodal spines. *Leaves* with 9 to 13 leaflets which are narrowly elliptic or lance-shaped, pointed at tip, pointed or roundish at base, downy on both surfaces at flowering time but smooth or nearly so when mature, ¾ to about 2 inches long. *Flowers* rose pink, 5 to 8 in a cluster on a more or less glandular-bristly axillary stalk; calyx teeth narrow, long-pointed, longer than the often glandular-hairy tube; blooming April to June. *Fruits* brown, densely glandular-bristly, 1½ to 2½ inches long; maturing June to September.

RANGE. Western North Carolina.

DWARF LOCUST *Robinia nana* Ell.

FIELD MARKS. A shrub 8 inches to about 1 foot high; growing in sandy open woods and on sandhills. *Branchlets* sometimes minutely downy; unarmed or occasionally with short nodal spines. *Leaves* with 7 to 11 (rarely 13) leaflets which are elliptic or narrowly egg-shaped, blunt or somewhat pointed at tip, roundish at base, smooth on both surfaces, 1 to 1½ inches long. *Flowers* pink, few in a cluster, on nodding and more or less glandular-bristly axillary stalks; blooming April or May. *Fruits* rarely maturing.

RANGE. Coastal plain and lower piedmont; North and South Carolina.

AMERICAN WISTERIA *Wisteria frutescens* (L.) Poir.

FIELD MARKS. A climbing, leaf-losing vine; growing on the borders of swamps and low woods or along streams. *Leaves* alternate, compound, 4 to 9 inches long; the 9 to 15 leaflets elliptic or egg-shaped, rounded to pointed at base, pointed at tip, untoothed on margin, smooth above, often sparingly hairy beneath, ¾ to 2¼ inches long. *Flowers* showy, lilac purple to white, in dense end clusters 2 to 4½ inches long; blooming April to June. *Fruits* knobby beanlike pods 2 to 4 inches long; maturing June to September.

RANGE. Chiefly coastal plain; eastern Maryland and Virginia south to Florida, west to Alabama.

KENTUCKY WISTERIA *Wisteria macrostachya* Nutt.

FIELD MARKS. A climbing vine similar to the preceding species but usually larger. *Leaves* 8 to 12 inches long; the leaflets usually 9 in number, rounded to slightly heart-shaped at base, often rather long-pointed at tip, smooth on both surfaces or sparingly downy beneath, 1 to 2¾ inches long. *Flowers* lilac to purple, showy, in rather dense and drooping end clusters 8 to 12 inches long; blooming June to August. *Fruits* knobby beanlike pods 2½ to nearly 5 inches long.

RANGE. Kentucky and southern Illinois to Missouri, south to Louisiana and Texas.

156

Kelsey Locust

Dwarf Locust

American Wisteria

Kentucky Wisteria

Northern Prickly-ash   **Southern Prickly-ash**

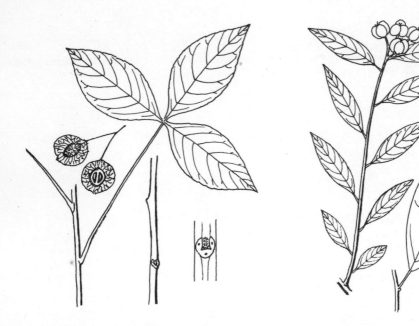

Hoptree   **Sebastianbush**

NORTHERN PRICKLY-ASH   *Zanthoxylum americanum* Mill.

FIELD MARKS. A leaf-losing shrub 4 to about 15 feet high; growing in rocky woods or along streams. *Branchlets* with pairs of broad-based nodal prickles, with a lemon-like odor when bruised; buds hairy, rusty-red. *Leaves* alternate, compound, 3 to 10 inches long; the 5 to 11 leaflets almost stalkless, egg-shaped, rounded to broadly pointed at base, pointed at tip, untoothed on margin, smooth or nearly so above, often slightly downy beneath, glandular-dotted, with lemon-like odor when crushed, 1 to 2½ inches long. *Flowers* small, greenish, clustered; blooming in April or May. *Fruits* dry, reddish-brown pods about 3/16 inch long, containing 1 or 2 shiny black seeds; maturing August or September.

RANGE. Quebec and Ontario to South Dakota; south to northern Georgia, Alabama, and northeastern Oklahoma.

Also called Toothache-tree; once used as a remedy for toothache, rheumatism, ulcers, colic, etc.

SOUTHERN PRICKLY-ASH   *Zanthoxylum clava-herculis* L.

FIELD MARKS. A large shrub or small somewhat evergreen tree; growing in dry sandy woods or on sandhills. *Branchlets* with paired nodal prickles and some scattered ones, on larger stems developing into corky knobs with a stout prickle at tip; lime-like odor when bruised. *Leaves* alternate, compound, 5 to 8 inches long; the 7 to 19 leaflets almost stalkless, often rather sickle-shaped, unevenly rounded or pointed at base, pointed at tip, margin bluntly toothed, somewhat leathery in texture, lustrous above, paler and usually smooth beneath, 1 to 2½ inches long, with limelike odor when crushed. *Flowers* small, greenish, clustered; blooming April to June. *Fruits* dry, reddish-brown pods about 3/16 inch long, containing 1 or 2 shiny black seeds; maturing July to September.

RANGE. Coastal plain; southeastern Virginia south to Florida, west to Texas; north in Mississippi Valley to Arkansas and southeastern Oklahoma.

HOPTREE   *Ptelea trifoliata* L.

FIELD MARKS. A leaf-losing shrub or small tree to 15 feet high, all parts of which are ill-scented when crushed; growing on sandy shores or rocky banks of streams. *Leaves* alternate, long-stalked, compound; the 3 leaflets egg-shaped, pointed at both ends, sometimes obscurely toothed on margin, smooth above, paler and sometimes downy beneath, minutely clear- or black-dotted, 2 to 6 inches long. *Flowers* small, greenish white, clustered; blooming April to July. *Fruits* wafer-like, roundish, thin, papery, with 2 seeds in a central chamber; maturing June to September.

RANGE. Southwestern Quebec to Ontario, south to Florida and Texas.

Also called Wafer-ash and Stinking-ash.

SPURGE FAMILY (Euphorbiaceae)

SEBASTIANBUSH   *Sebastiania ligustrina* (Michx.) Muell.-Arg.

FIELD MARKS. An erect half-evergreen shrub 3 to 12 feet high; growing in wet woods, swamps, or along streams. *Branchlets* slender, exuding a milky sap when broken. *Leaves* alternate, elliptic to oval, pointed at both ends or long-pointed at tip, margin untoothed, smooth or nearly so on both surfaces, slightly paler beneath, ¾ to 3 inches long; stipules small but quite evident. *Flowers* small, greenish, in short clusters; blooming May or June. *Fruits* 3-lobed, yellowish-green capsules about ¼ inch in diameter; maturing July or August, persisting until about October.

RANGE. Coastal plain; North Carolina south to Florida, west to Louisiana.

ALABAMA CROTON *Croton alabamensis* E. A. Smith

FIELD MARKS. A rare evergreen or semi-evergreen shrub 5 to 10 feet high; growing on shale or limestone river bluffs in Tuscaloosa and Bibb counties, Alabama. *Branchlets* pale brownish gray, minutely scaly, with a strong odor when broken. *Leaves* elliptic to broadly lance-shaped, roundish at base, blunt or rounded at tip, untoothed on margin, bright green and smooth above, silvery white with minute scales beneath, 2 to about 4 inches long; leafstalks slender. *Flowers* small, arranged in short and narrow end clusters; blooming February or March. *Fruits* 3-parted, silvery grayish, minutely scaly capsules ¼ to ⅜ inch long.

STILLINGIA *Stillingia aquatica* Chapm.

FIELD MARKS. A leaf-losing shrub 2 to about 6 feet high, with a solitary spindle-shaped stem which branches above; growing in shallow pineland ponds. *Branchlets* slender, smooth. *Leaves* alternate, rather crowded, narrow and willow-like, pointed at both ends, short-stalked, very finely but sharply toothed on margin, yellowish green and smooth on both surfaces, 1 to about 2¼ inches long. *Flowers* small, yellowish green, in a rather short and narrow end cluster; blooming May to September. *Fruits* 3-parted capsules about ⅜ inch long.

RANGE. Coastal plain; southeastern South Carolina south to Florida, west to Mississippi.

CACTUS FAMILY (Cactaceae)

EASTERN PRICKLY-PEAR *Opuntia compressa* (Salisb.) Macbr.

FIELD MARKS. A more or less prostrate and sometimes mat-forming plant; growing in sandy or rocky, open places. *Stems* made up of firmly attached, flattened, thick and fleshy joints which are inversely egg-shaped to elliptic or roundish in outline, pale green, 2 to 4 inches long, and commonly with 1 or a few slender spines an inch or less in length. *Leaves* thick, scalelike, spirally arranged, about 3/16 inch long, and soon shed; bearing in their axils little clusters of prickly bristles. *Flowers* bright yellow, often with a red center, about 2 inches across; blooming May or June. *Fruits* inversely egg-shaped, red or purplish berries 1 to about 2 inches long; ripening August to October.

RANGE. Coastal plain; Massachusetts south to Florida, west to Alabama; inland to Tennessee and the mountains of West Virginia.

Also known as Indian-fig, as the fruits are edible.

DRUMMOND PRICKLY-PEAR *Opuntia drummondii* Graham

FIELD MARKS. A small prostrate or mat-forming plant growing on sand dunes and in sandy pinelands near the coast. *Stems* made up of loosely attached fleshy joints which are pale green or partly purplish, usually ¾ to (seldom) 2 inches long, and viciously armed with slender spines which are often 1 inch or more long and commonly in groups of 2 to 4. *Leaves* thick, scalelike, and soon shed. *Flowers* similar to those of the preceding species; blooming in May or June. *Fruits* also similar but usually smaller; ripening August to October.

RANGE. North Carolina south to Florida, west to Mississippi.

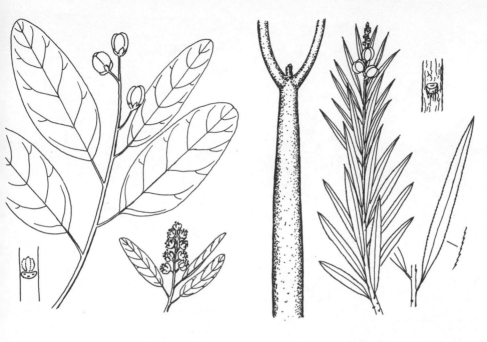

Alabama Croton

Stillingia

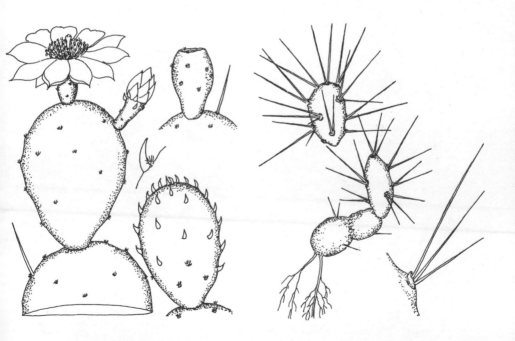

Eastern Prickly-pear

Drummond Prickly-pear

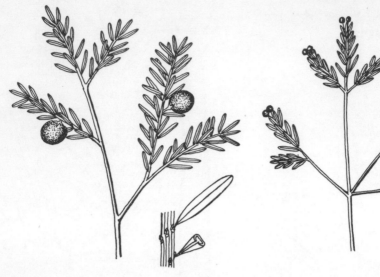

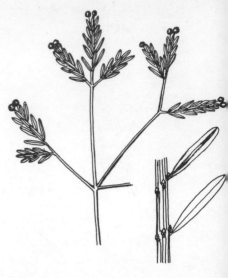

Black Crowberry

Broom-crowberry

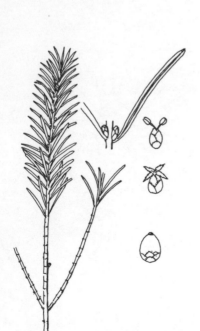

Sandhill-rosemary

American Smoketree

CROWBERRY FAMILY (Empetraceae)

BLACK CROWBERRY   *Empetrum nigrum* L.

FIELD MARKS. A prostrate and spreading evergreen shrub; growing in cold, sandy, or rocky places. *Branchlets* smooth or sometimes sticky-hairy. *Leaves* alternate or sometimes whorled, very narrow or narrowly elliptic, blunt at tip, margin rolled and roughish,thick, dark green, smooth or nearly so, ⅛ to ¼ inch long. *Flowers* small, purplish, solitary in the axils of the upper leaves; blooming June or July. *Fruits* round, berry-like, black or purple, juicy, 6- to 9-seeded, slightly less than ¼ inch in diameter; ripening July to November.
RANGE. Arctic region south to New England, northern New York, northern Michigan, northern Minnesota, southern Alberta, and northern California; also on eastern Long Island.

PURPLE CROWBERRY   *Empetrum atropurpureum* Fern. & Wieg.

FIELD MARKS. A shrub similar to the preceding but with trailing branchlets and leaves white-wooly when young. *Fruits* red to purplish-black.
RANGE. Labrador to Quebec, south to Nova Scotia and the mountains of northern New England. (Not illustrated)

BROOM-CROWBERRY   *Corema conradii* Torr.

FIELD MARKS. A spreading evergreen shrub 6 inches to about 2 feet high; growing in sandy or rocky places. *Leaves* alternate or in 3's, very narrow, blunt at tip, bright green and smooth when mature, ⅛ to 3/16 inch long. *Flowers* small, purplish, in heads at tips of the branchlets; blooming March to June. *Fruits* round, brownish, berry-like, usually 3-seeded, almost dry, less than ⅛ inch in diameter; ripening July to September.
RANGE. Newfoundland south near the coast to New Jersey; also in Shawangunk Mountains, New York.

SANDHILL-ROSEMARY   *Ceratiola ericoides* Michx.

FIELD MARKS. A much-branched, evergreen, aromatic shrub 1 to about 5 feet high; growing in dry and sandy coastal-plain pinelands and on sandhills. *Branchlets* slender and stiffly erect. *Leaves* alternate but closely crowded, spreading, very narrow, the margins so inrolled that the leaves appear to be needle-like or tubular, ¼ to about ½ inch long. *Flowers* small and inconspicuous, red or yellowish, 2 or 3 together in the axils of the upper leaves; stamen-bearing and pistil-bearing flowers usually on separate plants; blooming spring or summer, or all year southward. *Fruits* roundish, berry-like, rather dry, yellow or red, scarcely ⅛ inch in diameter.
RANGE. Coastal plain; South Carolina south to Florida, west to Mississippi.

CASHEW FAMILY (Anacardiaceae)

AMERICAN SMOKETREE   *Cotinus obovatus* Raf.

FIELD MARKS. A leaf-losing shrub or small tree 6 to sometimes 30 feet high; growing on rocky ridges and bluffs. *Branchlets* aromatic and exuding a gummy sap when broken. *Leaves* alternate, oval or broadest above the middle, somewhat pointed at base, rounded or notched at tip, untoothed and with a slightly rolled margin, dark green and smooth above, paler and often somewhat downy beneath, 2 to 5 inches long. *Flowers* small, yellowish green, a number in a much-branched pyramidal end cluster 6 to 8 inches long; blooming April or May. *Fruits* small, podlike, lopsided, dry; maturing June to September.
RANGE. Eastern Tennessee to Missouri, Arkansas, and Oklahoma; south to Alabama and Texas.
The hairy stalks of the flower clusters resemble puffs of smoke at a distance. Occasionally cultivated for its brilliant red and orange fall foilage.

SMOOTH SUMAC *Rhus glabra* L.

FIELD MARKS. A leaf-losing shrub or small tree 2 to about 15 feet high; growing in old fields, along fence rows, etc. *Branchlets* stout, smooth, whitened with a bloom, exuding milky sap when cut. *Leaves* alternate, compound, 12 to 20 inches long; the 11 to 31 leaflets stalkless, oblong lance-shaped, usually roundish at base, pointed at tip, sharply toothed on margin, smooth, whitened beneath, 2 to 5 inches long. *Flowers* small, yellowish green, in dense erect end clusters; blooming June or July. *Fruits* roundish, red, sticky-hairy, 1-seeded, about ⅛ inch in diameter, in compact end clusters; maturing August or September and persisting.

RANGE. Maine and Quebec to British Columbia, south to Florida and California.

Young fruits of this and other red-fruited sumacs have been used to make a pleasantly acid, lemonade-like drink. The fruits are eaten by many birds, but usually only in an emergency. Twigs and bark are often eaten by rabbits and deer.

STAGHORN SUMAC *Rhus typhina* L.

FIELD MARKS. Similar to the preceding but usually larger, to about 30 feet high. *Branchlets* are velvety-hairy. Leaves are usually both whitened and downy beneath, and the leafstalks are downy. The flowers and fruits are similar to those of Smooth Sumac.

RANGE. Nova Scotia to Quebec and Minnesota; south to northern Georgia, Tennessee, Illinois, and Iowa.

DWARF SUMAC *Rhus copallina* L.

FIELD MARKS. A leaf-losing shrub or small tree 2 to about 10 feet high; growing in open woods, thickets, fence rows, and old fields. *Branchlets* moderate, smooth or finely downy, exuding a clear sap when cut. *Leaves* alternate, compound, 6 to 12 inches long, with conspicuous wings between the leaflets; the 9 to 21 leaflets stalkless, egg-shaped to lance-shaped, pointed or unevenly rounded at base, pointed at tip, untoothed or nearly so on margin, usually lustrous above, paler and often downy beneath, 1½ to 3 inches long. *Flowers* small, yellowish green, numerous, in large end clusters; blooming July to September. *Fruits* roundish, red, hairy, about ⅛ inch in diameter, in large and often somewhat drooping end clusters; maturing September or October.

RANGE. Southern Maine to New York, Michigan, central Wisconsin, and eastern Kansas; south to Florida and Texas.

Also called Shining Sumac. Rich in tannin used in tanning hides.

MICHAUX SUMAC *Rhus michauxii* Sarg.

FIELD MARKS. A rather rare shrub. *Branchlets* moderate, densely brownish-hairy. *Leaves* with brownish-hairy leafstalks and 9 to 15 leaflets which are coarsely toothed on margin, brownish-hairy and green beneath. *Fruits* red and densely hairy.

RANGE. Coastal plain and lower piedmont; North Carolina south to Georgia. (Not illustrated)

POISON SUMAC *Rhus vernix* L.

CAUTION: All parts of this plant contain a dangerous skin irritant.

FIELD MARKS. A shrub or small tree 4 to about 15 feet high; growing in swamps, bogs, and other wet places. *Branchlets* moderately stout, smooth, the end bud present. *Leaves* alternate, compound, 6 to 12 inches long; the 7 to 13 leaflets short-stalked, elliptic or egg-shaped, broadly pointed at base, pointed at tip, margin untoothed, rather lustrous above, paler beneath, smooth, 2 to 4 inches long; leafstalks usually reddish. *Flowers* small, greenish, in axillary clusters; blooming May to July. *Fruits* roundish, smooth, waxy white, about 3/16 inch in diameter, in rather loose and drooping clusters; ripening August or September and persisting.

RANGE. Southwestern Maine to Ontario and Minnesota, south to Florida and Texas.

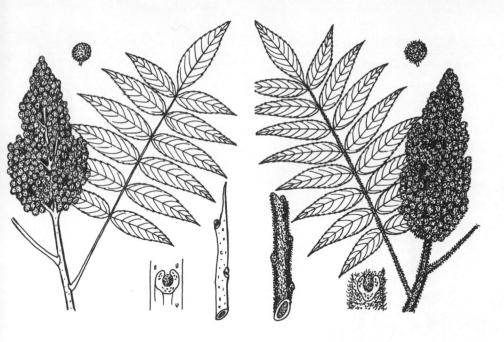

Smooth Sumac

Staghorn Sumac

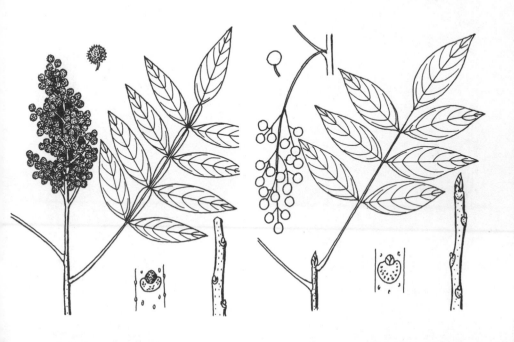

Dwarf Sumac

Poison Sumac

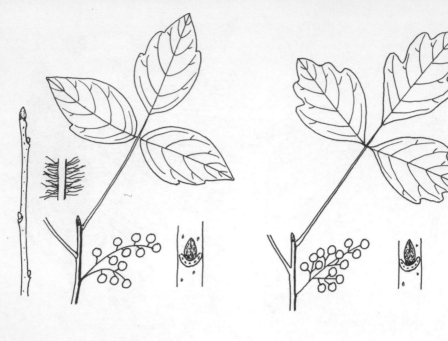

Poison-ivy

Poison-oak

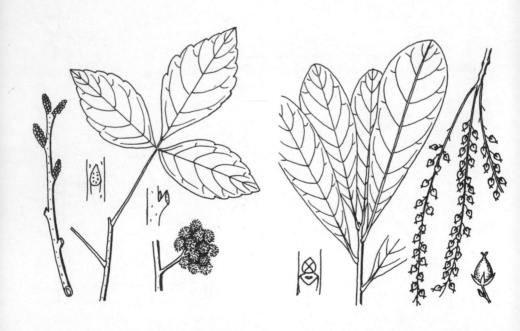

Fragrant Sumac

Swamp Cyrilla

POISON-IVY *Rhus radicans* **L.**

CAUTION: All parts of this plant contain a dangerous skin irritant.

FIELD MARKS. An erect or trailing leaf-losing shrub, or a woody vine climbing by means of aerial rootlets on the stems; growing in wooded areas, thickets, clearings, or along fence rows and roadsides. *Leaves* alternate, long-stalked, compound, 4 to 12 inches long; the 3 leaflets oval or egg-shaped, rounded or broadly pointed at base, pointed at tip, usually with a few coarse teeth on margin, often lustrous above, paler and slightly downy beneath, 1½ to 8 inches long; the end leaflet rather long-stalked, the side ones almost stalkless. *Flowers* small, yellowish green, in axillary clusters; blooming May to July. *Fruits* roundish, waxy white, about 3/16 inch in diameter; maturing August to October and persisting.

RANGE. Nova Scotia to British Columbia; south to Florida, Texas, and Arizona.

POISON-OAK *Rhus toxicodendron* **L.**

CAUTION: All parts of this plant contain a dangerous skin irritant.

FIELD MARKS. A stiffly erect, simple or sparingly branched, leaf-losing shrub 1 to 2½ feet high; growing in dry sandy pine and oak woods and clearings. *Leaves* alternate, long-stalked, compound, 3 to 8 inches long; the 3 leaflets often broadly egg-shaped, pointed at base, blunt at tip, with 3 to 7 often deep lobes, somewhat downy above, more densely so and paler beneath, 2 to 5 inches long; the end leaflet rather long-stalked, the side ones almost stalkless; leafstalks downy. *Flowers* and *fruits* similar to those of Poison-ivy but usually more downy.

RANGE. Chiefly coastal plain; New Jersey and Maryland south to Florida; Tennessee to eastern Oklahoma south to Alabama and Texas.

FRAGRANT SUMAC *Rhus aromatica* **Ait.**

FIELD MARKS. A leaf-losing, aromatic shrub 2 to 6 feet high; growing on dry rocky banks and hillsides. *Branchlets* pleasantly fragrant when bruised, often with catkin-like flower buds. *Leaves* alternate, rather long-stalked, compound, 4 to 6 inches long; leaflets 3, the end one short-stalked and commonly diamond-shaped, the side ones egg-shaped and almost stalkless, all usually pointed at base, pointed or blunt at tip, coarsely and irregularly toothed on margin, somewhat downy, 1 to 3 inches long. *Flowers* small, yellowish green, in catkin-like clusters; blooming March or April. *Fruits* roundish, red, densely hairy, about 1¼ inch in diameter; maturing July or August.

RANGE. Vermont and southwestern Quebec to Indiana, Kansas, Nebraska, and Oklahoma; south to Florida and Texas.

CYRILLA FAMILY (Cyrillaceae)

SWAMP CYRILLA *Cyrilla racemiflora* **L.**

FIELD MARKS. A shrub or small tree to 15 (rarely 30) feet high; forming thickets on borders of swamps and ponds. *Leaves* alternate, narrowly elliptic or broadest above the middle, wedge-shaped at base, rounded or blunt-pointed at tip, untoothed on margin, thin but somewhat leathery, lustrous above, paler beneath, smooth, 2 to 4 inches long; leafstalks short. *Flowers* small, white; in long, narrow, drooping end clusters; blooming late April to July. *Fruits* small, yellowish-brown, 4-seeded capsules about ⅛ inch long; maturing August or September and persisting.

RANGE. Coastal plain; Virginia south to Florida, west to Texas.

Also called White-titi. Flowers are important source of honey. Leaves usually turn red in the fall but persist most of the winter.

BUCKWHEAT-TREE *Cliftonia monophylla* (Lam.) Britt.

FIELD MARKS. A large evergreen shrub or small tree usually 5 to 15 (sometimes to 30) feet high, often forming dense thickets on the borders of swamps or along streams. *Leaves* alternate, narrowly elliptic or broadest above the middle, wedge-shaped at base, rounded or bluntly pointed at tip, margin untoothed, lustrous green above, paler and dull beneath, smooth, 1 to 2 inches long; the leafstalks very short. *Flowers* small, white or pinkish, fragrant, in narrow end clusters; blooming March or April. *Fruits* 2- to 4- winged, dry, light-brown capsules about ¼ inch long.

RANGE. Coastal plain; Georgia and Florida west to Louisiana.

An important honey plant. Also called Black-titi.

HOLLY FAMILY (Aquifoliaceae)

MOUNTAIN-HOLLY *Nemopanthus mucronata* (L.) Trel.

FIELD MARKS. An erect leaf-losing shrub 3 to 12 feet high; growing in cool, moist, rocky woods, lakeshores, and bogs. *Leaves* alternate, often clustered on short spurs, elliptic, pointed to roundish at base, blunt but with an abrupt little point at tip, (rarely) with a few teeth on margin, thin in texture, smooth, slightly paler beneath, ¾ to 2 inches long; leafstalks smooth and very slender. *Flowers* small, greenish white, on long and slender stalks; blooming about May. *Fruits* berry-like, 3- to 5-seeded, roundish, dull red, about ¼ inch in diameter, on long and slender stalks; ripening July to September.

RANGE. Newfoundland to Minnesota; south to West Virginia, Indiana, and northern Illinois.

HOLLIES (Ilex L.)

(Key Appendix H)

The hollies are evergreen or leaf-losing shrubs or trees with alternate and simple leaves. They have small greenish-white flowers which bloom in the spring. As a rule the stamens and pistils are in separate flowers, and they are found on separate plants. The fruits are roundish, berry-like, with 4 to 6 large bony nutlets and a mealy or pulpy flesh. Hollies are important as ornamental and honey plants; their fruits are eaten by many kinds of wild birds. The American Holly (*Ilex opaca* Ait.) is a tree commonly 20 to 40 feet or more high, the berried branches of which are widely used for Christmas decorations.

WINTERBERRY *Ilex verticillata* (L.) Gray

FIELD MARKS. A leaf-losing shrub 3 to 15 feet high; growing along streams and in low wet woods and swamps. *Leaves* oval to lance-shaped or broadest above the middle, pointed at both ends, sharply and rather coarsely toothed on margin, sometimes slightly leathery in texture, dull green above, slightly paler and sometimes slightly downy beneath, 1½ to 3 inches long; remaining green until frost, then turning black. *Flowers* bearing the stamens and those bearing the pistils both short-stalked; blooming April to June. *Fruits* bright red (rarely yellow), short-stalked, about ¼ inch in diameter; ripening September and October and persisting after the leaves fall.

RANGE. Newfoundland to Minnesota; south to Georgia, southeastern Louisiana, and Missouri.

Also called Black-alder.

SMOOTH WINTERBERRY *Ilex laevigata* (Pursh) Gray

FIELD MARKS. A leaf-losing shrub similar to the preceding and growing in similar swampy situations. *Leaves* oval to narrowly elliptic, pointed at both ends, with rather low but sharp teeth on margin, thin in texture, lustrous green above, paler and smooth or nearly so on both surfaces, 1½ to 3 inches long. *Flowers* bearing the stamens much longer than those bearing pistils; blooming April to June. *Fruits* orange red (rarely yellow), short stalked, about ¼ inch in diameter; ripening August to October, usually persisting after the leaves fall.

RANGE. Chiefly coastal plain; southern Maine and New York south to Georgia.

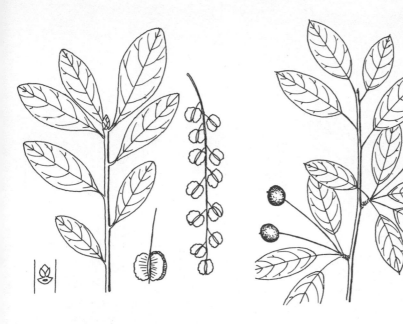

Buckwheat-tree

Mountain-holly

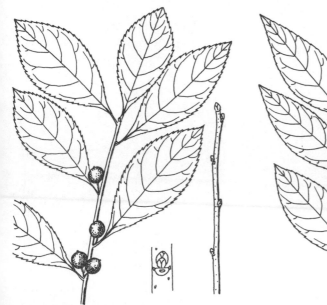

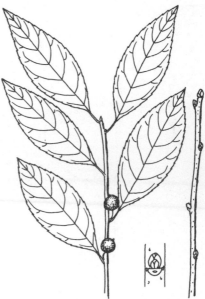

Winterberry

Smooth Winterberry

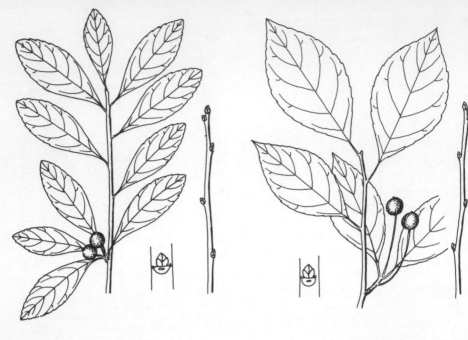

Deciduous Holly

Long-stalked Holly

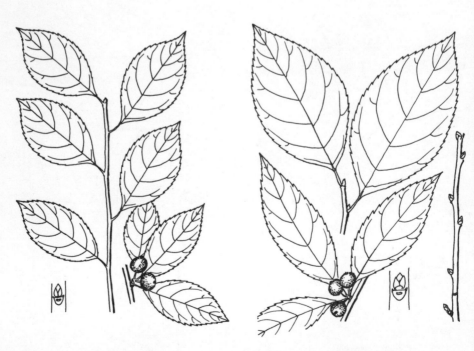

Carolina Holly

Largeleaf Holly

DECIDUOUS HOLLY   *Ilex decidua* Walt.

FIELD MARKS. A leaf-losing shrub or small tree 5 to 25 feet high; growing in upland forests, about swamps, and along streams. *Leaves* sometimes clustered on short spurlike branches, narrowly elliptic or broadest above the middle, wedge-shaped at the base, broadly pointed or blunt at tip, margin with low and bluntish teeth above the middle, light green above, paler beneath, smooth or nearly so on both surfaces, 1½ to 3 inches long; leafstalks short and sometimes downy. *Flowers* blooming in April or May. *Fruits* bright red, short-stalked, about ¼ inch in diameter; ripening September and October and usually persisting.

RANGE. Virginia to southern Illinois, Missouri, and Oklahoma; south to Florida and south central Texas.

Also called Possum-haw.

LONG-STALKED HOLLY   *Ilex decidua* var. *longipes* (Chapm.) Ahles

FIELD MARKS. A leaf-losing shrub 6 to 12 feet high; growing in upland woods and thickets and on cool rocky slopes. *Leaves* broadly lance-shaped to broadly elliptic, pointed at both ends, margin with rather widely spaced and bluntish teeth, thin in texture, smooth on both surfaces or sometimes sparingly hairy beneath, 2 to 4½ inches long. *Flowers* blooming in April or May. *Fruits* red or purplish (rarely yellow), about ¼ inch in diameter on stalks ½ to 1¼ inches long; ripening September or October.

RANGE. Virginia, West Virginia, and Tennessee; south to Florida and Alabama.

Also called Georgia Holly.

CAROLINA HOLLY   *Ilex ambigua* (Michx.) Torr.

FIELD MARKS. A leaf-losing shrub or small tree usually 5 to 15 feet high; growing in sandy or rocky upland woods. *Leaves* often clustered on short lateral spurlike branches, elliptic to oval, roundish or broadly pointed at base, pointed at tip, sharply toothed on margin often nearly to base, smooth on both surfaces or somewhat downy beneath, 1 to about 2½ inches long. *Flowers* blooming April to June. *Fruits* bright red, short-stalked, about ¼ inch in diameter; ripening August or September but scarcely persisting.

RANGE. Coastal plain; North Carolina south to Florida, west to Texas, and north into Arkansas.

LARGELEAF HOLLY   *Ilex ambigua* var. *montana* (T. & G.) Ahles

FIELD MARKS. A leaf-losing shrub or small tree 5 to 20 feet high; growing in cool, moist, wooded areas. *Leaves* often clustered on short lateral spurlike branches, elliptic to egg-shaped or lance-shaped, roundish to pointed at base, pointed at tip, sharply toothed on margin, thin in texture, bright green and smooth above, sometimes with scattered soft hairs beneath, 2½ to 5 inches long. *Flowers* blooming April to June. *Fruits* bright red, short-stalked, about ⅜ inch in diameter; ripening August to October but scarcely persisting.

RANGE. Southwestern Massachusetts to western New York; south along the mountains to northern Georgia.

SARVIS HOLLY *Ilex amelanchier* M. A. Curtis

FIELD MARKS. A rather rare leaf-losing shrub 3 to 6 feet high; growing along streams and in sandy swamps. *Leaves* elliptic or oblong and sometimes broadest above the middle, pointed to roundish at both ends, margin with small and inconspicuous teeth, veiny, smooth above, paler and somewhat downy beneath, 1½ to 3 inches long; the leafstalks slender. *Flowers* blooming in April or May. *Fruits* dull red, about ⅜ inch in diameter, on slender stalks ¼ to ⅜ inch long; ripening in October or November.

RANGE. Coastal plain; North Carolina south to Georgia, also in Louisiana.

INKBERRY *Ilex glabra* (L.) Gray

FIELD MARKS. An evergreen shrub 1 to about 4 feet high; growing in low sandy woods and about the borders of swamps or bogs. *Leaves* narrowly elliptic to oval and often broadest above the middle, wedge-shaped at base, broadly pointed at tip, margin with some low and bluntish teeth above the middle, thickish and leathery in texture, dark green and lustrous above, paler and smooth and with minute black dots beneath, ¾ to 2 inches long. *Flowers* blooming May to August. *Fruits* black, about ¼ inch in diameter, on stalks about ⅜ inch long; ripening September to November and persisting.

RANGE. Coastal plain; Nova Scotia south to Florida, west to Louisiana.

Also called Gallberry. An important honey plant in the southeast. The fruits are eaten by many birds, including the bobwhite quail and wild turkey.

LARGE GALLBERRY *Ilex coriacea* (Pursh) Chapm.

FIELD MARKS. An evergreen shrub 4 to about 10 feet high; growing in wet sandy woods and swampy places. *Leaves* narrowly elliptic to oval and often broadest above the middle, wedge-shaped at base, usually pointed at tip, margin untoothed or with a few spiny-tipped teeth above the middle, thickish and leathery in texture, dark green and lustrous above, paler and smooth and with minute black dots beneath, 1 to 3½ inches long. *Flowers* blooming in April or May. *Fruits* black, about ⅜ inch in diameter, on stalks ¼ to ⅜ inch long; ripening in September or October and persisting.

RANGE. Coastal plain; southeastern Virginia south to Florida, west to Louisiana.

YAUPON HOLLY *Ilex vomitoria* Ait.

FIELD MARKS. An evergreen shrub or small tree 4 to about 20 feet high; growing in sandy woods and on dunes. *Branchlets* stiff and spiky. *Leaves* oval to elliptic or egg-shaped, rounded to broadly pointed at the base, bluntly pointed at tip, margin with rounded or bluntish teeth, thickish and leathery in texture, lustrous green above, slightly paler beneath, smooth on both surfaces, ½ to 1½ inches long; the leafstalks very short. *Flowers* blooming March to May. *Fruits* bright red (rarely yellow) short-stalked, about ¼ inch in diameter; ripening in October or November and persisting.

RANGE. Coastal plain; southeastern Virginia south to Florida, west to south central Texas; north in the Mississippi Valley to Arkansas and Oklahoma.

Also called Cassine and Christmas-berry. The leaves have been used as a substitute for tea and were formerly used by the Indians to make their ceremonial "black drink." Cultivated as an ornamental shrub.

172

Sarvis Holly

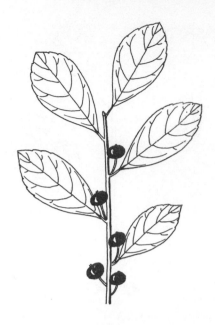

Inkberry

Large Gallberry

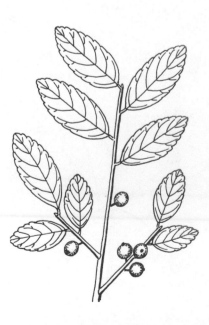

Yaupon Holly

Dahoon Holly

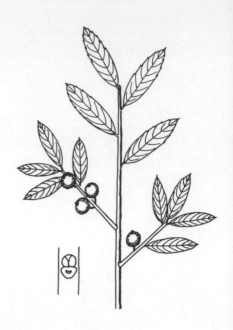

Myrtle-leaf Holly

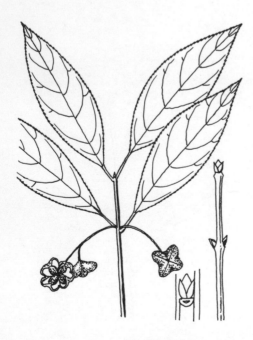

Burning-Bush

Strawberry-Bush

DAHOON HOLLY   *Ilex cassine* L.

FIELD MARKS. An evergreen shrub or small tree 5 to 25 feet high; growing about the borders of swamps and cypress ponds. *Leaves* elliptic or oblong egg-shaped, pointed at base, pointed or blunt at tip, margin untoothed or with a few spiny teeth above the middle, thickish and leathery in texture, dark green and smooth above, usually with minute pale hairs along midrib beneath, 1½ to 3 inches long. *Flowers* blooming in May or June. *Fruits* red (rarely yellow), short-stalked, about ¼ inch in diameter; ripening October or November and persisting.

RANGE. Coastal plain; North Carolina south to Florida, west to Louisiana.

MYRTLE-LEAF HOLLY   *Ilex cassine* var. *myrtifolia* (Walt.) Sarg.

FIELD MARKS. An evergreen shrub or small tree; growing in swampy woods and shallow pineland ponds. *Branchlets* straight, stiff, and spiky. *Leaves* narrowly elliptic, roundish or broadly pointed at base, abruptly tipped with a small spine, margin rolled and untoothed or with some small and inconspicuous teeth above the middle, stiff and leathery in texture, dark green above, paler beneath, smooth, ½ to 1½ inches long; the leafstalks very short. *Flowers* blooming in May or June. *Fruits* bright red (rarely yellow), short-stalked, about ¼ inch in diameter; ripening October or November and persisting.

RANGE. Coastal plain; North Carolina south to Florida, west to Louisiana.

STAFFTREE FAMILY (Celastraceae)

SPINDLETREES (Euonymus)

Members of this genus are shrubs, or sometimes small trees, with opposite and simple leaves. The branchlets are characteristically green and 4-sided or 4-lined. They have small greenish-white to greenish-yellow or purplish flowers which have 4 or 5 petals. The fruits are 3- to 5-lobed capsules which split open at maturity and expose the seeds, which have fleshy bright-red coats. Many species, including the following native ones, are cultivated as ornamental shrubs.

BURNING-BUSH   *Euonymus atropurpureus* Jacq.

FIELD MARKS. An erect leaf-losing shrub 6 to about 15 feet high; growing in rich, moist woods, ravines, and stream bottoms. *Branchlets* roundish and 4-lined. *Leaves* oblong egg-shaped to broadly lance-shaped, usually pointed at base and sharply pointed at tip, finely and sharply toothed on margin, thin-textured, dark green and smooth above, paler and usually somewhat downy beneath, 2 to 5 inches long; leafstalks slender, ¼ to ¾ inch long. *Flowers* purplish brown, about ¼ inch across, in clusters of 5 to 15 from the leaf axils; blooming in June. *Fruits* smooth, purplish pink, about ¾ inch across before bursting; ripening September or October.

RANGE. Western New York and southern Ontario to southern Michigan, central Minnesota, and Montana; south to eastern Virginia, northern Georgia and Alabama, Arkansas, and Oklahoma.

Also known as Wahoo.

STRAWBERRY-BUSH   *Euonymus americanus* L.

FIELD MARKS. An erect or straggling leaf-losing shrub 2 to 6 feet high; growing in rich woods, ravines, and along stream banks. *Branchlets* 4-sided. *Leaves* egg-shaped to broadly lance-shaped, usually pointed at base and sharply pointed at tip, finely and sharply toothed on margin, bright green and smooth above, slightly paler and smooth or nearly so beneath, 1 to 3½ inches long; almost stalkless. *Flowers* greenish purple, about ¼ inch across, solitary or 2 or 3 in cluster from leaf axils; blooming in May or June. *Fruits* rough-warty, crimson, ½ to ¾ inch across before bursting; ripening September or October.

RANGE. Southeastern New York and Pennsylvania to southern Illinois, Missouri, and Oklahoma; south to Florida and Texas.

Also known as Bursting-heart.

RUNNING STRAWBERRY-BUSH   *Euonymus obovatus* Nutt.

FIELD MARKS. A trailing leaf-losing shrub, rooting at the nodes, with ascending branchlets 6 to 12 inches high; growing in cool moist woods. *Branchlets* 4-sided. *Leaves* elliptical or broadest above the middle, pointed at base, broadly or abruptly pointed at tip, finely and sharply toothed on margin, thin in texture, dull light green above, slightly paler beneath, smooth or nearly so on both surfaces, ¾ to 2 inches long, very short-stalked. *Flowers* yellowish green, about ¼ inch across, 1 to 3 on stalks from leaf axils; blooming May or June. *Fruits* rough-warty, pale orange red, about ½ inch across before bursting; ripening September or October.

RANGE. Western New York to southern Ontario and southern Michigan; south to northern Georgia, Tennessee, and Missouri.

MOUNTAIN LOVER   *Pachystima canbyi* Gray

FIELD MARKS. A low, trailing, evergreen, mat-forming shrub with upright 4-sided branchlets 4 to 12 inches high; growing on rocky slopes in the mid-southern Appalachians. *Leaves* opposite, narrowly oblong or sometimes broader above the middle, pointed at base, blunt at tip, margin rolled and finely toothed, leathery in texture, green and smooth on both surfaces, ¼ to 1 inch long, almost stalkless. *Flowers* small, greenish or brownish, 1 to 3 on stalks from leaf axils; blooming April or May. *Fruits* small capsules about ⅛ inch in diameter, splitting at maturity in August or September.

RANGE. South central Pennsylvania and southeastern Ohio south to West Virginia, western Virginia, and eastern Kentucky.

Used in gardening as a ground cover or rock garden plant.

AMERICAN BITTERSWEET   *Celastrus scandens* L.

FIELD MARKS. A twining, leaf-losing, woody vine climbing to a height of 20 or more feet or scrambling over low vegetation and sometimes trailing on the ground; growing in moist thickets and along the banks of streams. *Leaves* alternate, oval or egg-shaped, rounded to broadly pointed at base, abruptly pointed at tip, finely toothed on margin, thin in texture, dull dark green above, paler beneath, smooth or nearly so on both surfaces, 2 to 4 inches long. *Flowers* yellowish-green, small, many in an elongate end cluster; blooming May or June. *Fruits* ball-shaped, dull orange capsules about ⅜ inch in diameter; splitting when mature in September or October and exposing the bright-scarlet, fleshy-coated seeds.

RANGE. Southern Quebec to southern Manitoba; south to Georgia, Mississippi, Arkansas, and Oklahoma.

Also called Climbing Bittersweet and Waxwort. Often cultivated as an ornamental vine. The fruits are eaten by several species of wild birds.

BLADDERNUT FAMILY (Staphyleaceae)

AMERICAN BLADDERNUT   *Staphylea trifolia* L.

FIELD MARKS. A shrub 3 to about 12 feet high; growing in moist thickets, on hillsides, and banks of streams. *Leaves* opposite, compound, long-stalked; the 3 leaflets egg-shaped or elliptic, pointed to roundish at base, abruptly pointed at tip, finely toothed on margin, dark green and smooth above, paler and sometimes downy beneath, end leaflet long-stalked, side ones short-stalked, 2 to 5 inches long. *Flowers* white or creamy white, bell-shaped, about ⅜ inch long, many in elongate and drooping clusters; blooming April to June. *Fruits* 3-sided, inflated, papery, baglike capsules 1 to 3 inches long which contain 3 to 5 light-brown and bony seeds which rattle when capsule is shaken; maturing August to October.

RANGE. Massachusetts to southwestern Quebec, southern Ontario, northern Michigan, and southern Minnesota; south to Georgia, Alabama, southeastern Oklahoma, and southeastern Nebraska.

176

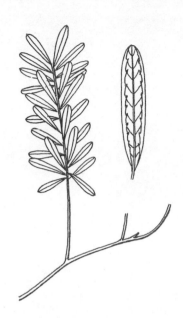

Running Strawberry-Bush

Mountain Lover

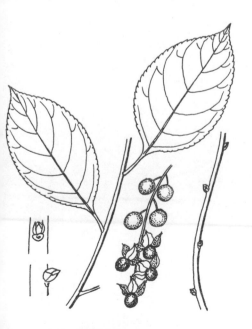

American Bittersweet

American Bladdernut

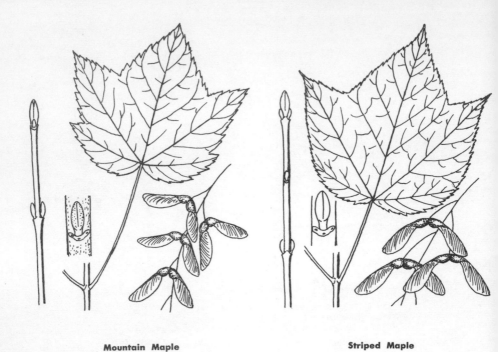

Mountain Maple

Striped Maple

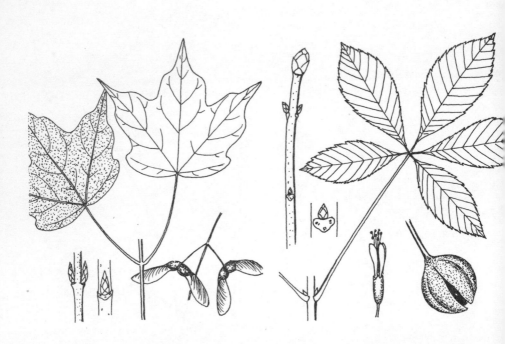

Chalk Maple

Red Buckeye

MAPLE FAMILY (Acer L.)

Maples are usually leaf-losing trees, sometimes shrubs, with opposite and usually simple 3- to 5-lobed leaves; with the main veins radiating from the summit of a long leafstalk. The flowers are rather small and seldom perfect. Maple fruits, called "keys," have a seed-bearing portion tipped with a broad flat wing. They are borne in pairs on slender stalks.

MOUNTAIN MAPLE *Acer spicatum* Lam.

FIELD MARKS. A shrub or small tree 5 to 20 feet high; growing in cool moist, usually rocky woods. *Leaves* usually heart-shaped at base, 3-lobed or sometimes 5-lobed above the middle, the lobes short but broad and pointed, margin coarsely toothed, smooth above, slightly paler and usually downy beneath, 3 to 5 inches broad. *Flowers* greenish yellow, in elongate upright clusters; blooming May or June. *Fruits* with wings slightly spread, about ½ inch long; maturing August or September.

RANGE. Newfoundland to Saskatchewan; south to New York, the region of the Great Lakes, northeastern Iowa, and in the mountains to northern Georgia.

STRIPED MAPLE *Acer pensylvanicum* L.

FIELD MARKS. A shrub or small tree to about 30 feet high; growing in cool, moist, rocky woods. *Bark* of the larger stems greenish and with conspicuous whitish streaks. *Leaves* rounded or heart-shaped at base, with 3 rather short but broad and taper-pointed lobes, margin finely toothed, smooth above, paler and smooth or nearly so beneath, 4 to 8 inches broad. *Flowers* greenish yellow, in loose drooping clusters; blooming May or June. *Fruits* with widely spread wings, about ¾ inch long; maturing August to October.

RANGE. Nova Scotia to Manitoba; south to New England, the region of the Great Lakes, and along the mountains to northern Georgia.

Also called Goosefoot Maple and Moosewood.

CHALK MAPLE *Acer saccharum* ssp. *leucoderme* (Small) Desmarais

FIELD MARKS. A shrub or small tree 10 to 25 feet high; growing along streams and on rocky wooded banks. *Bark* light gray or whitish. *Leaves* with 3 to 5 long-pointed, broad, sparingly blunt-toothed lobes, usually heart-shaped at base, smooth above, paler yellowish green and downy beneath, 2 to 3 inches broad. *Flowers* yellowish green, on slender stalks in end clusters; blooming in April. *Fruits* with spreading wings about ½ inch long; maturing September or October.

RANGE. North Carolina south to Florida, west to Louisiana, north in Mississippi Valley to Tennessee and Arkansas.

HORSECHESTNUT FAMILY (Hippocastanaceae)

BUCKEYES (Aesculus L.)

Buckeyes are leaf-losing trees or shrubs with opposite, compound leaves; with 5 to 7 leaflets radiating from the summit of a long leafstalk. They have showy flowers in large, upright end clusters. The fruits are leathery pods with 1 to 3 large shiny-brown seeds having a conspicuous lighter-colored scar. The seeds are poisonous if eaten.

RED BUCKEYE *Aesculus pavia* L.

FIELD MARKS. A shrub or small tree usually 3 to 10 (rarely 30) feet high, spreading by underground runners; growing in hammocks and pinelands near the coast. *Leaves* with 5 (rarely 7) leaflets which are elliptic or broadest above the middle, wedge-shaped at base, pointed at tip, finely toothed on margin, paler yellowish green and smooth to downy beneath, 4 to 6 inches long. *Flowers* bright red, in erect clusters 5 or 6 inches long; blooming April or May. *Fruits* smooth, 1 to 2 inches across; maturing July or August.

RANGE. Coastal plain; Virginia south to Florida, west to Louisiana, north in Mississippi Valley to southern Illinois and Oklahoma.

179

PAINTED BUCKEYE   *Aesculus sylvatica* Bartr.

FIELD MARKS A shrub or small tree usually 2 to 10 (rarely 30) feet high, spreading by underground runners; growing in rich woods or along streams. *Leaves* usually with 5 leaflets which are lance-shaped or broadest above the middle, wedge-shaped at base, pointed at tip, finely toothed on margin, smooth above, paler and smooth to downy beneath, 3 to 8 inches long. *Flowers* pale yellow or greenish yellow, often tinged with red or sometimes wholly red, in erect clusters 4 to 8 inches long; blooming April or May. *Fruits* smooth, 1 to 1½ inches across, usually 1-seeded; maturing July or August.

RANGE. Chiefly piedmont; Virginia southwest to Georgia and Alabama; also in Tennessee.

BOTTLE-BRUSH BUCKEYE   *Aesculus parviflora* Walt.

FIELD MARKS. A suckering shrub 4 to 10 feet high; growing in rich woods. *Leaves* with 5 to 7 leaflets which are almost stalkless, elliptic or broadest above the middle, wedge-shaped at base, finely toothed on margin, smooth above, paler and grayish-downy beneath, 2 to 7 inches long. *Flowers* small, white or pinkish, in slender upright clusters 6 to 12 inches long. *Fruits* smooth, 1 to 1½ inches across.

RANGE. Coastal plain and piedmont; Georgia, Alabama, and northern Florida.

A handsome ornamental often cultivated much farther north. (Not illustrated)

SOAPBERRY FAMILY (Sapindaceae)

FLORIDA SOAPBERRY   *Sapindus marginatus* Willd.

FIELD MARKS. A large leaf-losing shrub or small tree to 30 feet high; growing in coastal hammocks. *Leaves* alternate, compound, 8 to 24 inches long; the 7 to 13 leaflets almost stalkless, lance-shaped, long-pointed at top, margin untoothed, smooth, lustrous above, paler beneath, 2 to 6 inches long; leafstalks with a narrow ridge on each side. *Flowers* small, reddish, in erect end clusters; blooming in spring. *Fruits* roundish, 3-lobed, smooth, pale yellowish berries about ¾ inch in diameter.

RANGE. Coastal plain; southeastern South Carolina (Small) south to Florida.

WESTERN SOAPBERRY   *Sapindus drummondii* Hook & Arn.

FIELD MARKS. Usually a small tree. *Leaves* 6 to 12 inches long; the 9 to 18 leaflets short-stalked, often more or less sickle-shaped, long-pointed at tip, untoothed on margin, 2 to 3 inches long. *Flowers* small, whitish, in dense end clusters. *Fruits* roundish, yellow, about ½ inch in diameter.

RANGE. Louisiana to Arizona; north to southwestern Missouri, Kansas, and Colorado. (Not illustrated)

BUCKTHORN FAMILY (Rhamnaceae)

SUPPLEJACK   *Berchemia scandens* (Hill) K. Koch

FIELD MARKS. A high-climbing, leaf-losing vine; growing in swamps, sandy woods, or along streams. *Leaves* alternate, elliptic or lance-shaped, roundish to broadly pointed at base, pointed at tip, slightly paler beneath, smooth, with 9 to 12 pairs of prominent straight veins, 1½ to 3 inches long. *Flowers* small, greenish white, in end clusters; blooming April to June. *Fruits* oval-shaped, bluish black, 1-seeded, about ¼ inch long; maturing August to October.

RANGE. Chiefly coastal plain; Virginia south to Florida, west to Texas; north in Mississippi Valley to Kentucky and Missouri.

SAGERETIA   *Sageretia minutiflora* (Michx.) Trel.

FIELD MARKS. A straggling leaf-losing shrub to 10 feet high, with long weak branches and often spine-tipped branchlets; growing on sand or shell dunes and in coastal hammocks. *Leaves* opposite, roundish to egg-shaped or lance-shaped, roundish at base, pointed at tip, finely and inconspicuously toothed on margin, lustrous above, often somewhat downy beneath, short-stalked, ½ to a bit over 1 inch long. *Flowers* small, creamy white, fragrant, clustered. *Fruits* roundish, dark purple, about ¼ inch in diameter, containing 3 leathery nutlets.

RANGE. Coastal plain; South Carolina south to Florida, west to Mississippi.

Sometimes called Buckthorn.

Painted Buckeye

Florida Soapberry

Supplejack

Sageretia

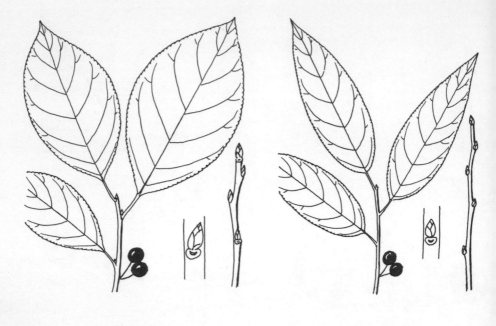

Alderleaf Buckthorn

Lanceleaf Buckthorn

Carolina Buckthorn

New Jersey-Tea

ALDERLEAF BUCKTHORN *Rhamnus alnifolia* L'Her.

FIELD MARKS. A leaf-losing shrub 1½ to about 3 feet high; growing in cold swamps and bogs. *Branchlets* reddish brown, smooth or nearly so. *Leaves* alternate, oval or elliptic, broadly pointed at base, pointed at tip, finely and bluntly toothed on margin, lustrous and with sunken veins above, paler and usually downy on the veins beneath, 2 to 4½ inches long. *Flowers* small, greenish yellow, fragrant, 1 to 3 in leaf axils; blooming May or June. *Fruits* roundish or slightly egg-shaped, black, 1- to 3-seeded, about ¼ inch in diameter; ripening July or August.

RANGE. Newfoundland to British Columbia; south to northern New Jersey, West Virginia, the region of the Great Lakes, Nebraska, Wyoming, and California.

LANCELEAF BUCKTHORN *Rhamnus lanceolata* Pursh

FIELD MARKS. A leaf-losing shrub 4 to 8 feet high; growing on hillsides and stream banks. *Branchlets* ashy gray, often downy. *Leaves* alternate, broadly lance-shaped or elliptic, rounded or broadly pointed at base, often abruptly pointed at tip, finely and bluntly toothed on margin, smooth above, paler and sometimes slightly downy beneath, 1¼ to 3½ inches long. *Flowers* small, greenish yellow, fragrant, 1 to 6 in leaf axils; blooming in May. *Fruits* roundish, black, 2-seeded, about ¼ inch in diameter; ripening August or September.

RANGE. Southeastern Pennsylvania, West Virginia, southern Ohio, Wisconsin, and Nebraska; south to Alabama and Texas.

CAROLINA BUCKTHORN *Rhamnus caroliniana* Walt.

FIELD MARKS. A leaf-losing shrub or small tree to 30 feet high; growing along streams and on wooded hillsides. *Branchlets* reddish brown to ashy brown; with an elongate, naked, hairy end bud. *Leaves* alternate, elliptic, rounded to broadly pointed at base, pointed at tip, obscurely toothed on margin, lustrous above, paler and sometimes downy beneath, prominently veined, 2 to 6 inches long. *Flowers* small, yellowish green, 3 to 5 clustered in leaf axils; blooming May or June. *Fruits* roundish, black, 2- to 4-seeded, about ⅓ inch in diameter; ripening September or October.

RANGE. Southwestern Virginia, West Virginia, the Ohio Valley, and Nebraska; south to Florida and Texas.

Also called Indian-cherry.

NEW JERSEY-TEA *Ceanothus americanus* L.

FIELD MARKS. A leaf-losing shrub 1 to 3 feet high; growing on dry, rocky, wooded slopes and in clearings. *Leaves* alternate, egg-shaped, rounded or somewhat heart-shaped at base, pointed at tip, finely toothed on margin, more or less hairy above, paler and downy beneath, 1 to 3 inches long, with 3 prominent veins from near summit of the short leafstalks. *Flowers* small, white, in dense, cylindrical, long-stalked clusters; blooming May to Auugst. *Fruits* small, 3-lobed capsules containing 3 pale-brown seeds; maturing August to October; the silvery-lined, cup-shaped bases persisting into the winter.

RANGE. Maine to southern Quebec and Manitoba; south to Florida and Texas.

The leaves were used as a substitute for tea during the American Revolution; and the large red roots yield a dye.

SOUTHERN REDROOT *Ceanothus americanus* var. *intermedius* (Pursh) K. Koch

A variety of the preceding, with leaves ¾ to 2 inches long and smaller flowers; found in sandy pinelands chiefly in the coastal plain. (Not illustrated)

REDROOT *Ceanothus ovatus* Desf.

FIELD MARKS. A leaf-losing shrub 1 to 2 feet high; growing on dry rocky or sandy soils. *Leaves* alternate, elliptic or lance-shaped, rounded to broadly pointed at base, bluntly pointed at tip, finely toothed on margin, smooth above, sometimes slightly downy on the veins beneath, ¾ to 2 inches long; with 3 prominent veins arising near the summit of the short leafstalk. *Flowers* small, white, in rather short and somewhat flat-topped end clusters which have stalks shorter than the leaves; blooming April to July. *Fruits* similar to those of New Jersey-Tea but with dark-brown seeds.

RANGE. Western Maine to Quebec and Manitoba, south to western Georgia and Texas.

SMALL-LEAF REDROOT *Ceanothus microphyllus* Michx.

FIELD MARKS. A diffusely branched evergreen shrub 1 to 2 feet high; growing in dry sandy pineland, pine-oak woods, or on sandhills. *Branchlets* yellowish brown, very slender, smooth, ascending. *Leaves* alternate, roundish to oval or elliptic, untoothed on margin, rather fleshy in texture, ⅛ to ¼ inch long, commonly with clusters of smaller leaves in the axils. *Flowers* small, white, in flat-topped, stalkless end clusters; blooming April or May. *Fruits* similar to those of New Jersey-Tea but smaller.

RANGE. Coastal plain; southern Georgia and Alabama south into Florida.

VINE FAMILY (Vitaceae)

PEPPER VINE *Ampelopsis arborea* (L.) Koehne

FIELD MARKS. A leaf-losing, somewhat bushy to high-climbing vine; growing in rich moist woods and thickets. Tendrils may be present opposite some of the leaves. *Leaves* alternate, twice or thrice compound, 2 to about 8 inches long; the leaflets more or less egg-shaped, rounded to pointed at base, pointed at tip, sharply and coarsely toothed on margin, smooth on both surfaces or slightly downy along the veins beneath, ½ to 1½ inches long. *Flowers* small, greenish, in loose, long-stalked clusters opposite some of the leaves; blooming June or July. *Fruits* roundish or slightly flattened, dark purple to black, 1- to 3-seeded berries about ¼ inch in diameter, bitter and inedible; ripening August to October.

RANGE. Eastern Maryland, West Virginia, southern Illinois, Missouri, and Oklahoma; south to Florida and Texas.

HEARTLEAF AMPELOPSIS *Ampelopsis cordata* Michx.

FIELD MARKS. A leaf-losing climbing vine; growing in swamps and stream bottoms. Tendrils may be present opposite some of the leaves. *Branchlets* with a white pith. *Leaves* alternate, egg-shaped or broadly so, heart-shaped to flattened at base, pointed at tip, coarsely and irregularly toothed on margin and sometimes 3-lobed, smooth above, paler and sometimes slightly downy beneath, 2 to 5 inches long. *Flowers* small, greenish, in long-stalked, forking clusters opposite some of the leaves; blooming May to July. *Fruits* roundish or slightly flattened, bluish, usually 2-seeded berries about ¼ inch in diameter, inedible; ripening August to October.

RANGE. Virginia to southern Ohio and Illinois, southeastern Missouri, and Oklahoma; south to Florida and Texas.

Often confused with Muscadine Grape, the branchlets of which have a brownish pith.

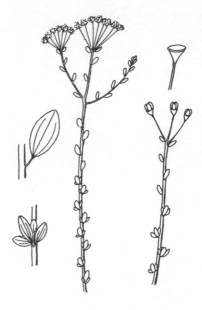

Redroot   **Small-leaf Redroot**

Pepper Vine   **Heartleaf Ampelopsis**

Virginia Creeper   **Thicket Creeper**

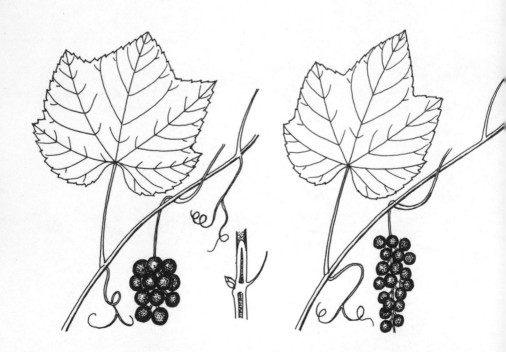

Fox Grape   **Summer Grape**

VIRGINIA CREEPER *Parthenocissus quinquefolia* (L.) Planch.

FIELD MARKS. A climbing or sometimes trailing leaf-losing vine; growing in moist woods and thickets. Tendrils opposite some of the leaves are 5- to 12-branched and end in small adhesive disks. *Leaves* alternate, compound, with usually 5 leaflets radiating from the summit of a long leafstalk; leaflets egg-shaped or elliptic, wedge-shaped at base, pointed or abruptly pointed at tip, margin sharply and coarsely toothed to or slightly below the middle, dull above, paler and sometimes downy beneath, 2 to 8 inches long. *Flowers* small, greenish, in branched end clusters; blooming June to August. *Fruits* roundish, dark blue, 2- to 3-seeded berries about ¼ inch in diameter; ripening August to October.

RANGE. Maine and Quebec to Minnesota, south to Florida and Texas.

Often confused with Poison-ivy. Cultivated as an ornamental.

THICKET CREEPER *Parthenocissus inserta* (Kern.) K. Fritsch

FIELD MARKS. Similar to the preceding species, but tendrils 2- to 5-branched and rarely ending in adhesive disks. Leaves are dark green and lustrous above, only slightly paler beneath. Flowers and fruits are in regularly forked clusters.

RANGE. Nova Scotia to Manitoba and Montana; south to Pennsylvania, the region of the Great Lakes, Missouri, Arizona, and California.

GRAPES (Vitis L.)

(Key Appendix I)

Grapes are usually high-climbing vines with shredding bark, alternate simple leaves, and forked tendrils. The branchlets usually have a brownish pith which is interrupted by harder partitions (diaphragms) at the nodes. The leaves have main veins radiating from the summit of a long leafstalk, are coarsely toothed on the margin, and are often lobed. The flowers are small, greenish yellow, fragrant, and borne in compact clusters opposite the leaves; blooming in spring as the new leaves begin to expand. The fruits are few-seeded, round, pulpy berries ripening in late summer or fall. They are an important food for wildlife. Although most of our wild grapes are too tart to be eaten raw, they make very good jelly and preserves.

FOX GRAPE *Vitis labrusca* L.

FIELD MARKS. A high-climbing vine; growing in rich woods, thickets, or along streams. *Branchlets* more or less rusty-woolly, with a tendril or flower cluster opposite each leaf. *Leaves* heart-shaped, shallowly or sometimes deeply 3-lobed, margin coarsely but shallowly toothed, somewhat leathery, smooth above, felted with tawny or rusty wool beneath, 4 to 8 inches long. *Fruits* purplish black, brownish purple, or (rarely) amber-colored, 3- to 6-seeded, about ½ inch across, usually sweet and somewhat musky.

RANGE. Southern Maine to Michigan, south to Florida and Mississippi.

Parent of Concord, Catawba, Niagra, and other cultivated grapes.

SUMMER GRAPE *Vitis aestivalis* Michx.

FIELD MARKS. A high-climbing vine; growing in woods, thickets, or on stream banks. *Branchlets* usually somewhat downy, no tendril or flower cluster opposite every third leaf. *Leaves* heart-shaped, unlobed or shallowly to deeply 3- to 5-lobed, basal sinus narrowly to broadly U-shaped, smooth above, whitish and with some loose tawny or rusty wool beneath, 3 to 8 inches long. *Fruits* black with a whitish bloom, 2- to 3-seeded, about ⅜ inch across, very tart.

RANGE. Massachusetts to Michigan and Wisconsin, south to Georgia and Texas.

BLUELEAF GRAPE *Vitis aestivalis* var. *argentifolia* (Munson) Fern.

FIELD MARKS. This variety is readily distinguished by its smooth branchlets, which are whitened with a powdery bloom, and by its leaves, which are smooth or nearly so and very white beneath. (Not illustrated)

RIVERBANK GRAPE *Vitis riparia* Michx.

FIELD MARKS. A trailing or high-climbing vine; growing along streams and in alluvial bottomlands. *Branchlets* smooth or nearly so, no tendril or flower cluster opposite every third leaf, pith with thin partitions at the nodes. *Leaves* heart-shaped, usually 3-lobed, margin with large and sharply pointed teeth, sinus at base V-shaped but broad and open, bright green and lustrous on both surfaces, sometimes slightly hairy on larger veins beneath, 2½ to 5 inches long. *Fruits* bluish black and with a white bloom, 2- to 4-seeded, about ⅜ inch in diameter, usually sour.
RANGE. New Brunswick to Manitoba; south to Virginia, Tennessee, Missouri, and Texas.

DUNE GRAPE *Vitis riparia* var. *syrticola* (Fern. & Wieg.) Fern.

A variety of the Riverbank Grape, with leafstalks and lower leaf surfaces densely covered with long and soft hairs. It grows on sand dunes about the Great Lakes from New York to Michigan and Indiana. (Not Illustrated)

FROST GRAPE *Vitis vulpina* L.

FIELD MARKS. A high-climbing vine; growing in low rich woods or thickets and along streams. *Branchlets* smooth or nearly so, no tendril or flower cluster opposite every third leaf, pith with thick partitions at the nodes. *Leaves* heart-shaped, unlobed or occasionally slightly 3-lobed, margin coarsely and sharply toothed, sinus at base deep and narrowly V-shaped, bright green on both surfaces, lustrous above, sometimes sparingly hairy along the veins beneath, 3 to 5 inches long. *Fruits* lustrous black, 2- to 3-seeded, about ⅜ inch in diameter, often sweet after frost.
RANGE. Southeastern New York and Pennsylvania to Illinois and eastern Kansas; south to Florida and Texas.

NEW ENGLAND GRAPE *Vitis novae-angliae* Fern.

FIELD MARKS. A high-climbing vine; growing in dry woods and thickets. *Branchlets* reddish-hairy, a tendril or flower cluster opposite each leaf. *Leaves* heart-shaped, unlobed or sometimes with a short pointed lobe on each side above the middle, margin with broad and sharply pointed teeth, sinus at base broadly V-shaped or the base almost flattened, lustrous above, smooth or nearly so on both surfaces at maturity, rusty-hairy when young, 2 to 4 inches long. *Fruits* black, usually with a white bloom, about ⅜ inch in diameter, sour.
RANGE. New England south to eastern New York, New Jersey, and central Pennsylvania.

WINTER GRAPE *Vitis cinerea* Engelm.

FIELD MARKS. A high-climbing vine; growing in dry woods and thickets. *Branchlets* angled, grayish-hairy, no tendril or flower cluster opposite every third leaf. *Leaves* heart-shaped, unlobed or with a short lobe on each side above the middle, sinus at base narrowly or broadly V-shaped, margin with broad and pointed teeth, smooth and dull green above, more or less whitish-wooly beneath, 2 to 6 inches long; leafstalks grayish-hairy. *Fruits* black, usually about a bloom, 1- to 3-seeded, about ⅜ inch in diameter, usually sweet when ripe.
RANGE. Southeastern Virginia to southern Ohio, Illinois, Iowa, and Nebraska; south to Florida and Texas.

PIGEON GRAPE *Vitis cinerea* var. *floridana* Munson

A variety of the Winter Grape, with rusty or reddish-brown hairs on the branchlets, leafstalks, and lower leaf surfaces. More common than the typical variety eastward. Eastern Virginia and Arkansas south to Florida and Texas. (Not illustrated)

Riverbank Grape

Frost Grape

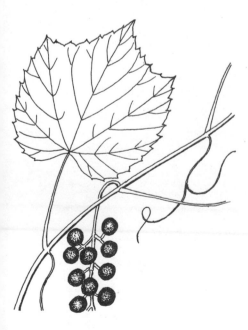

New England Grape

Winter Grape

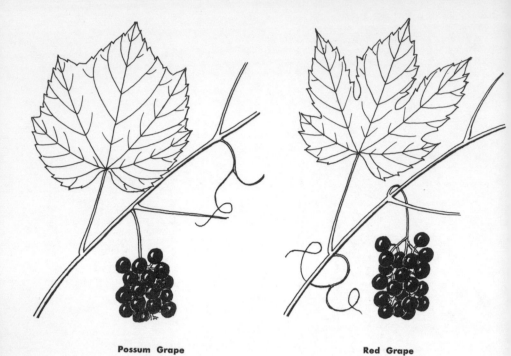

Possum Grape

Red Grape

Bush Grape

Muscadine Grape

POSSUM GRAPE *Vitis baileyana* Munson

FIELD MARKS. A high-climbing vine; growing in rich thickets and along the banks of streams. *Branchlets* angled when young, woolly-hairy, no tendril or flower cluster opposite every third leaf. *Leaves* roundish, base heart-shaped, usually with a short lobe on each side near the tip, margin with rather small teeth, bright green above, grayish and downy on the veins beneath, 2 to 5 inches long. *Fruits* black, with little or no bloom, seeds small, about ⅜ inch in diameter.

RANGE. Eastern Virginia to Kentucky and Missouri south to Georgia and Arkansas.

RED GRAPE *Vitis palmata* Vahl

FIELD MARKS. A slender, high-climbing vine; growing in low, moist woods, borders of ponds, sloughs, etc. *Branchlets* at first bright red, later turning reddish brown, smooth or nearly so, no tendril or flower cluster opposite every third leaf. *Leaves* egg-shaped, sinus at base broadly U-shaped, deeply 3- to 5-lobed with rounded sinuses between the long-pointed lobes, margin coarsely and irregularly toothed, dark green and smooth above, bright green and sometimes downy on the veins (which are commonly red) beneath, 2 to 5 inches long. *Fruits* black, without a bloom, 1- or 2-seeded, about ⅜ inch across.

RANGE. Southern Indiana and Illinois to southeastern Iowa, south to Louisiana and Texas.

Also called Cat or Catbird Grape.

POST OAK GRAPE *Vitis lincecumii* Buckl.

FIELD MARKS. A high-climbing vine; growing in woods, thickets, and glades. Closely resembles the Summer Grape. *Leaves* with loose, rusty wool on lower surface (or, in var. *glauca* Munson, smooth and whitened with only the main veins sometimes rusty-downy). *Fruits* purplish black with a slight white bloom, ⅜ to 1 inch in diameter, pleasant-tasting.

RANGE. Southern Indiana and Missouri, south to Mississippi and Texas. (Not illustrated)

BUSH GRAPE *Vitis rupestris* Scheele

FIELD MARKS. A low, bushy, or slightly climbing shrub; growing on sandy banks and rocky slopes. *Branchlets* only occasionally with tendrils. *Leaves* roundish to broadly heart-shaped, the sinus at the base very broadly V-shaped, unlobed or sometimes slightly 3-lobed, margin with coarse and broad but sharply pointed teeth, lustrous above, slightly paler and smooth or nearly so beneath, 2 to 4 inches long. *Fruits* black, usually with a white bloom, 2- to 4-seeded, about ⅜ inch in diameter, sweet; in small but compact clusters.

RANGE. Maryland and southern Pennsylvania to Missouri; south to western Virginia, Tennessee, Arkansas, and Texas.

Also called Sand Grape and Sugar Grape.

MUSCADINE GRAPE *Vitis rotundifolia* Michx.

FIELD MARKS. A high-climbing vine; growing in woods, thickets, sandhills, and swamps. Differs from all other grapes in having smooth bark dotted with paler lenticels, no woody partitions in the pith at the nodes, and tendrils which are not branched. *Leaves* roundish or broadly egg-shaped, the sinus at the base broadly V-shaped and shallow, margin with large and triangular teeth, lustrous above, yellowish green and sometimes slightly downy on the veins beneath, 2 to 4 inches wide. *Fruits* purplish black to bronze, without a bloom, with very tough skin, sweet with musky flavor, ½ to 1 inch in diameter.

RANGE. Southern Delaware and Virginia to southern Indiana, southeastern Missouri, and Oklahoma; south to Florida and Texas.

SILKY-CAMELLIA *Stewartia malachodendron* L.

FIELD MARKS. A leaf-losing shrub or small tree 5 to about 20 feet high; growing in rich deciduous woods, usually near streams. *Leaves* alternate, elliptic, wedge-shaped at base, pointed or abruptly pointed at tip, minutely toothed and hairy-fringed on margin, dark green and smooth above, paler and downy at least on the veins beneath, 2½ to 4 inches long. *Flowers* very showy, 3 to 4 inches across, the 5 creamy-white petals crimped and ragged on margin, stamens purple; styles united; blooming May or June. *Fruits* roundish capsules ½ inch or slightly more in diameter; seeds shiny, not winged.

RANGE. Chiefly coastal plain; Virginia south to Florida, west to Louisiana, north in Mississippi Valley to Tennessee and eastern Arkansas.

MOUNTAIN-CAMELLIA *Stewartia ovata* (Cav.) Weath.

FIELD MARKS. A leaf-losing shrub or small tree similar to the preceding; growing in rich woods, usually along streams, chiefly in the mountains. *Leaves* alternate, oblong-elliptic or egg-shaped, mostly rounded at base, sharply pointed at tip, minutely toothed and hairy-fringed on margin, dark green and smooth above, grayish green and slightly hairy beneath, 2 to 5 inches long. *Flowers* similar to those of the Silky-camellia, but the stamens usually with yellow (rarely purple) anthers and the styles distinct; blooming June to August. *Fruits* egg-shaped, pointed, sharply 5-angled capsules about ⅝ inch long; seeds dull and winged.

RANGE. Virginia and southeastern Kentucky; south to central North Carolina, and northern Georgia and Alabama.

ST. JOHN'S-WORT FAMILY (Hypericaceae)

ST. PETER'S-WORTS AND ST. JOHN'S-WORTS (Hypericum L.)

(Key Appendix J)

These are herbaceous or shrubby plants, with opposite simple leaves with untoothed margins and usually with minute clear or blackish dots. The branchlets are commonly more or less 2-edged below the leaves, and often there are clusters of smaller leaves in the axils of the larger ones.

ST. PETER'S-WORT *Hypericum stans* (Michx.) Adams & Robson.

FIELD MARKS. A shrub with a simple or sparingly branched, more or less erect stem 1 to 3 feet high; growing in sandy woods and fields. *Branchlets* prominently 2-edged or 2-winged. *Leaves* oblong-oval, stalkless, rounded to somewhat heart-shaped and often clasping the stem at the base, rounded at tip, thickish and firm in texture, smooth, ½ to 1½ inches long. *Flowers* ¾ to 1¼ inches across, with 4 bright yellow petals, 2 outer sepals which are large and heart-shaped and 2 inner ones very much smaller and narrow, pistil with 3 or 4 styles; blooming July to September. *Fruits* egg-shaped capsules about ⅜ inch long.

RANGE. Southeastern Massachusetts to southeastern Pennsylvania and Kentucky, south to Florida and Texas.

DWARF ST. PETER'S-WORT *Hypericum suffruticosum* Adams & Robson.

FIELD MARKS. A shrub resembling the preceding but smaller and with prostrate stems often forming mats, the erect flowering branches only a few inches high; growing in sandy coastal-plain pinelands. *Leaves* stalkless, oval to narrowly elliptic, ⅛ to about 5/16 inch long. *Flowers* yellow, about ½ inch across, the 2 outer sepals very small or absent. *Fruits* about 3/16 inch long.

RANGE. North Carolina south to Florida, west to Mississippi.

192

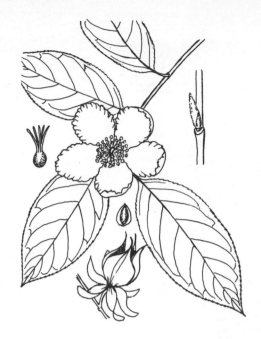

Silky-camellia

Mountain-camellia

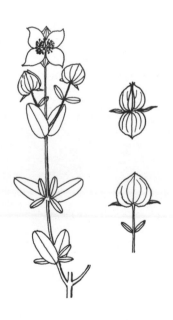

St. Peter's-wort

Dwarf St. Peter's-wort

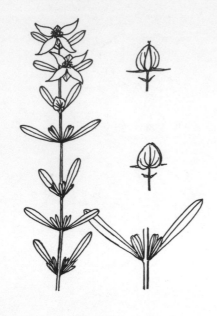

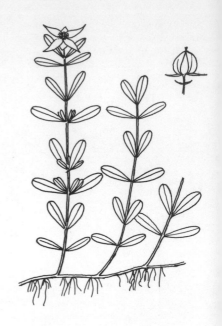

St. Andrew's-cross   Reclining St. Andrew's-cross

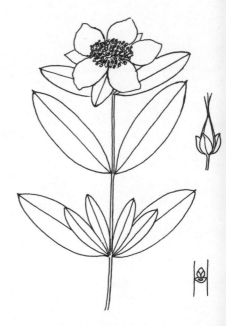

Shrubby St. John's-wort   Golden St. John's-wort

ST. ANDREW'S-CROSS *Hypericum hypericoides* (L.) Crantz

FIELD MARKS. A more or less erect and branching shrub to about 3 feet high; growing in dry sandy or rocky fields and open woods. *Branchlets* flattened and 2-edged. *Leaves* stalkless, ¼ to about 1 inch long and mostly less than ⅛ inch wide, broadest toward the tip, wedge-shaped at base, blunt at tip, smooth. *Flowers* about ½ inch across, with 4 bright-yellow petals, 2 outer sepals which are large and egg-shaped or heart-shaped and 2 inner ones very much smaller and narrow, pistil with 2 styles; blooming May to September. *Fruits* narrowly egg-shaped and somewhat flattened 2-celled capsules about ¼ inch long.

RANGE. Virginia and Tennessee south to Florida and Texas.

RECLINING ST. ANDREW'S-CROSS *Hypericum stragalum* Adams & Robson.

FIELD MARKS. A shrub similar to the preceding but with reclining stems and numerous erect branchlets 5 inches to about 1 foot high; growing in dry sandy or rocky woods and clearings. *Leaves* similar to those of the preceding species but usually shorter and broader. *Flowers* and *fruits* also similar.

RANGE. Southeastern Massachusetts to southern Pennsylvania, Illinois, and Kansas; south to Georgia and Texas.

SHRUBBY ST. JOHN'S-WORT *Hypericum spathulatum* (Spach) Steud.

FIELD MARKS. An erect, bushy-branched, leaf-losing shrub 2 to about 4 feet high; usually growing in moist sandy or rocky open woods, fields, and slopes. *Leaves* very short-stalked, narrowly oblong or sometimes broadest toward the tip, pointed at base, blunt at tip, light green above, pale beneath, smooth on both surfaces, ¾ to 3 inches long. *Flowers* bright yellow, about ¾ inch across, 5-petalled, clustered in the axils of the upper leaves; blooming June to September. *Fruits* narrowly egg-shaped, 3-celled capsules about ½ inch long.

RANGE. Southeastern New York to Ontario and Minnesota; south to Georgia, Mississippi, and Arkansas.

One of our most showy species of St. John's-worts; sometimes cultivated and locally escaping as far north as Massachusetts.

GOLDEN ST. JOHN'S-WORT *Hypericum frondosum* Michx.

FIELD MARKS. A widely branched, often semi-evergreen shrub 2 to about 6 feet high; growing on limestone or shale bluffs in the southern Appalachians. *Leaves* stalkless or nearly so, oblong to narrowly oblong, narrowed at base, roundish or blunt at tip but often with an abrupt little point, bluish green above, pale or somewhat whitened beneath, smooth on both surfaces, 1 to 3 inches long. *Flowers* bright golden yellow, 1 to 2 inches across, 5-petalled, stamens very numerous, sepals large and leaflike but not all of the same size; blooming June to August. *Fruits* narrowly egg-shaped, somewhat 3-celled capsules ½ to ¾ inch long, more or less enclosed by the sepals.

RANGE. Kentucky and southern Indiana; south to Georgia, Alabama, and Texas.

Sometimes cultivated for its large showy flowers.

KALM ST. JOHN'S-WORT *Hypericum kalmianum* L.

FIELD MARKS. A widely branching leaf-losing shrub 1 to 2½ feet high; growing in sandy or rocky open woods and clearings. *Leaves* stalkless, narrowly oblong or broadest toward the tip, pointed at base, blunt to pointed at tip, smooth on both surfaces, whitened beneath, 1 to 2 inches long. *Flowers* bright yellow, ¾ to 1 inch across, 5-petalled and with 5 distinct styles; blooming July to September. *Fruits* narrowly egg-shaped, usually 5-celled capsules about ⅜ inch long.

RANGE. Region of the Great Lakes from western New York and western Quebec to Illinois and western Ontario.

BUSHY ST. JOHN'S-WORT *Hypericum densiflorum* Pursh

FIELD MARKS. A much-branched, bushy, leaf-losing shrub 1 to about 6 feet high; growing in swamps, swales, boggy places or sometimes in dry woods. *Leaves* stalkless or almost so, very narrow or narrowly oblong, pointed at base, blunt or somewhat pointed at tip, margin slightly rolled beneath, light green above, slightly paler beneath, smooth on both surfaces, ¾ to 2 inches long. *Flowers* bright yellow, about ⅜ inch across, 5-petalled, in rather crowded, forking, flat-topped end clusters; blooming June to September. *Fruits* narrowly egg-shaped, 3-celled capsules usually less than ¼ inch long.

RANGE. Southeastern New York to southern Pennsylvania and Kentucky; south to Georgia and Alabama.

STRAGGLING ST. JOHN'S-WORT *Hypericum dolabriforme* Vent.

FIELD MARKS. A straggling shrub, prostrate at the base and with ascending or erect branches ½ to about 1½ feet high; growing in rocky woods or on balds and barrens. *Branchlets* slightly angled or quite round. *Leaves* narrow or narrowly lance-shaped, tapered at base, pointed or blunt at tip, smooth on both surfaces, ¾ to about 2 inches long. *Flowers* bright yellow, nearly 1 inch across, the sepals almost as long as the 5 oblique petals, in a forking, few-flowered, leafy-bracted end cluster; blooming June to August. *Fruits* egg-shaped, pointed, 1-celled capsules about ¼ inch long.

RANGE. Kentucky south to Georgia, west to southeast Missouri.

MYRTLE-LEAF ST. JOHN'S-WORT *Hypericum myrtifolium* Lam.

FIELD MARKS. A simple or sparingly-branched evergreen shrub 1 to 3 feet high; growing in low wet pinelands or shallow ponds. Leaves stalkless or nearly so, egg-shaped or elliptic, rounded at base, blunt at tip, veiny, smooth on both surfaces, paler beneath, more or less coated with a waxy bloom, ½ to 1¼ inches long. *Flowers* bright yellow, about ¾ inch across, 5-petalled, with large and leaflike sepals; blooming May to August. *Fruits* egg-shaped capsules about ¼ inch long.

RANGE. Coastal plain; Georgia and Florida west to Mississippi.

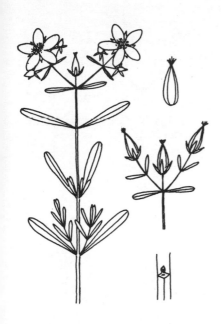

Kalm St. John's-wort

Bushy St. John's wort

Straggling St. John's-wort

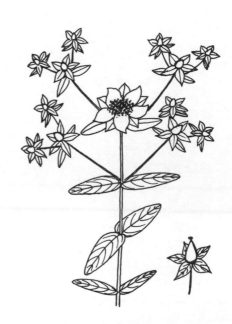

Myrtle-leaf St. John's-wort

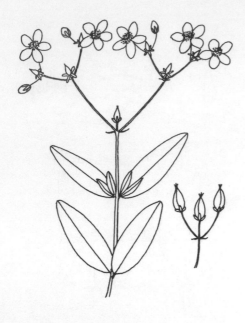

Naked-flowered St. John's-wort

Round-podded St. John's-wort

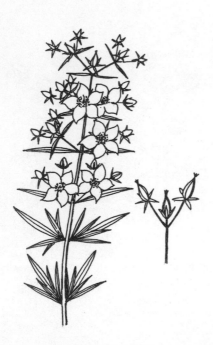

Bedstraw St. John's-wort

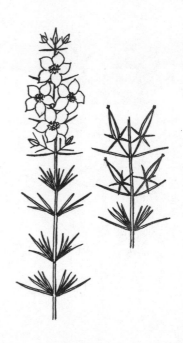

Sandweed

NAKED-FLOWERED ST. JOHN'S-WORT *Hypericum nudiflorum* Michx. ex. Willd.

FIELD MARKS. A shrub 1 to 3 feet high, often more or less herbaceous above; growing in low woods, swamps, or along the banks of streams. *Branchlets* 2-edged, brown. *Leaves* elliptic or narrowly egg-shaped, pointed or roundish at base, blunt or bluntly pointed at tip, thin in texture, smooth, ¾ to 2¾ inches long. *Flowers* bright yellow, ½ inch or slightly more across, 5-petalled, in a forking and rather flat-topped end cluster; blooming May to September. *Fruits* narrowly egg-shaped, more or less 1-celled capsules about ¼ inch long.

RANGE. Virginia and Tennessee south to Florida and Mississippi.

ROUND-PODDED ST. JOHN'S-WORT *Hypericum cistifolium* Lam.

FIELD MARKS. A simple or sparingly-branched shrub 1 to 2½ feet high; growing in low pinelands and savannahs. *Branchlets* more or less erect, dark purplish brown, 4-angled. *Leaves* narrowly oblong or narrowly elliptic, stalkless or nearly so, narrowed or roundish at base, blunt or broadly pointed at tip, smooth on both surfaces, paler below, ¾ to about 2 inches long. *Flowers* bright yellow, about ½ inch across, 5-petalled, in a forking and rather flat-topped end cluster; blooming June to August. *Fruits* roundish egg-shaped, 1-celled capsules about 3/16 inch long.

RANGE. Coastal plain; North Carolina south to Florida, west to Mississippi.

BEDSTRAW ST. JOHN'S-WORT *Hypericum galioides* Lam.

FIELD MARKS. An evergreen shrub 1 to about 4 feet high; growing in low wet pinelands and swamps. *Branchlets* slender, nearly round. *Leaves* stalkless, flat, narrow but usually slightly broadened upward, pointed at tip, tapering to base, thickish and firm in texture, dark green above, slightly paler beneath, smooth on both surfaces, ½ to about 2 inches long. *Flowers* bright yellow, about ½ inch across, 5-petalled, the sepals narrow and similar to the leaves, in rather narrow and elongate end clusters; blooming June to August. *Fruits* conical egg-shaped, pointed capsules about ¼ inch long.

RANGE. Coastal plain; North Carolina south to Florida, west to Louisiana.

SANDWEED *Hypericum fasciculatum* Lam.

FIELD MARKS. An evergreen shrub 1 to about 4 feet high; growing in low, wet, sandy pinelands and the borders of shallow ponds. *Branchlets* slender, 4-angled. *Leaves* stalkless, narrow and almost needle-like, leathery in texture, bright green, ⅜ to ¾ inch long; those of the axillary clusters often about as long; with a hand lens 2 longitudinal groves may be seen on the lower leaf surface. *Flowers* bright yellow, about ½ inch across, 5-petalled, the sepals narrow like the leaves, in rather narrow and elongate end clusters; blooming May to September. *Fruits* narrowly egg-shaped capsules about ¼ inch long.

RANGE. Coastal plain; South Carolina south to Florida, west to Texas.

SANDWEED *Hypericum nitidum* Lam.

This species is similar to the preceding but often taller (up to 10 feet high), and the leaves are not distinctly grooved beneath. It grows in wet places in the coastal plain from North Carolina south to Florida, west to Alabama. (Not illustrated)

SANDWEED *Hypericum reductum* P. Adams

Similar to *H. fasciculatum* but growing in moist to dry sandy woods in the coastal plain from southeastern North Carolina south to Georgia and Alabama. The largest leaves are less than ½ inch long. (Not illustrated)

SANDWEED *Hypericum lloydii* (Svenson) P. Adams

Similar to *H. fasciculatum* but with the main stems reclining and with upright branches 1 foot or less high. It grows in dry sandy or rocky woodlands in the coastal plain from North Carolina south to Florida. (Not illustrated)

199

MOUNTAIN ST. JOHN'S-WORT *Hypericum buckleyi* M. A. Curtis

FIELD MARKS. A low, creeping, somewhat woody, often matted, leaf-losing plant with ascending branches 4 to 12 inches high; growing in rock crevices and on seepage slopes in the southern Appalachians. *Branchlets* slender, 4-angled. *Leaves* short-stalked, elliptic or broadest above the middle, wedge-shaped at base, rounded at tip, smooth on both surfaces, paler beneath, ¼ to ¾ inch long. *Flowers* bright yellow, ¾ to 1 inch across, 5-petalled, with spoon-shaped sepals; blooming June to August. *Fruits* egg-shaped, pointed, 3-celled capsules ¼ to ⅜ inch long.

RANGE. North Carolina south to Georgia, in mountains above 3,500 feet.

ROCKROSE FAMILY (Cistaceae)

BEACH-HEATHER *Hudsonia tomentosa* Nutt.

FIELD MARKS. An intricately branched and matted evergreen shrub 4 to 8 inches high, densely coated with soft white wooly hair; growing in dry sands and on sand dunes. *Leaves* scalelike, usually less than ⅛ inch long, overlapping and closely pressed to the branchlets. *Flowers* bright yellow, 5-petalled, about ¼ inch across, stalkless or nearly so, and solitary at the tips of the branchlets; blooming May to July. *Fruits* small capsules enclosed by the calyx.

RANGE. Labrador south along the coast to North Carolina, inland chiefly about the Great Lakes to Minnesota and Saskatchewan; also in Pendelton County, West Virginia.

GOLDEN-HEATHER *Hudsonia ericoides* L.

FIELD MARKS. A bushy-branched, tufted, evergreen shrub 4 to about 7 inches high, softly hairy but green throughout; growing in dry sandy or rocky places. *Leaves* slender, awl-shaped, more or less spreading, about ¼ inch long; densely crowded and with bases overlapping on the younger branchlets, more widely scattered on the older ones. *Flowers* bright yellow (rarely white), 5-petalled, about ⅜ inch across, on slender hairy stalks ¼ to ½ inch long, and solitary at the tips of the branchlets; blooming May to July. *Fruits* small capsules enclosed by the calyx.

RANGE. Newfoundland south chiefly along the coast to Virginia, and in the mountains of central New Hampshire.

MOUNTAIN-HEATHER *Hudsonia montana* Nutt.

This species is very similar to the preceding one. It occurs on the summits of a few mountains in the North Carolina Blue Ridge. (Not illustrated)

LOOSESTRIFE FAMILY (Lythraceae)

SWAMP LOOSESTRIFE *Decodon verticillatus* (L.) Ell.

FIELD MARKS. A soft-woody plant with angled, recurved stems 3 to 9 feet long, which are thickened and spongy at the base; growing in shallow waters of lakes, ponds, streams, and marshes. *Leaves* opposite or in 3's, lance-shaped, pointed at both ends, untoothed on margin, bright green and smooth above, paler and often downy beneath, 2 to 5 inches long. *Flowers* purplish, about 1 inch across, 5-petalled, in axillary clusters; blooming July to September. *Fruits* urn-shaped capsules about ¼ inch across, with remnants of the sepals at the summit.

RANGE. Maine to southern Ontario south to Florida and Louisiana.

Also called Water-willow.

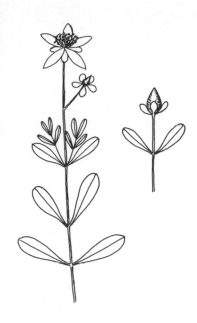

Mountain St. John's-wort

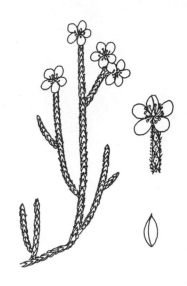

Beach-heather

Golden-heather

Swamp Loosestrife

Leatherwood

Canada Buffaloberry

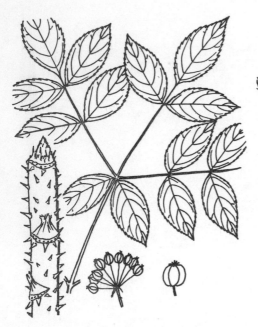

Hercules'-club

Bristly Sarsaparilla

MEZEREUM FAMILY (Thymelaeaceae)

LEATHERWOOD   *Dirca palustris* L.

FIELD MARKS. A leaf-losing shrub 2 to 8 feet high, often with a solitary trunklike stem; growing in rich moist woods. *Branchlets* tough, pliable, enlarged at nodes and at tip, and appearing jointed. *Leaves* alternate, short-stalked, oval to elliptic or broadest above the middle, pointed to roundish at base, blunt or broadly pointed at tip, margin untoothed, smooth or nearly so, 1½ to 3½ inches long. *Flowers* small, pale yellow, 2 to 4 in clusters; blooming April or May, before the leaves appear. *Fruits* berry-like, oval, red, 1-seeded, about ⅜ inch long; ripening May or June.

RANGE. New Brunswick to Ontario and Minnesota, south to Florida and Mississippi.

Bark was used by Indians for bow strings, cordage, and baskets. Taken internally it induces vomiting and purging; externally it may irritate the skin.

OLEASTER FAMILY (Elaeagnaceae)

CANADA BUFFALOBERRY   *Shepherdia canadensis* (L.) Nutt.

FIELD MARKS. A leaf-losing shrub 3 to 5 feet high; growing in sandy or rocky woods and along streams. *Branchlets* slender; densely coated with rusty, branlike scales. *Leaves* opposite, short-stalked, elliptic to egg-shaped, roundish to broadly pointed at base, blunt at tip, margin untoothed, dull green above, coated with silvery starry-branched hairs and rusty scales beneath, ¾ to 1½ inches long. *Flowers* small, yellowish green, bell-shaped, clustered; blooming April or May, before the leaves appear. *Fruits* berry-like, egg-shaped, reddish or yellowish, 1-seeded, about ¼ inch in diameter; ripening June to August.

RANGE. Newfoundland to Alaska; south to Maine, Vermont, the region of the Great Lakes, South Dakota, and New Mexico.

GINSENG FAMILY (Araliaceae)

HERCULES'-CLUB   *Aralia spinosa* L.

FIELD MARKS. A leaf-losing shrub or small tree 5 to 15 or more feet high; growing in woods, clearings, or along streams. *Branchlets* very stout and armed with prickles. *Leaves* alternate, 2 to 3 feet long, doubly or triply compound; the numerous leaflets egg-shaped, rounded or broadly pointed at base, pointed at tip, sharply toothed on margin, smooth above, paler and sometimes downy beneath, 1½ to 3½ inches long. *Flowers* small, white, in numerous clusters (umbels) and in a large pyramid-shaped end group; blooming June to September. *Fruits* berry-like, egg-shaped, black, about ¼ inch long; ripening August to October.

RANGE. Southern New England and central New York to Michigan and Iowa, south to Florida and Texas.

BRISTLY SARSAPARILLA   *Aralia hispida* Vent.

FIELD MARKS. A woody-based, leaf-losing plant 1½ to about 10 feet high; growing in rocky or sandy open woods and clearings. *Branchlets* moderate; with numerous weak, needle-like or bristly prickles. *Leaves* alternate, 4 to 12 inches long, usually twice compound; the leaflets egg-shaped to lance-shaped, rounded to pointed at base, pointed at tip, sharply toothed on margin, paler beneath and sometimes bristly along the veins, 1 to 2 inches long. *Flowers* small, white, in 2 to about 7 clusters (umbels) at stem tip; blooming June to August. *Fruits* berry-like, roundish, purplish black, about ¼ inch in diameter; ripening August or September.

RANGE. Newfoundland to Manitoba; south to western Virginia, West Virginia, and the region of the Great Lakes.

DEVIL'S-CLUB *Oplopanax horridus* (Sm.) Miq.

FIELD MARKS. A leaf-losing shrub 6 to 10 feet high; growing in rocky places. *Branchlets* stout, covered with slender prickles. *Leaves* alternate, roundish, heart-shaped at base, margin sharply and irregularly toothed and with 3 to 11 pointed lobes, 4 to 12 inches wide; the long leafstalks and veins of the lower leaf surfaces prickly. *Flowers* small, greenish white, the many clusters (umbels) in an elongate end group; blooming June to August. *Fruits* berry-like, red, roundish, about ¼ inch in diameter; ripening August to October.

RANGE. Western Ontario and Isle Royale (Michigan) to Alaska, south to Montana and California.

DOGWOOD FAMILY (Cornaceae)
DOGWOODS (Cornus L.)
(Key Appendix K)

Dogwoods are leaf-losing shrubs or small trees with opposite (rarely alternate), simple leaves which are untoothed on the margin and have veins which curve and tend to parallel the margin or to meet at the tip. The flowers are small, perfect, greenish yellow or whitish, and borne in open or compact end clusters. The fruits have a large stone enclosing the seed surrounded by a fleshy portion. The Flowering Dogwood (*Cornus florida* L.) is a well-known small tree, with showy bracts surrounding the flower clusters.

RED-OSIER DOGWOOD *Cornus stolonifera* Michx.

FIELD MARKS. A shrub 3 to 9 feet high, often with stems partly prostrate and rooting; growing in wet or swampy places. *Branchlets* purplish red to blood-red, with a large white pith. *Leaves* elliptic to egg-shaped, roundish or broadly pointed at base, pointed at tip, veins 4 to 6 pairs, smooth or minutely hairy on both surfaces, whitened beneath, 2 to 4 inches long. Flowers whitish, in flat-topped clusters; blooming May to July. *Fruits* roundish, white, about ¼ inch in diameter; ripening July to September.

RANGE. Newfoundland to Yukon; south to western Maryland, West Virginia, the region of the Great Lakes, Iowa, New Mexico, and California.

BAILEY DOGWOOD *Cornus stolonifera* var. *baileyi* (Coult. & Evans) Dresch.

Differs from the Red-Osier Dogwood in having more brownish branchlets and lower leaf surfaces densely woolly-hairy. Ontario to Alaska; south to the region of the Great Lakes and South Dakota. (Not illustrated)

SILKY DOGWOOD *Cornus amonum* Mill.

FIELD MARKS. A shrub 4 to about 10 feet high; growing in wet places and along streams. *Branchlets* purplish red, more or less covered with minute closely pressed hairs; pith large and brownish. *Leaves* egg-shaped to broadly elliptic, rounded at base, pointed at tip, veins 3 to 5 pairs, smooth or nearly so above, pale and usually with some small reddish hairs beneath, 2 to 4 inches long. *Flowers* creamy white, in flat-topped to slightly convex clusters; blooming May to July. *Fruits* roundish, dull blue or partly white, about ¼ inch in diameter; ripening August to October.

RANGE. Southern Maine to Illinois, south to Georgia and Alabama.
Also called Kinnikinnik.

PALE DOGWOOD *Cornus obliqua* Raf.

FIELD MARKS. A shrub very similar to the preceding and by some botanists considered to be merely a variety of it. It differs in having lance-shaped or narrowly egg-shaped leaves which are pointed at both ends, and with whitish, closely pressed hairs beneath.

RANGE. New Brunswick to North Dakota; south to New Jersey, West Virginia, Kentucky, Arkansas, and Oklahoma.

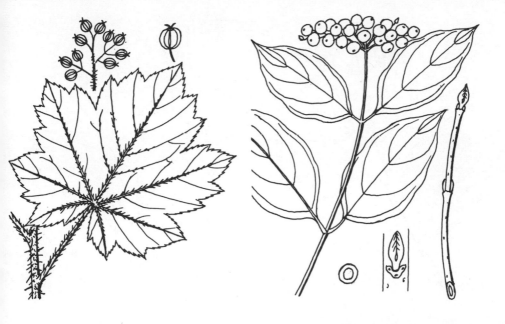

Devil's-club

Red-Osier Dogwood

Silky Dogwood

Pale Dogwood

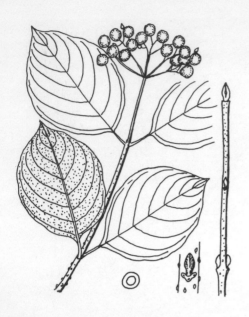

Roundleaf Dogwood

Gray-stemmed Dogwood

Rough-leaf Dogwood

Stiff Dogwood

ROUNDLEAF DOGWOOD *Cornus rugosa* Lam.

FIELD MARKS. An erect, rather losely branched shrub 3 to 8 feet high; growing in dry to well-drained, rocky woods. *Branchlets* greenish usually spotted with purple, warty-dotted, and with white pith. *Leaves* broadly egg-shaped to roundish, rounded or broadly pointed at base, pointed at tip, usually with 7 to 9 pairs of veins, often with scattered close-pressed hairs on upper surface, pale and woolly or downy beneath, 2½ to 5 inches long. *Flowers* white, in flat-topped clusters; blooming May to July. *Fruits* lead-colored or pale blue, roundish, about ¼ inch in diameter; ripening August and September.

RANGE. Nova Scotia and eastern Quebec to Manitoba; south to New England, western Virginia, West Virginia, the Great Lakes region, and northeastern Iowa.

GRAY-STEMMED DOGWOOD *Cornus racemosa* Lam.

FIELD MARKS. A much-branched, very twiggy, gray-stemmed shrub 3 to 8 feet high; growing in dry to moist thickets, borders of woods, fence rows, etc. *Branchlets* very slender, light brown, and with pale brown or whitish pith. *Leaves* narrowly egg-shaped to lance-shaped, usually pointed at base, long-pointed at tip, with 3 to 5 pairs of veins, smooth or with minute close-pressed hairs on both surfaces, pale or whitened beneath, 1½ to 3 inches long. *Flowers* creamy white, in cone-shaped clusters; blooming June and July. *Fruits* white, roundish, about 3/16 inch in diameter, on bright-red stalks; ripening August or September.

RANGE. Central Maine to southern Ontario and Minnesota; south to Delaware, West Virginia, North Carolina, Kentucky, and Oklahoma.

Also called Panicled Dogwood.

ROUGH-LEAF DOGWOOD *Cornus drummondii* Meyer

FIELD MARKS. A shrub or small tree 4 to about 15 feet high; growing in moist woods, along streams, and on shores of lakes and ponds. *Branchlets* brownish or reddish brown, rough-hairy, with brownish (rarely whitish) pith. *Leaves* elliptic to broadly egg-shaped, usually rounded at base, pointed at tip, with 3 to 5 pairs of veins, rough-hairy above, downy beneath, 1½ to 5 inches long. *Flowers* creamy white, in flat or slightly convex clusters; blooming May and June. *Fruits* white, roundish, ⅛ to ¼ inch in diameter; ripening August or September.

RANGE. Southern Ontario and Michigan to Iowa and Nebraska; south to Alabama, Mississippi, and eastern Texas.

STIFF DOGWOOD *Cornus stricta* Lam.

FIELD MARKS. A shrub or small tree 5 to 15 feet high; growing in wet woods, swamps, and along streams. *Branchlets* slender, smooth, reddish or partly green and becoming gray, with a white pith. *Leaves* elliptic to egg-shaped or broadly lance-shaped, usually pointed at base, pointed at tip, smooth or nearly so on both surfaces, dark dull green above, slightly paler beneath, with 4 or 5 pairs of veins, 2 to 5 inches long. *Flowers* creamy white, in a flat-topped cluster; blooming April to June. *Fruits* pale blue, roundish, about ¼ inch in diameter; ripening July to September.

RANGE. Eastern Virginia to southern Indiana and southeastern Missouri; south to Florida and eastern Texas.

SOUTHERN ROUGH-LEAF DOGWOOD *Cornus asperifolia* Michx.

FIELD MARKS. A leaf-losing shrub 5 or more feet high; growing in low woods and swamps. *Branchlets* slender, brownish, with a white pith. *Leaves* elliptic, pointed to roundish at base, rather long-pointed at tip, thin in texture, roughish above, scarcely paler and rather hairy beneath, 1½ to about 3 inches long. *Flowers* creamy white, in rather small flat-topped clusters; blooming May or June. *Fruits* roundish, pale blue, ⅛ to 3/16 inch in diameter; ripening August or September.

RANGE. Coastal plain; South Carolina south to Florida.

ALTERNATE-LEAF DOGWOOD *Cornus alternifolia* L. f.

FIELD MARKS. A shrub or small tree 4 to sometimes 25 feet high, with almost horizontally spreading branches, and larger stems dark green and often streaked with white; growing in moist woods and along streams. *Branchlets* greenish and with a white pith. *Leaves* alternate, very often crowded toward the tips of the branchlets, rather long and slender stalked, oval or broadly egg-shaped, broadly pointed at base, pointed at tip, bright green and smooth above, paler and sometimes slightly downy beneath, 2 to 5 inches long. *Flowers* creamy white, in flat-topped clusters; blooming May or June. *Fruits* bluish black, roundish, ¼ to ⅜ inch in diameter, on bright-red stalks; ripening August or September.

RANGE. Newfoundland to southern Ontario, southeastern Manitoba, and eastern Minnesota; south to Florida, Alabama, and northern Arkansas.

Also called Blue or Pagoda Dogwood.

WHITE-ALDER FAMILY (Clethraceae)

SWEET-PEPPERBUSH *Clethra alnifolia* L.

FIELD MARKS. A leaf-losing shrub 3 to 10 feet high, the older stems with dark gray or blackish and flaky bark; growing in wet or swampy, and usually sandy, woods and thickets. *Branchlets* slender, grayish brown, minutely downy. *Leaves* alternate, broadest above the middle, wedge-shaped at base, bluntly pointed or abruptly sharp-pointed at tip, sharply and doubly toothed on margin to somewhat below the middle, green and smooth or nearly so on both surfaces, 1½ to 3 inches long. *Flowers* white or (rarely) pinkish, 5-petaled, fragrant, in narrow end clusters from 2 to 6 inches in length; blooming June to September. *Fruits* roundish capsules about ⅛ inch in diameter, on ascending stalks; maturing September or October.

RANGE. Chiefly coastal plain; southern Maine and New Hampshire, south to Florida, west to eastern Texas.

WOOLLY SWEET-PEPPERBUSH *Clethra alnifolia* var. *tomentosa* (Lam.) Michx.

FIELD MARKS. Differs from the preceding in having whitish-woolly branchlets and lower leaf surfaces. It grows in wet coastal plain pinelands from southeastern Virginia south to Florida and west to Mississippi. (Not illustrated)

MOUNTAIN SWEET-PEPPERBUSH *Clethra acuminata* Michx.

FIELD MARKS. A leaf-losing shrub 4 to about 15 feet high, the older stems with reddish-brown or cinnamon-colored bark which comes off in long strips; growing in rich, moist woods and along streams in the southern Appalachians. *Branchlets* slender, pale brown or ashy, more or less downy. *Leaves* alternate, rather long-stalked, oval to oblong-elliptic, pointed or roundish at base, pointed at tip, finely and sharply toothed on margin nearly to base, bright green and smooth above, paler and usually somewhat downy beneath, 2 to 7 inches long. *Flowers* white, 5-petaled, fragrant, in narrow end clusters from 4 to 8 inches in length; blooming July to September. *Fruits* roundish or slightly egg-shaped capsules about 3/16 inch in diameter, on nodding stalks; maturing September or October.

RANGE. Western Pennsylvania, western Virginia, and West Virginia south to northern Georgia.

Also known as Cinnamon Clethra.

Southern Rough-leaf Dogwood

Alternate-leaf Dogwood

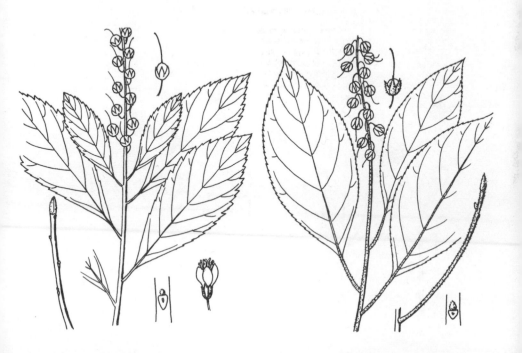

Sweet-pepperbush

Mountain Sweet-pepperbush

Spotted Wintergreen

Pipsissewa

Tar-flower

Southern-plume

WINTERGREEN FAMILY (Pyrolaceae)

SPOTTED WINTERGREEN *Chimaphila maculata* (L.) Pursh

FIELD MARKS. A low, semiherbaceous, evergreen plant with creeping underground stems and upright, leafy branches 4 to 10 inches high; growing in dry woods. *Leaves* crowded toward tips of stems or nearly in whorls of 3's, egg-shaped to lance-shaped, broadly pointed to roundish at base, pointed at tip, sharply toothed on margin, dark green mottled with white along the veins and lustrous above, usually purplish beneath, 1 to 3 inches long. *Flowers* white or pinkish, 5-petalled, about ⅝ inch across, 2 to 5 in a long-stalked end cluster; blooming June or July. *Fruits* slightly flattened, roundish, 5-parted capsules about ¼ inch in diameter.

RANGE. New Hampshire to Ontario and Michigan; south to Georgia, Alabama, and Tennessee.

Also called Spotted Pipsissewa.

PIPSISSEWA *Chimaphila umbellata* (L.) Bart. var. *cisatlantica* Blake

FIELD MARKS. A low, semiherbaceous, evergreen plant with creeping underground stems and upright, leafy branches 4 to 12 inches high; growing in dry woods. *Leaves* crowded toward tips of stems and appearing to be whorled; broadest above the middle, wedged-shaped at base, blunt or broadly pointed at tip, sharply toothed on margin, bright green on both surfaces, very lustrous above, ¾ to 2½ inches long. *Flowers* white or pinkish, 5-petalled, about ½ inch across, 3 to 6 in a long-stalked end cluster; blooming July or August. *Fruits* slightly flattened, roundish, 5-parted capsules about 3/16 inch in diameter.

RANGE. Nova Scotia to Ontario; south to northeastern North Carolina, West Virginia, Ohio, northern Illinois, and Minnesota.

Also called Prince's-pine, King's-cure, and Wintergreen. Used medicinally by the Indians for a variety of ailments.

HEATH FAMILY (Ericaceae)

TAR-FLOWER *Befaria racemosa* Vent.

FIELD MARKS. An evergreen shrub 2 to about 6 feet high, with upright branches; growing in sandy pinelands. *Branchlets* long, slender, hairy. Leaves alternate, elliptic to oval, broadly pointed at base, sharply pointed at tip, untoothed on margin, thick and leathery in texture, ½ to 2 inches long. *Flowers* very showy, white or pink-tinged fragrant, usually 7-petalled, 1½ to 2 inches across; blooming June to August. *Fruits* somewhat flattened, roundish, 5-parted capsules about ¼ inch in diameter.

RANGE. Costal plain; southern Georgia and Florida.

Also called Fly-catcher, as the sticky-hairy buds and calyxes of the flowers often catch small insects.

SOUTHERN-PLUME *Elliottia racemosa* Muhl.

FIELD MARKS. A leaf-losing shrub or small tree 3 to about 15 feet high; growing on oak ridges or sandhills. *Leaves* alternate, oval to oblong-elliptic, broadly pointed at base, pointed at tip, untoothed on margin, dull green and smooth above, paler and somewhat downy beneath, 2 to 5 inches long. *Flowers* showy, white, usually 4-petalled, about ½ inch long; blooming July or August. *Fruits* somewhat flattened, roundish, usually 4-parted capsules nearly ⅜ inch in diameter.

RANGE. Southern South Carolina and Georgia.

One of the rarest of American shrubs, known only from a few localities within its range.

SANDMYRTLE *Leiophyllum buxifolium* (Berg.) Ell.

FIELD MARKS. A much-branched evergreen shrub 6 inches to 2½ feet high, with upright branches; growing in sandy pinelands and on rocky places in the mountains. *Leaves* mostly opposite, short-stalked, elliptic to oval, blunt at both ends, untoothed on margin, smooth, leathery, lustrous above, paler and dull beneath, smooth, ⅛ to ⅝ inch long. *Flowers* small, white, 5-petalled, in rather dense end clusters; blooming March to June. *Fruits* egg-shaped, 2- to 5-parted capsules about ⅛ inch long.

RANGE. Coastal plain, New Jersey to South Carolina; upper piedmont and mountains, eastern Kentucky, North and South Carolina.

PROSTRATE SANDMYRTLE *Leiophyllum buxifolium* var. *prostratum* (Loud) Gray

FIELD MARKS. A prostrate or spreading, much-branched, evergreen shrub usually less than 6 inches high; growing on rocky mountain summits. *Leaves* opposite, crowded, oval to broadly elliptic, blunt at both ends, margin untoothed and rolled inward beneath, leathery, lustrous above, paler and dull beneath, ⅛ to about ¼ inch long. *Flowers* small, white, in few-flowered end clusters; blooming April to June. *Fruits* egg-shaped capsules slightly more than 1/16 inch long.

RANGE. Western North Carolina and eastern Tennessee.

LABRADOR-TEA *Ledum groenlandicum* Oeder

FIELD MARKS. An evergreen shrub 1 to (rarely) 3 feet high; growing in peaty soils and cold bogs. *Branchlets* rusty-woolly when young. *Leaves* alternate, short-stalked, elliptic to narrowly oblong, roundish at base, bluntly pointed at tip, margin untoothed and strongly rolled inward beneath, leathery, smooth and bright green above, densely rusty-wooly beneath, ½ to 2 inches long. *Flowers* white, 5-petalled, about ⅜ inch across, in rather dense end clusters; blooming May or June. *Fruits* narrowly oblong capsules about ¼ inch long, opening upward from base into 5 parts.

RANGE. Greenland and Labrador to Alaska; south to northern parts of New Jersey, Pennsylvania, and Ohio, Michigan, Alberta, and Washington.

RHODODENDRONS AND AZALEAS (Rhododendron L.)

(Key Appendix L)

These are evergreen or leaf-losing shrubs with alternate, simple leaves. They have clusters of showy flowers arising from end buds formed the previous season. The fruits are narrowly egg-shaped or oblong, 5-parted, woody capsules which contain a large number of very small seeds. Rhododendrons and azaleas are among the most beautiful of our native shrubs, and many of them are grown as ornamentals. The rhododendrons are evergreen shrubs with leathery leaves; our native azaleas are all leaf-losing shrubs.

ROSEBAY RHODODENDRON *Rhododendron maximum* L.

FIELD MARKS. An evergreen shrub or small tree commonly 5 to 15 feet (rarely to 40 feet) high; growing along streams and on moist, rocky, wooded slopes and sometimes forming dense thickets. *Leaves* usually broadest above the middle, tapering to a wedge-shaped base, broadly pointed at tip, untoothed on margin, very thick and leathery, lustrous above, paler and dull and sometimes downy beneath, 4 to 8 inches long. *Flowers* white to rose pink, spotted with olive green to orange, open bell-shaped with 5 rounded lobes, about 1½ inches across, in large clusters; blooming June or July. *Fruits* downy, ¾ to 1 inch long.

RANGE. Southwestern Maine to New York, southern Ontario, and Ohio; south in the mountains to northern Georgia and Alabama.

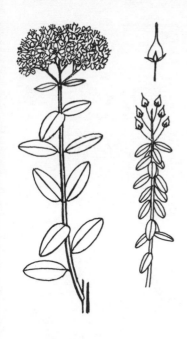

Sandmyrtle

Prostrate Sandmyrtle

Labrador-tea

Rosebay Rhododendron

Catawba Rhododendron

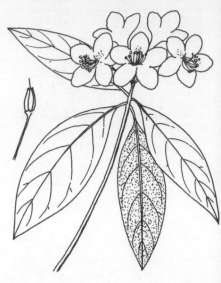

Carolina Rhododendron

Lapland Rhododendron

Pinkshell Azalea

CATAWBA RHODODENDRON *Rhododendron catawbiense* Michx.

FIELD MARKS. A spreading and often thicket-forming evergreen shrub usually 4 to 10 (rarely 20) feet high; growing on rocky slopes, ridges, and mountain tops, usually above 3,000 feet.. *Leaves* elliptic or oblong, rounded at base, blunt or slightly pointed at tip, margin untoothed, very thick and leathery, smooth, dark green and lustrous above, paler or whitened and dull beneath, 3 to 5 inches long. *Flowers* lilac purple to rose purple spotted with olive green, open bell-shaped with 5 rounded lobes, about 2 inches across, in large and showy clusters; blooming April to June. *Fruits* narrowly oblong, rusty-hairy, ¾ to 1 inch long.

RANGE. Southwestern Virginia, southern West Virginia, and southeastern Kentucky; south to northern Georgia and Alabama; locally eastward to north-central North Carolina.

Also called Purple Rhododendron and Mountain Rosebay. Often cultivated and a parent of many cultivated hybrid rhododendrons.

CAROLINA RHODODENDRON *Rhododendron minus* Michx.

FIELD MARKS. An evergreen shrub 3 to about 8 feet high; growing on exposed or wooded slopes and along streams. *Leaves* elliptic to narrowly elliptic, pointed at both ends, margin untoothed, thick and leathery, dark green and smooth above, pale or whitened and covered with minute dotlike brown scales beneath, 2 to about 4 inches long. *Flowers* white to deep rose pink, often spotted with olive-green or orange, open bell-shaped with 5 rounded lobes, 1 to 1½ inches across, in dense or fairly open clusters; blooming April to July or later. *Fruits* oblong egg-shaped, ⅜ to ¾ inch long, rusty brown.

RANGE. South-central and western North Carolina, eastern Tennessee, and north-western South Carolina south into Georgia and Alabama.

Also known as Piedmont and Small Rhododendron.

LAPLAND RHODODENDRON *Rhododendron lapponicum* (L.) Wahlenb.

FIELD MARKS. A prostrate or mat-forming evergreen shrub 2 to rarely 12 inches high; growing on tundras and southward on the rocky alpine summits of high mountains. *Leaves* short-stalked, elliptic to oval, pointed or rounded at base, blunt or abruptly short-pointed at tip, margin untoothed, leathery, dark green and wrinkled in appearance above, densely covered with small brownish scales beneath, ¼ to ¾ inch long. *Flowers* purple, open bell-shaped with 5 rounded lobes, ½ to ¾ inch across, in clusters of 3 to 6; blooming June or July. *Fruits* about ¼ inch long.

RANGE. Arctic south to Newfoundland, eastern Quebec; mountains of Maine, New Hampshire, and New York; and in Dells of Wisconsin River, Wisconsin.

PINKSHELL AZALEA *Rhododendron vaseyi* Gray

FIELD MARKS. A leaf-losing, bushy shrub 3 to 15 feet high; growing in boggy places, along streams, and in high mountain forests. *Branchlets* light reddish brown, smooth or sparingly hairy, later becoming grayish brown with flaking bark. *Leaves* elliptic, pointed at both ends, margin somewhat wavy and hairy-fringed, dark green above, paler beneath, smooth or with a few hairs along the midrib, 2 to 5 inches long. *Flowers* pale to deep rose pink spotted with yellowish orange to reddish orange, open bell-shaped with a short tube and 5 rounded lobes, 1½ to 2 inches across, 5 to 8 in a cluster; blooming in May or June. *Fruits* elliptical but somewhat lopsided, smooth or nearly so, light reddish brown, about ½ inch long.

RANGE. Jackson, Macon, and Watauga Counties, North Carolina.

Beautiful flowering shrub of very limited natural distribution but sometimes cultivated and reported as escaping from cultivation in Massachusetts.

RHODORA *Rhododendron canadense* (L.) Torr.

FIELD MARKS. A leaf-losing shrub 1 to 3 feet high; growing in cold bogs and moist rocky barrens. *Branchlets* smooth, often whitened with a bloom. *Leaves* elliptic or oblong, pointed at both ends, margin slightly rolled and hairy-fringed, dull green above, pale or whitened beneath and with some rusty hairs along the midrib, ¾ to 2 inches long. *Flowers* rose purple, 2-lipped, with a short tube, 5 to 8 in a cluster; blooming April or May. *Fruits* oblong egg-shaped, uneven at base, downy, ½ to ⅝ inch long.

RANGE. Labrador and Newfoundland to south-central Quebec; south to northern New Jersey, northeastern Pennsylvania, and central New York.

FLAME AZALEA *Rhododendron calendulaceum* (Michx.) Torr.

FIELD MARKS. A leaf-losing shrub 3 to (rarely) 15 feet high; growing in oak or pine woods and on mountain balds. *Branchlets* downy and with scattered spreading hairs. *Leaves* elliptic or broadest above the middle, pointed at both ends, margin hairy-fringed, bright green and often with scattered hairs above, paler and downy and with stiff hairs along midrib beneath, 1 to 3 inches long. *Flowers* yellow, orange, or scarlet, the tube with gland-tipped hairs, not fragrant, 1½ to 2 inches across, 5 to 9 in a cluster; blooming April to June, as new leaves unfold. *Fruits* narrowly egg-shaped, somewhat downy and with spreading hairs, about ¾ inch long.

RANGE. Southwestern Pennsylvania, southeastern Ohio, and West Virginia; south to northern Georgia and Alabama.

Often cultivated as an ornamental shrub.

SHOWY AZALEA *Rhododendron speciosum* (Willd.) Sweet.

Very similar to the preceding, but flower tubes have hairs without glands, and perhaps just a variety. It grows at lower elevations in Georgia. (Not illustrated)

CUMBERLAND AZALEA *Rhododendron cumberlandense* E. L. Br.

Much like the Flame Azalea but not blooming until the leaves are grown, and the branchlets are smooth. Oak woods, eastern Kentucky and western Virginia. (Not illustrated.

ALABAMA AZALEA *Rhododendron alabamense* Rehd.

FIELD MARKS. A leaf-losing shrub 2 to about 4 feet high; growing on rich but often dry wooded slopes. *Branchlets* with scattered stiff hairs. *Leaves* elliptic or broadest above the middle, pointed at base, broadly pointed to rounded at tip, margin fringed with short hairs, dark green above, paler or slightly whitened and somewhat hairy and with stiff hairs along the midrib beneath, 1¼ to 2¼ inches long. *Flowers* white, fragrant, the tube downy and with short gland-tipped hairs on the outside; blooming in May, when the leaves are well developed. *Fruits* narrowly egg-shaped, somewhat downy and glandular-bristly, about ⅝ inch long.

RANGE. South-central South Carolina south to Florida, west to Mississippi.

PINXTER-FLOWER *Rhododendron nudiflorum* (L.) Torr.

FIELD MARKS. A leaf-losing shrub 2 to 6 (rarely 10) feet high, the stems often unbranched below but with more or less whorled branches above; growing in moist woods, clearings, and swamps. *Branchlets* smooth or with scattered spreading hairs. *Leaves* elliptic or oblong and often broadest above the middle, pointed at tip and wedge-shaped at base, margin fringed with short hairs, dull green and smooth above, paler and with stiff hairs along the midrib beneath, 2 to 4 inches long. *Flowers* pink to almost white, delicately or faintly fragrant, the tube hairy but seldom with gland-tipped hairs on the outside, about 1½ inches across; blooming March to May, before the leaves appear. *Fruits* narrowly egg-shaped, hairy, ½ to ¾ inch long.

RANGE. Massachusetts to New York and southern Illinois; south to central South Carolina and northern Georgia.

Also called Pink or Purple Azalea and Purple-honeysuckle.

Rhodora

Flame Azalea

Alabama Azalea

Pinxter-Flower

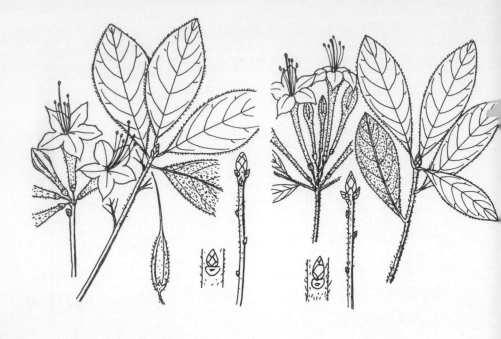

Mountain Azalea

Hoary Azalea

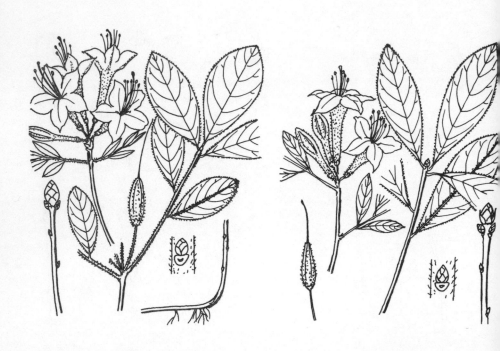

Dwarf Azalea

Swamp Azalea

MOUNTAIN AZALEA *Rhododendron roseum* (Loisel.) Rehd.

FIELD MARKS. A leaf-losing shrub 3 to 10 feet high; growing in upland woods and on rocky slopes. *Branchlets* grayish-downy and with scattered stiff hairs. *Leaves* elliptic or broadest above the middle, wedge-shaped at base, broadly pointed at tip, margin hairy-fringed, upper surface often with scattered hairs, grayish-downy and with stiff hairs along midrib beneath, 1 to 3 inches long. *Flowers* usually bright pink, tube about as long as the lobes and downy and sticky-glandular, fragrant, about 1½ inches across, 5 to 9 in a cluster; blooming April to June. *Fruits* narrowly oblong, downy, glandular-hairy capsules about ¾ inch long.

RANGE. Maine to Quebec; south to western Virginia, Tennessee, and Missouri. Also called Rose, Early, or Honeysuckle Azalea.

HOARY AZALEA *Rhododendron canescens* (Michx.) Sweet

FIELD MARKS. A shrub similar to the preceding; growing in moist woods, swamps, and along streams. *Branchlets* and *leaves* quite similar to those of the preceding species. *Flowers* pink or (rarely) white, the glandular-sticky and downy tube slender and about twice as long as the lobes, fragrant, about 1½ inches across, 5 to 9 in a cluster; blooming March or April, often before the leaves begin to expand. *Fruits* similar to those of the preceding species.

RANGE. Chiefly coastal plain; northern Delaware and northeastern Maryland; south to Florida, west to Texas, and north to Arkansas and Tennessee.

DWARF AZALEA *Rhododendron atlanticum* (Ashe) Rehd.

FIELD MARKS. A leaf-losing shrub forming colonies by means of creeping underground stems, the erect branches 8 inches to 2 feet high; growing in moist to dry sandy pinelands. *Branchlets* more or less bristly-hairy. *Leaves* elliptic or broadest above the middle, wedge-shaped at base, bluntly pointed to roundish at tip, margin hairy-fringed, smooth above, pale or somewhat whitened and with stiff hairs along midrib beneath, 1¼ to 2½ inches long. *Flowers* white to pink or pale purple, tube longer than the lobes and with rows of sticky stalked glands, very fragrant, about 1½ inches across, 4 to 10 in a cluster; blooming April or May, often before the new leaves begin to appear. *Fruits* narrowly egg-shaped, bristly-hairy, about ⅝ inch long.

RANGE. Coastal plain; Delaware and southeastern Pennsylvania south to Georgia and Alabama.

SWAMP AZALEA *Rhododendron viscosum* (L.) Torr.

FIELD MARKS. A leaf-losing shrub 3 to 10 feet high; growing in swamps, bogs, along streams, and occasionally on mountain summits. *Branchlets* with scattered, stiff, brownish hairs. *Leaves* narrowly elliptic or broadest above the middle, wedge-shaped at base, blunt or short-pointed at tip, hairy-fringed on margin, dark green and smooth above, pale or slightly whitened and with stiff brownish hairs along midrib beneath, ¾ to 2½ inches long. *Flowers* white to pale pink, tube somewhat longer than the lobes and very sticky-glandular, very fragrant, about 1¼ inches across, 4 to 9 in a cluster; blooming May to July after the leaves are grown. *Fruits* narrowly egg-shaped, glandular-bristly capsules ½ to ¾ inch long.

RANGE. Southwestern Maine to northeastern Ohio; south to Georgia and Tennessee. Also called the Clammy Azalea and White- or Clammy-honeysuckle.

SOUTHERN SWAMP AZALEA *Rhododendron viscosum* var. *serrulatum*
(Small) Ahles

A shrub similar to the preceding but often taller, and with larger leaves finely toothed as well as hairy-fringed on the margin. The flowers have slender tubes about twice as long as the lobes. Coastal Plain; North Carolina south to Florida, west to Mississippi. (Not illustrated)

SMOOTH AZALEA   *Rhododendron arborescens* (Pursh) Torr.

FIELD MARKS. A leaf-losing shrub 5 to 20 feet high; growing in moist rocky woods, along streams, and in swamps and bogs. *Branchlets* smooth, somewhat lustrous, often with a whitish bloom. *Leaves* elliptic or broadest above the middle, wedge-shaped at base, short-pointed to blunt at tip, margin fringed with short hairs, thick and firm in texture, dark green and lustrous above, pale or whitened beneath and sometimes with a few stiff hairs along the midrib, 1 to 3 inches long. *Flowers* white or sometimes pale pink, about 1½ inches across, very sticky-hairy on the outside, the corolla tube longer than the lobes, very fragrant, 3 to 6 in a cluster; blooming late May to July. *Fruits* narrowly egg-shaped, densely glandular-hairy, ½ to ¾ inch long.

RANGE. Southern Pennsylvania to Kentucky, south to northern Georgia and Alabama. Also called Sweet or Tree Azalea.

RED AZALEA   *Rhododendron prunifolium* (Small) Millais

FIELD MARKS. A leaf-losing shrub 4 to 10 feet high; growing in moist woods and ravines. *Branchlets* smooth. *Leaves* elliptic to narrowly elliptic or broadest above the middle, wedge-shaped at base, broadly pointed to long-pointed at tip, margin fringed with short hairs and also minutely toothed, dark green and smooth above, paler green and with some stiff hairs along the midrib beneath, 1½ to 5 inches long. *Flowers* bright red, about 1½ inches across, the corolla tube smooth or merely with occasional hairs, 3 to 5 in a cluster; blooming July and August.

RANGE. Coastal plain; southern Georgia and Alabama.

ALLEGHENY MENZIESIA   *Menziesia pilosa* (Michx.) Juss.

FIELD MARKS. A rather straggling leaf-losing shrub 2 to 6 feet high, with bark freely shredding; growing in bogs or on thinly wooded slopes and balds in the southern Appalachians. *Branchlets* bristly-hairy and somewhat rusty-chaffy. *Leaves* alternate, often crowded toward tips of branchlets, elliptic to oval or broadest above the middle, pointed at base, abruptly pointed at tip, untoothed but hairy-fringed on margin, roughish-hairy above, pale or whitened and usually rusty-chaffy along the veins beneath, ¾ to 2 inches long. *Flowers* greenish white or greenish yellow often tinged with red, bell-shaped, about ¼ inch long, 3 to 6 in a cluster and nodding on slender stalks; blooming May to July. *Fruits* egg-shaped, bristly-hairy capsules about 3/16 inch long; maturing August to October.

RANGE. Southern Pennsylvania and West Virginia south to eastern Tennessee and northern Georgia.

Also called Minniebush.

ALPINE-AZALEA   *Loiseleuria procumbens* (L.) Desv.

FIELD MARKS. A much-branched, mat-forming, evergreen shrub seldom 8 inches high; growing on tundras or mountain tops, and in cold bogs. *Leaves* opposite, crowded, elliptic to oval, blunt at tip, margin rolled and untoothed, leathery in texture, smooth, dark green above, often whitened beneath, ⅛ to ⅜ inch long. *Flowers* white or pink, bell-shaped, about ⅛ inch long, 2 to 5 in end clusters; blooming June and July. Fruits 2- to 3-parted, egg-shaped capsules about ⅛ inch long.

RANGE. Greenland and Newfoundland to Alaska; south to mountain summits in Maine and New Hampshire, Quebec, and Alberta.

220

Smooth Azalea

Red Azalea

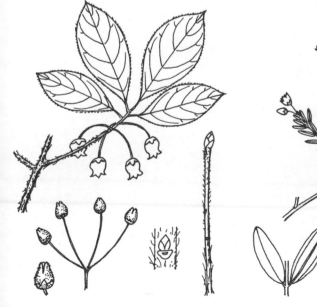

Allegheny Menziesia

Alpine-Azalea

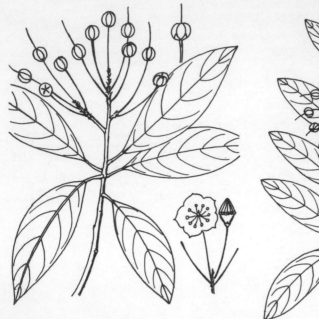

Mountain-Laurel

Sheep-Laurel

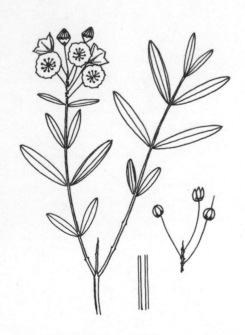

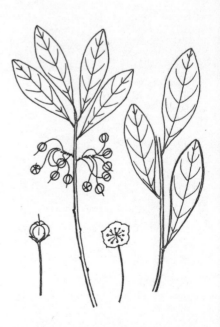

Pale-Laurel

White Wicky

LAURELS (Kalmia L.)

These are shrubs with alternate, opposite, or whorled simple leaves with untoothed margins. Their showy flowers have a saucer-shaped or shallowly bowl-shaped, 5-lobed corolla. The anthers of the 10 stamens fit into small pouches in the corolla until they are released by an insect touching the springlike filaments. The fruits are 5-parted roundish or slightly flattened capsules containing a number of small seeds. Leaves of these plants are known to be poisonous to livestock, and honey made from the nectar of the flowers is said to be poisonous to humans. Although these are commonly called laurels in America, the true laurels are members of the Laurel family.

MOUNTAIN-LAUREL *Kalmia latifolia* L.

FIELD MARKS. An evergreen shrub or small tree 3 to (rarely) 35 feet high; growing in rocky or sandy woods. *Leaves* mostly alternate but crowded toward ends of the branchlets, elliptic, pointed at both ends, thick and leathery, smooth, lustrous above, paler yellowish green beneath, 2 to about 4 inches long. *Flowers* deep pink to whitish, about ¾ inch across, in dense end clusters; blooming April to July. *Fruits* about 3/16 inch in diameter.

RANGE. New Brunswick and Maine to Ontario, southern Indiana, and western Kentucky; south to Florida and Louisiana.

Also called Ivy (in southern Appalachians), Calicobush, and Spoonwood. Often cultivated as an ornamental shrub.

SHEEP-LAUREL *Kalmia angustifolia* L.

FIELD MARKS. An evergreen shrub 1 to about 3 feet high; growing in bogs and rocky or sandy woods. *Leaves* opposite or in 3's, narrowly elliptic to oblong, pointed at both ends, thin but leathery in texture, smooth above, paler green or slightly whitened and smooth beneath (or grayish-downy beneath in var. *caroliniana* [Small] Fern.), 1 to 2½ inches long. *Flowers* deep pink to rose purple (rarely white), about ⅜ inch across, in clusters on branchlets of the previous year at base of the new growth; blooming April to August. *Fruits* about ⅛ inch in diameter.

RANGE. Newfoundland and Labrador to Manitoba, south to Pennsylvania and Michigan; var. *caroliniana* from Virginia and Tennessee south to Georgia.

PALE-LAUREL *Kalmia polifolia* Wang.

FIELD MARKS. A straggling evergreen shrub 6 inches to 2 feet high; growing in cold northern bogs. *Branchlets* strongly 2-edged. *Leaves* opposite or in 3's, stalkless or nearly so, very narrowly elliptic, narrowed at base, blunt or short-pointed at tip, margin rolled, smooth, lustrous above, strongly whitened beneath, ½ to 1¼ inches long. *Flowers* rose purple, about ½ inch across, in end clusters; blooming May to July. *Fruits* about ⅛ inch in diameter.

RANGE. Newfoundland and Labrador to Alaska; south to New Jersey, northern Pennsylvania, Michigan, Minnesota, and Oregon.

Also called Swamp- or Bog-laurel.

WHITE WICKY *Kalmia cuneata* Michx.

FIELD MARKS. A leaf-losing shrub 8 inches to about 3 feet high; growing in wet places in the Carolina sandhills. *Branchlets* downy. *Leaves* alternate, narrowly elliptic or broadest above the middle, wedge-shaped at base, usually blunt at tip, margin slightly rolled, smooth above, downy beneath, ¾ to 2 inches long. *Flowers* white or pinkish, about ⅝ inch across, in few-flowered clusters on branchlets of the previous year at base of the new growth; blooming May or June. *Fruits* about ⅛ inch in diameter.

RANGE. North and South Carolina.

HAIRY-LAUREL *Kalmia hirsuta* Walt.

FIELD MARKS. An evergreen shrub 6 inches to about 2 feet high, with ascending branches; growing in moist, sandy pinelands. *Branchlets* hairy. *Leaves* alternate, stalkless or nearly so, elliptic to oval, broadly pointed at both ends, margin sometimes slightly rolled, dark green above, paler beneath, with spreading hairs on both surfaces, ⅛ to ½ inch long. *Flowers* pink or rose purple with hairy calyx and pointed corolla lobes, ⅜ to ⅝ inch across, usually solitary in the axils of leaves toward the ends of the branchlets; blooming May to August. *Fruits* about ⅛ inch in diameter.

RANGE. Coastal plain; southeastern Virginia south to Florida, west to Mississippi.

MOUNTAIN-HEATH *Phyllodoce caerulea* (L.) Bab.

FIELD MARKS. A prostrate evergreen shrub with ascending branches 4 to 8 inches high; growing on arctic tundras and southward on alpine summits of high mountains. *Leaves* alternate, crowded, narrow, flattened, blunt at tip, on short stalks running slightly down the branchlets, margin roughish or minutely toothed, 3/16 to ⅜ inch long. *Flowers* purplish, urn-shaped, ¼ to ⅜ inch long, solitary or 2 to 6 at ends of the branchlets; blooming June to August. *Fruits* egg-shaped, 5-parted capsules about 3/16 inch long.

RANGE. Arctic regions south to Newfoundland, Quebec, and the higher mountains of Maine and New Hampshire.

BOG ROSEMARY *Andromeda glaucophylla* Link

FIELD MARKS. A spreading evergreen shrub 4 inches to 2 feet high, growing in bogs and shallow pools. *Branchlets* whitened. *Leaves* alternate, very short-stalked, narrowly lance-shaped or narrowly oblong, pointed at base, short-pointed at tip, margin strongly rolled, thick and leathery in texture, dark bluish green and lustrous above, very white and minutely downy beneath, ¾ to about 2 inches long. *Flowers* white or pinkish, globeshaped, about ¼ inch long, in end clusters; blooming May to July or later. *Fruits* turban-shaped, 5-parted capsules about 3/16 inch in diameter.

RANGE. Southwestern Greenland and Labrador to eastern Manitoba; south to northern New Jersey, West Virginia, Indiana, Wisconsin, and Minnesota.

ZENOBIA *Zenobia pulverulenta* (Bartr.) Pollard

FIELD MARKS. A leaf-losing shrub 3 to about 10 feet high; growing in damp sandy or peaty pinelands. *Branchlets* reddish to brown, often more or less whitened with a bloom. *Leaves* alternate, elliptic to oval, pointed at base, blunt or sometimes pointed at tip, untoothed or with rather obscure wavy teeth or margin, leathery in texture, smooth on both surfaces, often whitened with a bloom but sometimes green on both surfaces, ¾ to 2½ inches long. *Flowers* white, broadly bell-shaped, about ¼ inch long, in clusters along growth of the preceding year; blooming May or June. *Fruits* roundish, 5-parted capsules nearly ¼ inch in diameter.

RANGE. Coastal plain; southeastern Virginia south to Georgia.

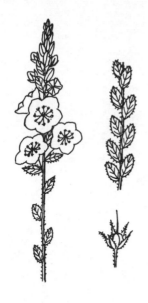

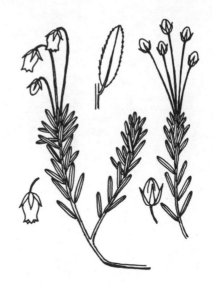

Hairy-Laurel

Mountain-Heath

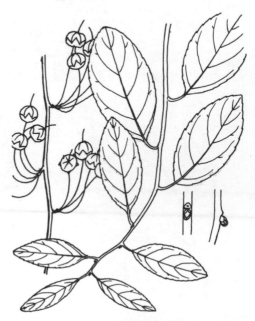

Bog Rosemary

Zenobia

Drooping Leucothoë

Coastal Leucothoë

Recurved Leucothoë

Swamp Leucothoë

DROOPING LEUCOTHOË   *Leucothoë fontanesiana* (Steud.) Sleumer

FIELD MARKS. An evergreen shrub 2 to about 6 feet high, with spreading and arching, reddish branches; growing in moist mountain woodlands. *Leaves* alternate, narrowly egg-shaped to lance-shaped, rounded or broadly pointed at base, long-pointed at tip, finely toothed on margin with bristle-tipped teeth, leathery in texture, dark green and lustrous above, paler and smooth beneath, 2½ to 6 inches long; leafstalks ⅜ to ⅝ inch long. *Flowers* white, bell-shaped, fragrant, about ⅜ inch long; in many-flowered, narrow, drooping clusters arising in the axils of the leaves; blooming April and May. *Fruits* roundish, somewhat flattened, 5-lobed capsules about 3/16 inch in diameter.
RANGE. Western Virginia south to northern Georgia and northern Alabama.
Also called Dog-hobble and Switch-ivy.

COASTAL LEUCOTHOË   *Leucothoë axillaris* (Lam.) D. Don.

FIELD MARKS. An evergreen shrub similar to the preceding species but growing in wet woods and swamps in the coastal region. *Leaves* alternate, elliptic or oblong lance-shaped, pointed at base, pointed or short-pointed (rarely long-pointed) at tip, margin toothed chiefly above the middle, leathery in texture, dark green and lustrous above, paler and smooth or nearly so beneath, 1½ to 5 inches long; leafstalks ⅛ to ⅜ inch long. *Flowers* white, bell-shaped, fragrant, about ⅜ inch long; in many-flowered, narrow, drooping clusters arising in the axils of the leaves; blooming February to May. *Fruits* roundish, somewhat flattened, 5-lobed capsules about 3/16 inch in diameter.
RANGE. Coasal plain; Southeastern Virginia south to Florida, west to Mississippi.

RECURVED LEUCOTHOË   *Leucothoë recurva* (Buckley) Gray

FIELD MARKS. A widely branched, straggling, leaf-losing shrub 3 to 10 feet high; growing on dry, often rocky, wooded slopes in the mountains. *Leaves* alternate, egg-shaped or elliptic, pointed at both ends, finely and sharply toothed on the margin, thin in texture, bright green and smooth above, paler and sometimes slightly downy on the veins beneath, 1½ to 4 inches long. *Flowers* white, narrowly bell-shaped, fragrant; many hanging downward in 1-sided, spreading and recurved, narrow end clusters; blooming April to June. *Fruits* roundish, somewhat flattened, deeply 5-lobed capsules about 3/16 inch in diameter.
RANGE. Western Virginia and West Virginia south to northern Georgia and northern Alabama.
Also called Redtwig Leucothoe. The leaves turn bright red in fall.

SWAMP LEUCOTHOË   *Leucothoë racemosa* (L.) Gray

FIELD MARKS. A leaf-losing shrub 5 to about 12 feet high, with ascending and spreading branches; growing in swampy thickets, along streams, and about shallow ponds. *Leaves* alternate, lance-shaped or elliptic, pointed at both ends, finely and sharply toothed on margin, bright green and smooth above, paler and usually somewhat downy on the veins beneath, 1 to 3 inches long. *Flowers* white or pale pink, narrowly bell-shaped, fragrant; many standing erect in long, narrow, stiffly spreading clusters; blooming April to June. *Fruits* roundish, somewhat flattened, 5-parted capsules about 3/16 inch in diameter.
RANGE. Massachusetts, southeastern New York, and southeastern Pennsylvania; south to Florida, west to Louisiana.

FETTERBUSH   *Lyonia lucida* (Lam.) K. Koch

FIELD MARKS. An evergreen shrub 3 to about 6 feet high, with arching or drooping and sharply 3-angled branches; growing in moist pinelands, swamps, and peaty thickets. *Leaves* alternate, elliptic to oval or sometimes broadest above the middle, pointed or broadly pointed at base, abruptly pointed at tip, stiff and leathery in texture, with a prominent vein paralleling the untoothed and narrowly rolled margin, dark green and lustrous above, paler and dull and glandular-dotted beneath, 1 to 3 inches long. *Flowers* white to deep rose pink, oblong bell-shaped, about ⅜ inch long, the 5 calyx lobes narrow and spreading, 3 to 10 in clusters in the leaf axils; blooming March to May. *Fruits* roundish, 5-parted capsules about 3/16 inch in diameter.

RANGE. Coastal plain, Southeastern Virginia south to Florida, west to Louisiana.

Also called Tetterbush and Hoorah-bush (Okefenokee region).

STAGGERBUSH   *Lyonia mariana* (L.) D. Don

FIELD MARKS. A leaf-losing shrub 8 inches to nearly 4 feet high, with slender upright branches; growing in peaty or sandy open woods. *Leaves* alternate, elliptic or broadest above the middle, pointed at base, sharply to bluntly pointed at tip, untoothed on margin, bright green and smooth above, paler and minutely black-dotted and sometimes downy on the veins beneath, 1 to 3 inches long. *Flowers* white or pale pink, barrel-shaped, about ⅜ inch long, the 5 calyx lobes narrow and spreading, in several whorled clusters on leafless tips of branchlets; blooming April to June. *Fruits* urn-shaped, 5-angled, point capsules about ¼ inch long.

RANGE. Chiefly coastal plain; Southern Rhode Island, southeastern New York, and southeastern Pennsylvania; south to Florida, west to Texas, and north in the Mississippi Valley to Arkansas and eastern Tennessee.

Foliage poisonous to calves and lambs if eaten.

MALEBERRY   *Lyonia ligustrina* (L.) DC.

FIELD MARKS. A leaf-losing shrub 3 to about 12 feet high; growing in moist to dry places, often along streams or in bogs. *Leaves* alternate, commonly elliptic to narrowly egg-shaped but often broadest above the middle, more or less pointed at both ends, usually very finely toothed but sometimes inconspicuously toothed or almost untoothed on margin, smooth above but usually more or less hairy beneath, commonly 1 to 2½ (rarely 4) inches long. *Flowers* white, globe-shaped, about ⅛ inch across, in leafless or leafy-bracted clusters from buds on growth of the previous year; blooming April to July. *Fruits* roundish but somewhat flattened, 5-celled capsules about ⅛ inch in diameter.

RANGE. Central Maine to central New York and Kentucky; south to Florida, Louisiana, and Oklahoma.

Very variable as to leaf size, hairiness of branchlets, etc. Also known as Privet-andromeda, Seedy-buckberry, and Male-huckleberry.

RUSTY LYONIA   *Lyonia ferruginea* (Walt.) G. Don.

FIELD MARKS. An evergreen shrub or small tree usually 3 to 10 (rarely 30) feet high; growing in hammocks and wet pinelands. *Leaves* alternate, those near the ends of the branchlets reduced in size and rusty in appearance, oval to narrowly elliptic or broadest above the middle, pointed at base, pointed to roundish at tip, untoothed on margin, leathery in texture; the larger ones pale green above, rusty-dotted beneath, 1 to 2½ inches long. *Flowers* white, globe-shaped, about 3/16 inch across, in small clusters in the leaf axils of the previous year; blooming March to May. *Fruits* narrowly egg-shaped, 5-angled capsules about ¼ inch long.

RANGE. Coastal plain; South Carolina south to Florida.

228

Fetterbush   **Staggerbush**

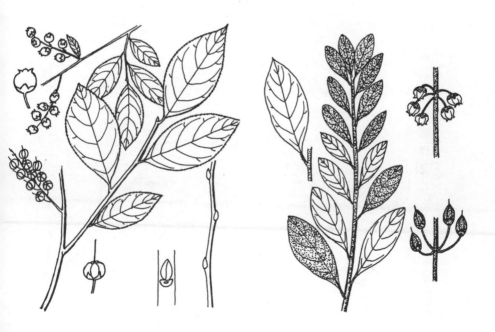

Maleberry   **Rusty Lyonia**

Mountain Fetterbush

Vine-wicky

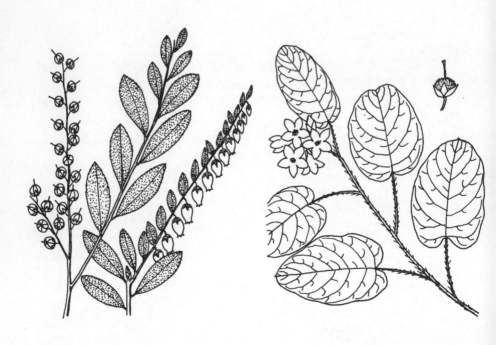

Leatherleaf

Trailing-Arbutus

MOUNTAIN FETTERBUSH *Pieris floribunda* (Pursh) B. & H.

FIELD MARKS. An evergreen shrub 3 to about 6 feet high; growing on dry to moist slopes or balds in the Appalachian Mountains. *Branchlets* slender, hairy, nearly erect. *Leaves* alternate, narrowly egg-shaped or oblong, pointed at base, sharply pointed at tip, finely toothed and bristly-hairy on margin, leathery in texture, smooth, green above, paler and minutely black-dotted beneath, 1½ to 3 inches long. *Flowers* white, vase-shaped, nodding, about 3/8 inch long, in a group of slender clusters at tips of branches; blooming March to June. *Fruits* egg-shaped, slightly 5-angled capsules about 3/16 inch long.

RANGE. West Virginia south to western North Carolina and eastern Tennessee.

Often cultivated as an ornamental shrub.

VINE-WICKY *Pieris phillyreifolia* (Hook.) DC.

FIELD MARKS. An evergreen vinelike shrub creeping up the trunks of cypress trees beneath their outer bark, often to a height of 20 to 30 feet, and sending out branches every few feet; more rarely a small shrub standing alone. *Leaves* alternate, elliptic to oval or broadest above the middle, pointed at base, broadly pointed or blunt at tip, margin toothed only above the middle, leathery in texture, bright green and smooth above, paler beneath, 1 to 3 inches long. *Flowers* white, vase-shaped, about ¼ inch long, in narrow clusters from the axils of the upper leaves; blooming February to April. *Fruits* roundish, slightly flattened, 5-celled capsules about 3/16 inch in diameter.

RANGE. Coastal plain; Southeastern Georgia, northern Florida, and southern Alabama.

Also called He-huckleberry. A very unique shrub, the branches seemingly growing out of the trunks of cypress trees.

LEATHERLEAF *Chamaedaphne calyculata* var. *angustifolia* (Ait.) Rehd.

FIELD MARKS. A much-branched, more or less evergreen shrub 1 to about 3 feet high, with spreading or horizontal branches; growing in peaty soils or in bogs. *Leaves* alternate, narrowly elliptic or broadest above the middle, pointed at base, bluntly pointed to roundish at tip, practically untoothed or with some minute teeth on the slightly rolled margin, dull green dotted with silvery scales above, brownish with minute rusty scales beneath, leathery in texture, ½ to 1½ inches long, often turning reddish in winter. *Flowers* white, bell-shaped, about ¼ inch long, in long and one-sided end clusters, each flower subtended by a leafy bract; blooming March to July. *Fruits* roundish, somewhat flattened, 5-celled capsules about ⅛ inch in diameter.

RANGE. Newfoundland to Alaska; south to the coastal plain and mountains of North Carolina, the region of the Great Lakes, northern Iowa, Alberta, and British Columbia.

TRAILING-ARBUTUS *Epigaea repens* L.

FIELD MARKS. A trailing evergreen shrub with slender stems which are usually bristly with rusty hairs; growing in dry rocky or sandy open woods and clearings. *Leaves* alternate, oblong-oval, roundish or heart-shaped at base, blunt to rounded at tip, untoothed but usually fringed with stiff hairs on margin, green and usually rough-hairy on both surfaces but sometimes quite smooth, ¾ to 2½ inches long. *Flowers* white to deep pink, about ½ inch long, very fragrant, in small clusters in the leaf axils or at tips of the stems; blooming March to May or June. *Fruits* roundish 5-celled capsules about ¼ inch in diameter.

RANGE. Labrador to Saskatchewan; south to Georgia, Alabama, and Iowa.

Also known as Mayflower.

TEABERRY *Gaultheria procumbens* L.

FIELD MARKS. An aromatic evergreen plant 2 to 6 inches high, with creeping underground stems; growing in sandy or rocky woods and clearings. *Leaves* with wintergreen odor when bruised, alternate, oval to roundish, margin with a few low and bristle-tipped teeth, leathery, smooth, lustrous above, paler green beneath, ¾ to 2 inches long. *Flowers* white, urn-shaped, about ¼ inch long, usually solitary in leaf axils; blooming June to August. *Fruits* roundish, bright red, about ⅜ inch in diameter, with spicy wintergreen odor when crushed; ripening September to November and persisting.

RANGE. Newfoundland to Manitoba; south to Georgia, Alabama, and Minnesota. Also called Mountain-tea, Checkerberry, and Wintergreen. Oil of wintergreen used as a flavoring and in medicines is obtained from the leaves.

CREEPING-SNOWBERRY *Gaultheria hispudula* (L.) Bigel.

FIELD MARKS. A creeping, aromatic, evergreen plant with very slender, brownish-hairy stems; growing in cold mossy woods and bogs. *Leaves* with a wintergreen odor when bruised, short-stalked, alternate, roundish egg-shaped, pointed or abruptly bristle-pointed at tip, broadly pointed to roundish at base, margin untoothed and rolled inward beneath, leathery, lustrous above, paler and with closely pressed brown hairs beneath, ⅛ to ⅜ inch long. *Flowers* white, bell-shaped, slightly over ⅛ inch long, solitary in leaf axils; blooming May or June. *Fruits* roundish, white, usually with some bristly brownish hairs, about ¼ inch in diameter, with wintergreen odor when crushed; ripening August or September.

RANGE. Newfoundland and Labrador to British Columbia; south to New England, West Virginia, Michigan, Minnesota, and Idaho.

MOSS-PLANT *Cassiope hypnoides* (L.) D. Don

FIELD MARKS. A prostrate or tufted, mosslike, evergreen plant 1 to 5 inches high; growing on tundras and southward on alpine mountain summits. *Leaves* narrow and needle-like, crowded in 4 rows along the branchlets, minutely downy, averaging about ⅛ inch long. *Flowers* white or pink, open bell-shaped, deeply 4- to 5-lobed, about ¼ inch long, nodding on slender stalks at tips of the branchlets; blooming June to August. *Fruits* small, roundish, 4- to 5-parted capsules.

RANGE. Arctic America south to mountains of Newfoundland, Quebec, Maine, New Hampshire, and New York.

BEARBERRY *Arctostaphylos uva-ursi* (L.) Spreng.

FIELD MARKS. A trailing evergreen shrub, the long and flexible branches often rooting at the nodes; growing on tundras and rocky or sandy open areas. *Branchlets* smooth to white-woolly or sticky-downy; later becoming reddish brown to grayish brown, and with papery peeling bark. *Leaves* alternate, short-stalked, usually broadest above the middle, wedge-shaped at base, rounded at tip, untoothed on margin, leathery, smooth or nearly so on both surfaces, lustrous above, paler beneath, ½ to 1¼ inches long. *Flowers* white or pinkish, urn-shaped, almost ¼ inch long, in small end clusters; blooming May to July and rarely October or November. *Fruits* roundish, red, about ¼ inch in diameter, with mealy flesh and 5 to 10 seeds; ripening August or September and persisting.

RANGE. Labrador to Alaska; south to eastern Virginia, the region of the Great Lakes, South Dakota, New Mexico, and California.

Leaves used medicinally, for tanning leather, and for making dyes. Mixed with tobacco by Indians and called Kinnikinnik. Berries eaten by grouse and bears.

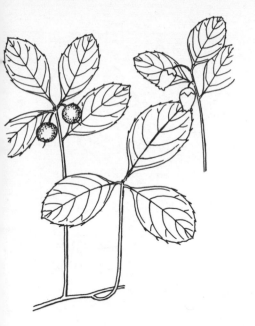

Teaberry

Creeping-snowberry

Moss-plant

Bearberry

Alpine Bearberry

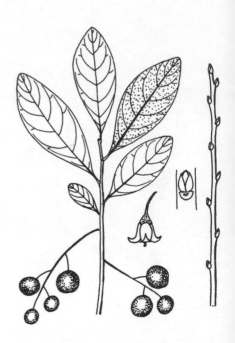

Box Huckleberry

Dwarf Huckleberry

Dangleberry

ALPINE BEARBERRY *Arctostaphylos alpina* (L.) Spreng.

FIELD MARKS. A trailing or mat-forming shrub with papery-barked and brittle branches; growing on tundras and southward on alpine mountains summits. *Leaves* alternate, broadest above the middle, wedge-shaped at base, pointed or blunt at tip, margin minutely toothed and often hairy-fringed toward base, wrinkled-veiny above, ⅜ to 1 inch long; turning bright red and withering in fall but persisting. *Flowers* white or pink-tinged, urn-shaped, 4- or 5-lobed, about 3/16 inch long, 2 to 4 in end clusters; blooming May or June. *Fruits* roundish, purple or purplish black, juicy, 4- or 5-seeded; ripening September or October.

RANGE. Arctic America south to Newfoundland, Maine, and New Hampshire.

HUCKLEBERRIES (Gaylussacia HBK)

(Key Appendix M)

Huckleberries are usually leaf-losing shrubs with alternate simple leaves which are dotted with small, glistening, yellowish resin globules. The fruits are berry-like, roundish, and have 10 rather large seedlike nutlets. These leaf and fruit characteristics readily distinguish them from the blueberries.

BOX HUCKLEBERRY *Gaylussacia brachycera* (Michx.) Gray

FIELD MARKS. An evergreen shrub forming colonies by creeping underground stems, branches 6 to 15 inches high; growing in sandy woods or on dry wooded slopes. *Branchlets* prominently angled, smooth. *Leaves* short-stalked, oval to egg-shaped, broadly pointed to blunt at both ends, margin with low blunt teeth and rolled inward beneath, leathery, smooth, bright green above, paler yellowish green beneath, ½ to 1 inch long. *Flowers* white or pinkish, urn-shaped, in small clusters; blooming May or June. *Fruits* blue, with a whitish bloom, about ⅜ inch in diameter; ripening June to August.

RANGE. Delaware and Pennsylvania south to South Carolina and Tennessee.

DWARF HUCKLEBERRY *Gaylussacia dumosa* (Andr.) T. & G.

FIELD MARKS. A leaf-losing shrub 6 inches to 2 feet high, with creeping underground stems; growing in dry sandy woods. *Branchlets* slender, zigzag, more or less downy. *Leaves* broadest above the middle, wedge-shaped at base, abruptly short-pointed at tip, margin untoothed, thickish, bright green on both sides, lustrous above, somewhat glandular-hairy and resin-dotted beneath, 1 to 2½ inches long. *Flowers* whitish to greenish pink or reddish, bell-shaped, in leafy-bracted clusters; blooming March to June. *Fruits* black, sometimes glandular-hairy, ¼ to ⅜ inch in diameter; ripening June to August.

RANGE. Newfoundland and New Brunswick to eastern Pennsylvania and Tennessee, south to Florida and Louisiana.

BRISTLY HUCKLEBERRY *Gaylussacia hirtella* (Ait. f.) Klotzch

Similar to the preceding but usually taller and with bristly-hairy stems and fruits. Sandy pinelands; Florida, Alabama, and Louisiana. (Not illustrated)

DANGLEBERRY *Gaylussacia frondosa* (L.) T. & G.

FIELD MARKS. A leaf-losing shrub 2 to 4 feet high; growing in rocky or sandy woods and bogs. *Branchlets* slender, smooth, often whitened with a bloom. *Leaves* elliptic to oval or broadest above the middle, pointed at base, bluntly pointed to roundish at tip, margin untoothed, pale green and smooth above, paler or whitened and resin-dotted beneath, 1 to 2½ inches long. *Flowers* greenish pink, bell-shaped, in rather long drooping clusters; blooming March to June. *Fruits* blue, whitened with a bloom, about ⅜ inch in diameter, sweet and juicy; ripening June to August.

RANGE. Massachusetts to southeastern New York and Ohio, south to Florida and Louisiana.

Also called Tangleberry, Blue-tangle, and Blue Huckleberry.

235

WOOLLY DANGLEBERRY *Gaylussacia frondosa* var. *tomentosa* Gray

FIELD MARKS A leaf-losing shrub with stiffly erect and sparingly branched stems 2 to 4 feet high; growing in moist pinelands. *Branchlets* densely downy or woolly-hairy. *Leaves* elliptic to oval or broadest above the middle, wedge-shaped at base, broadly pointed or blunt at tip, pale green and wrinkled-veiny above, densely coated beneath with pale to brownish wool and also resin-dotted, 1 to 3 inches long. *Flowers* white or pinkish, bell-shaped, in rather long drooping clusters; blooming March to May. *Fruits* dull blue, whitened with a bloom, about ⅜ inch in diameter; ripening June to August.

RANGE. Coastal plain; southeastern South Carolina south to Florida, west to Alabama.

CREEPING DANGLEBERRY *Gaylussacia nana* (Gray) Small

FIELD MARKS. A leaf-losing shrub with creeping underground stems and erect branches 8 inches to 2 feet high; growing in sandy oak and pine woods. *Branchlets* finely downy, often whitened with a bloom and resin-dotted. *Leaves* elliptic or broadest above the middle, pointed to roundish at base, broadly pointed or rounded at tip, margin untoothed but slightly rolled, wrinkled-veiny, smooth above, often finely downy and resin-dotted beneath, whitened on both surfaces, ¾ to 1½ inches long. *Flowers* creamy white or greenish white, often tinged with red, bell-shaped, in drooping clusters; blooming March or April. *Fruits* blue, whitened with a bloom, about ¼ inch in diameter; ripening June or July.

RANGE. Coastal plain; Georgia and Florida.

BLACK HUCKLEBERRY *Gaylussacia baccata* (Wang.) K. Koch

FIELD MARKS. A leaf-losing shrub 1½ to 3 feet high, with erect branches and with young growth copiously dotted with sticky resin globules; growing in dry sandy or rocky woods and sometimes in bogs. *Leaves* elliptic to oval or oblong lance-shaped (rarely broadest above the middle) pointed at base, pointed to blunt at tip, margin untoothed, yellowish green above and scarcely paler beneath, resin-dotted on both surfaces but more densely so beneath, 1 to 2½ inches long. *Flowers* greenish tinged with pink or red, egg-shaped, in short clusters; blooming April to June. *Fruits usually* lustrous black, about ¼ inch in diameter, sweet; ripening July and August.

RANGE. Newfoundland to Saskatchewan, south to Georgia and Louisiana.

BUCKBERRY *Gaylussacia ursina* (M. A. Curtis) T. & G.

FIELD MARKS. A leaf-losing shrub 2 to about 4 feet high; growing throughout woodlands of the southern Appalachians. *Branchlets* somewhat downy when young. *Leaves* elliptic or sometimes broadest above the middle, pointed to roundish at base, pointed at tip, margin untoothed but often hairy-fringed, thin in texture, bright green and smooth or nearly so except for some hairs along the midrib beneath, minutely and rather inconspicuously resin-dotted on the lower surface, 1½ to 4 inches long. *Flowers* greenish white to reddish, bell-shaped, about 3/16 inch across, in elongate clusters; blooming May or June. *Fruits* lustrous black, about ⅜ inch in diameter, insipid to rather sweet; ripening July to September.

RANGE. Southwestern North Carolina and eastern Tennessee, south into northwestern South Carolina and northern Georgia.

Woolly Dangleberry

Creeping Dangleberry

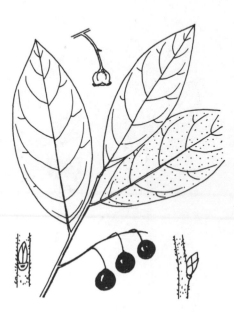

Black Huckleberry

Buckberry

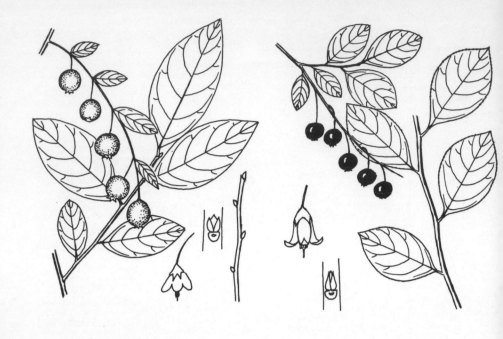

Deerberry

Sparkleberry

Bog Bilberry

Dwarf Bilberry

BLUEBERRIES, BILBERRIES, AND CRANBERRIES (Vaccinium L.)

These are shrubs with alternate and simple leaves. The fruits are roundish berries containing a large number of small seeds. Blueberries and cranberries are well known for their edible fruits. The blueberries are a difficult group, and various botanists have described numerous species. Other botanists regard them as mere variations of the species included here.

DEERBERRY *Vaccinium stamineum* L.

FIELD MARKS. A leaf-losing shrub 2 to 10 feet high; growing in dry rocky or sandy woods and thickets. *Branchlets* reddish purple, often downy or with a whitish bloom. *Leaves* elliptic or egg-shaped, pointed to rounded at base, usually pointed at tip, untoothed on margin, thin, smooth above, smooth or downy and often whitened beneath, 1 to 3½ inches long. *Flowers* greenish white or purple-tinged, open bell-shaped, in leafy-bracted clusters; blooming April to June. *Fruits* greenish or pale purplish, often whitened with a bloom, 5/16 to ½ inch in diameter, rather sour but edible when cooked; ripening July to October.

RANGE. Massachusetts to southern Ontario and Kansas; south to Florida and Louisiana.

Also called Squaw-huckleberry.

BLACK DEERBERRY *Vaccinium stamineum* var. *melanocarpum* Mohr

Similar to the above but with downy branchlets and lower leaf surfaces and with purplish-black, downy fruits. North Carolina and Missouri south to Florida and Louisiana. (Not illustrated)

SPARKLEBERRY *Vaccinium arboreum* Marsh.

FIELD MARKS. A leaf-losing, or southward an evergreen, shrub or small tree 4 to 30 feet high; growing in dry sandy or rocky woods. *Leaves* elliptic to oval or broadest above the middle, more or less pointed at both ends, margin sometimes minutely toothed or slightly rolled inward on lower surface, somewhat leathery in texture, lustrous above, paler and sometimes downy beneath, ¾ to 2 inches long. *Flowers* white, bell-shaped, in leafy-bracted clusters; blooming April to June. *Fruits* black, lustrous, about ¼ inch in diameter, rather dry and insipid; ripening September or October.

RANGE. Virginia to southern Indiana and Illinois, Missouri, and Oklahoma; south to Florida and Texas.

Also called Farkleberry and Tree-huckleberry.

BOG BILBERRY *Vaccinium uliginosum* var. *alpinum* Bigel.

FIELD MARKS. A spreading, much-branched, leaf-losing shrub 6 to 12 inches high; growing on tundras and southward on alpine mountain summits and lakeshores. *Leaves* almost stalkless, oval or broadest above the middle, wedge-shaped at base, rounded or blunt at tip, untoothed on margin, smooth and dull above, paler or whitened and sometimes downy beneath, 3/16 to ¾ inch long. *Flowers* pinkish, urn-shaped, 2 to 4 in a cluster; blooming June and July. *Fruits* bluish black, with whitish bloom, about ¼ inch in diameter, sweet and edible; ripening July to September.

RANGE. Arctic America south to New England, New York, Michigan, and Minnesota.

DWARF BILBERRY *Vaccinium caespitosum* Michx.

FIELD MARKS. A tufted leaf-losing shrub 2 to 12 inches high; growing in rocky woods or on gravelly shores. *Leaves* short-stalked, broadest above the middle, wedge-shaped at base, blunt or broadly pointed at tip, finely toothed on margin, thin, smooth, lustrous green on both sides, ⅜ to 1½ inches long. *Flowers* white or pink, narrowly bell-shaped, solitary in leaf axils; blooming June or July. *Fruits* light blue, with whitish bloom, about ¼ inch in diameter, sweet and edible; ripening July or August.

RANGE. Labrador to Alaska; south to New England, New York, Michigan, Wisconsin, Colorado, and California.

THINLEAF BILBERRY   *Vaccinium membranaceum* Dougl.

FIELD MARKS. An erect leaf-losing shrub 1 to 4½ feet high, with peeling bark; growing in cool, moist, northern woods and thickets. *Branchlets* somewhat 4-angled. Leaves elliptic or egg-shaped, pointed at both ends, sharply and finely toothed on margin, thin in texture, bright green and smooth or nearly so on both surfaces, ¾ to 2¾ inches long. *Flowers* greenish or purplish, solitary in leaf axils; blooming June or July. *Fruits* dark purple or black, about 5/16 inch across, rather sour; ripening July to September.

RANGE. Western Ontario, northern Michigan, and southwestern South Dakota; southern Alberta and southern British Columbia south to California.

OVAL-LEAF BILBERRY   *Vaccinium ovalifolium* Sm.

FIELD MARKS. A straggling, slender, leaf-losing shrub 1 to 5 feet high; growing in cool northern woods and on peaty slopes. *Branchlets* sharply 4-angled. *Leaves* elliptical, roundish or broadly pointed at base, rounded or blunt at tip, untoothed or slightly wavy-toothed on margin, thin in texture, dull green above, pale or whitened beneath, smooth on both surfaces, 1 to 2 inches long. *Flowers* pinkish, bell-shaped, solitary in the axils of developing leaves; blooming June or July. *Fruits* blue, with a white bloom, about ⅜ inch in diameter, rather unpalatable; ripening September and October.

RANGE. Newfoundland and southeastern Labrador to western Ontario and northern Michigan; Alaska south to Idaho and Oregon.

EVERGREEN BLUEBERRY   *Vaccinium myrsinites* Lam.

FIELD MARKS. A much-branched evergreen shrub 8 inches to 2 feet high; growing in open sandy woods and pinelands. *Leaves* elliptic to egg-shaped or broadest above the middle, more or less pointed at both ends, margin untoothed or with small and low bristle-tipped teeth, thickish in texture, dark green and lustrous above, paler and sometimes slightly downy or whitened beneath, ¼ to ¾ inch long. *Flowers* white or pinkish, cylindrical bell-shaped, in umbel-like end clusters; blooming late February to April. *Fruits* bluish black, sometimes with a whitish bloom; ripening April or May.

RANGE. Coastal plain; North Carolina south to Florida.

VELVET-LEAF BLUEBERRY   *Vaccinium myrtilloides* Michx.

FIELD MARKS. A much-branched, leaf-losing shrub 8 inches to about 2 feet high; growing in cool, moist woods and swamps. *Branchlets* densely velvety with whitish hairs and warty-dotted. *Leaves* short-stalked, narrowly elliptic to oblong lance-shaped, pointed at both ends, untoothed on margin, thin in texture, green and somewhat downy above, densely downy beneath with pale hairs, ¾ to 1½ inches long. *Flowers* greenish white or pinkish, narrowly bell-shaped, in dense clusters; blooming May or June. *Fruits* blue, with a white bloom, ¼ to ⅜ inch in diameter, usually quite sour; ripening July and August.

RANGE. Newfoundland and Quebec to British Columbia; south to western New England, Pennsylvania, the Great Lakes region, northeastern Iowa, and Montana, and in the Appalachian Mountains to western Virginia and West Virginia.

Also called Canada Blueberry and Sourtop.

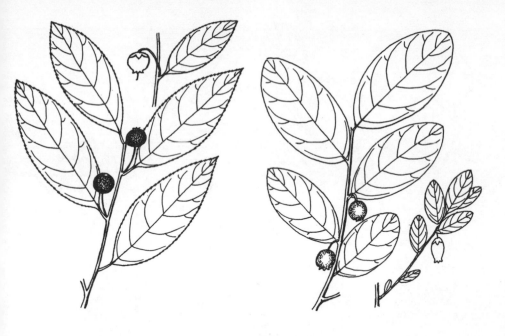

Thinleaf Bilberry

Oval-leaf Bilberry

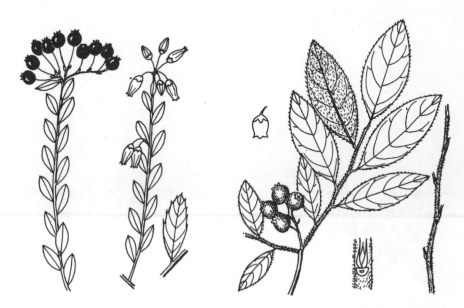

Evergreen Blueberry

Velvet-leaf Blueberry

Late Low Blueberry

Early Low Blueberry

Hairy Blueberry

Small Black Blueberry

LATE LOW BLUEBERRY *Vaccinium vacillans* Torr.

FIELD MARKS. A spreading leaf-losing shrub 8 inches to about 2 feet high; growing in dry sandy or rocky woods and clearings. *Branchlets* yellowish green, warty-dotted, somewhat angled. *Leaves* short-stalked, oval to egg-shaped or broadest above the middle, usually broadly pointed at both ends, untoothed or sometimes finely toothed on margin, smooth on both surfaces, paler and sometimes slightly whitened beneath, ½ to 2 inches long. *Flowers* greenish white or pink-tinged, cylindrical urn-shaped, clustered; blooming March to June, when leaves are partly grown. *Fruits* dark blue, usually with a whitish bloom, ¼ to ⅜ inch in diameter, sweet and juicy; ripening June to September.

RANGE. Western Nova Scotia to southern Ontario, Michigan, and northeastern Iowa; south to Georgia, Alabama, and eastern Kansas.

EARLY LOW BLUEBERRY *Vaccinium angustifolium* Ait.

FIELD MARKS. A spreading leaf-losing shrub 8 inches to about 2 feet high; growing in open rocky woods and clearings. *Branchlets* olive green to yellowish green, somewhat grooved, warty-dotted. *Leaves* short-stalked, narrowly elliptic or lance-shaped, pointed at both ends, finely and sharply toothed on margin, bright green and smooth above, paler green and sometimes whitened or downy beneath, ½ to 1½ inches long. *Flowers* white or pink-tinged, urn-shaped, clustered; blooming April to June. *Fruits* blue, with a heavy whitish bloom, or sometimes lustrous black, about ¼ inch in diameter, sweet and juicy; ripening June to August.

RANGE. Labrador to Saskatchewan; south to western Virginia, West Virginia, Indiana, Minnesota, and northeastern Iowa.

The common commercial wild blueberry of New England.

HAIRY BLUEBERRY *Vaccinium hirsutum* Buckl.

FIELD MARKS. A leaf-losing shrub 1 to 2½ feet high; growing in sandy open woods and balds in the southern Appalachians. *Branchlets* densely soft-hairy. *Leaves* elliptic or egg-shaped, usually pointed at both ends, untoothed on margin, hairy on both surfaces but paler and more densely so beneath, ½ to 2 inches long. *Flowers* cylindrical urn-shaped, greenish white or reddish-tinged, densely hairy, clustered; blooming in April or May. *Fruits* bluish black, densely hairy, ¼ inch or slightly more in diameter, sweet and juicy; ripening June or July.

RANGE. Mountains of southwestern North Carolina, western Tennessee, and northern Georgia at altitudes of 1,700 to about 5,000 feet.

SMALL BLACK BLUEBERRY *Vaccinium tenellum* Ait.

FIELD MARKS. A leaf-losing shrub with creeping underground stems and often nearly unbranched upright stems 8 inches to 2 feet high; growing in dry sandy woods and pinelands. *Leaves* broadest above the middle, wedge-shaped at base, more broadly pointed at tip, finely and rather inconspicuously toothed on margin, green and smooth above, paler and with gland-tipped hairs beneath at least when young, ½ to about 1 inch long. *Flowers* white or pink-tinged, rather narrowly cylindric, clustered; blooming March to May. *Fruits* black, about ¼ inch in diameter, rather dry but sweet; ripening June or July.

RANGE. Southeastern Virginia south to Florida and west to Mississippi.

HIGHBUSH BLUEBERRY *Vaccinium corymbosum* L.

FIELD MARKS. A leaf-losing shrub 3 to about 10 feet high; growing in low wet grounds, bogs, swamps, and moist rocky woods. *Branchlets* yellowish green to reddish, warty-dotted, often hairy in lines. *Leaves* short-stalked, elliptic to egg-shaped or broadly lance-shaped, pointed to rounded at base, pointed at tip, untoothed or sometimes with very fine or bristly teeth on margin, paler green and sometimes whitened or slightly downy beneath, 1 to about 3 inches long. *Flowers* white, greenish white, or pinkish, cylindrical urn-shaped, clustered; blooming late February to June, before the leaves or when the leaves are partly grown. *Fruits* blue or bluish black, whitened with a bloom, ¼ to nearly ½ inch in diameter, sweet and juicy; ripening June to August.
RANGE. Nova Scotia to southern Quebec and Wisconsin; south to Florida and Louisiana.
The parent of most cultivated varieties of blueberries. Most common southward in coastal plain but also present in the mountains.

BLACK HIGHBUSH BLUEBERRY *Vaccinium atrococcum* (Gray) Heller

FIELD MARKS. A leaf-losing shrub 3 to about 10 feet high; similar to the preceding species and growing in similar places. *Branchlets* densely downy. *Leaves* short-stalked, elliptic to egg-shaped, usually pointed at both ends, untoothed on margin, paler and densely downy beneath, 1 to 3 inches long, *Flowers* greenish white to yellowish green and often tinged with red, cylindrical urn-shaped, clustered; blooming late February to June, before or with the expanding leaves. *Fruits* lustrous black, about ⅜ inch in diameter, sweet and juicy; ripening June to August.
RANGE. New England, New York, and southern Ontario; south to Georgia and Arkansas.
Found southward chiefly in the coastal plain and piedmont.

ELLIOTT BLUEBERRY *Vaccinium elliottii* Chapm.

FIELD MARKS. A leaf-losing shrub 3 to about 8 feet high; growing along streams, in sandy woods, and in swamps. *Branchlets* warty-dotted, greenish, often downy. *Leaves* almost stalkless, egg-shaped to elliptic or oval, mostly rounded at base, blunt to pointed at tip, finely toothed or almost untoothed on margin, lustrous green and smooth above, duller and often somewhat downy beneath, ⅜ to about 1 inch long. *Flowers* pink or reddish, narrowly urn-shaped or vase-shaped, clustered; blooming March or April, as the leaves are expanding. *Fruits* black or bluish black, about 5/16 inch in diameter, sweet but rather dry; ripening June or July.
RANGE. Southeastern Virginia south to Florida, west to Louisiana; north in Mississippi Valley to Arkansas.

SOUTHERN MOUNTAIN-CRANBERRY *Vaccinium erythrocarpum* Michx.

FIELD MARKS. A leaf-losing shrub 1 to about 6 feet high, with spreading branches; growing in cool moist woods or bogs in the southern Appalachians. *Branchlets* downy. *Leaves* short-stalked, egg-shaped to oblong lance-shaped, rounded to broadly pointed at base, tapering to a sharp point at tip, margin finely toothed with bristle-tipped teeth, green and often slightly downy on both surfaces, 1 to about 3 inches long. *Flowers* pale red with 4 recurved corolla lobes, solitary in the axils of leaves or leaf-like bracts; blooming May to July. *Fruits* dark purplish red, about 3/16 inch in diameter, sweetish to sour or insipid; ripening August and September.
RANGE. Western Virginia and West Virginia south to northern Georgia and eastern Tennessee.
Also called Bearberry.

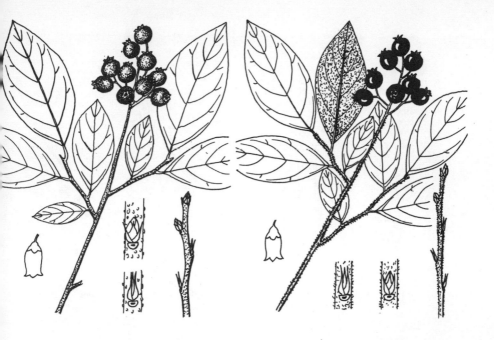

Highbush Blueberry

Black Highbush Blueberry

Elliott Blueberry

Southern Mountain-cranberry

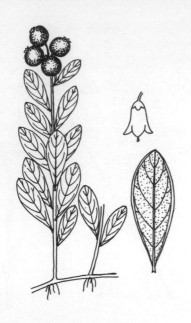

Mountain-cranberry

Creeping Blueberry

Large Cranberry

Small Cranberry

MOUNTAIN-CRANBERRY *Vaccinium vitis-idea* var. *minima* Lodd.

FIELD MARKS. An evergreen mat-forming shrub with creeping underground stems and upright branches 1 to about 6 inches high; growing in cool, moist, rocky places and bogs. *Leaves* short-stalked, oval or broadest above the middle, wedge-shaped at base, blunt or rounded at tip, margin rolled and sometimes sparingly toothed, dark green and lustrous above, pale and with minute black dots beneath, ¼ to ¾ inch long. *Flowers* white or pinkish, bell-shaped with 4 short lobes, in small end clusters; blooming June or July. *Fruits* dark red, ¼ to ⅜ inch in diameter, acid and slightly bitter but edible when cooked; ripening August and September.

RANGE. Arctic region south to Newfoundland, New England, southwestern Ontario, northern Michigan and Minnesota, Manitoba, and British Columbia.

Also called Cowberry.

CREEPING BLUEBERRY *Vaccinium crassifolium* Andr.

FIELD MARKS. A trailing evergreen shrub with slender stems up to 3 feet long from a thickened base; growing in wet peaty soils of pineland bogs. *Leaves* very short-stalked, elliptic or oval, usually broadly pointed at both ends or blunt at tip, margin thickened or slightly rolled and minutely toothed, leathery in texture, smooth, deep green above, paler green beneath, ¼ to ½ inch long. *Flowers* white or pink, globe-shaped, in small axillary clusters; blooming April or May. *Fruits* black or purplish black, lustrous, little more than ⅛ inch in diameter; ripening June or July.

RANGE. Coastal plain; southeastern Virginia south to Georgia.

In habit this plant very much resembles the cranberries.

LARGE CRANBERRY *Vaccinium macrocarpum* Ait.

FIELD MARKS. A trailing evergreen shrub with slender stems up to 3 feet long; growing in wet peaty soils and sphagnum bogs. *Leaves* very short-stalked, oblong-elliptic, roundish or blunt at both ends, margin untoothed and sometimes slightly rolled, smooth, leathery in texture, dark green and lustrous above, pale or somewhat whitened beneath, ¼ to ⅝ inch long. *Flowers* pink, with 4 recurved lobes, solitary or 2 to 4 on slender stalks in end clusters; blooming May to August. *Fruits* red, ⅜ to ¾ inch in diameter, sour; ripening August to November.

RANGE. Newfoundland to Minnesota; south to coastal plain and mountains of North Carolina, Tennessee, the region of the Great Lakes, and Arkansas.

The familiar cranberry grown commercially and sold in markets. Also called American Cranberry.

SMALL CRANBERRY *Vaccinium oxycoccus* L.

FIELD MARKS. A trailing evergreen shrub with almost threadlike stems up to 18 inches in length; growing in cold sphagnum bogs (sometimes along with the preceding species). *Leaves* very short-stalked, egg-shaped or triangular, broadly rounded or slightly heart-shaped at base, pointed at tip, margin untoothed and rolled, dark green and lustrous above, white beneath, ⅛ to rarely ½ inch long. *Flowers* similar to those of the preceding species but much smaller; blooming May to July. *Fruits* red, rarely ⅜ inch in diameter, very sour; ripening August to October.

RANGE. Labrador to Alaska; south to New Jersey, West Virginia, northern Ohio, Michigan, Wisconsin, Manitoba, Saskatchewan, and Oregon.

SAPODILLA FAMILY (Sapotaceae)

BUMELIAS (Bumelia Sw.)

Bumelias are shrubs or small trees with alternate, simple leaves which are often clustered on short lateral spurs. The branchlets are armed with short thorns and exude a milky sap when they are cut or broken. They have small, 5-parted, whitish flowers which are borne in dense clusters in the leaf axils. The fruits are berry-like in appearance but have a single large seed, surrounded by a pulp with a bittersweet taste.

BUCKTHORN BUMELIA *Bumelia lycioides* (L.) Pers.

FIELD MARKS. A leaf-losing shrub or small tree 5 to 20 feet or more high; growing in swampy woods or on stream banks, bluffs, and dunes. *Leaves* narrowly elliptic or broadest above the middle, wedge-shaped at base, short-pointed to rounded at tip, untoothed on margin, smooth or nearly so on both surfaces, 2 to 6 inches long. *Flowers* blooming June to August. *Fruits* black, oblong, about ½ inch long; ripening September or October.

RANGE. Southeastern Virginia south to Florida, west to Texas; north in Mississippi Valley to southern Indiana, Illinois, and southeastern Missouri.

Also called Southern-buckthorn and False-buckthorn.

WOOLLY BUMELIA *Bumelia lanuginosa* (Michx.) Pers.

FIELD MARKS. A shrub or small tree 10 feet or more high, with more or less persistent leaves; growing in moist to dry sandy or rocky woods and thickets. *Leaves* narrowly elliptic, wedge-shaped at base, abruptly pointed at tip, untoothed on margin, dark green and lustrous above, sparsely to densely coated with tawny to white hairs beneath, 1 to about 4 inches long. *Flowers* blooming June or July. *Fruits* black, roundish to oval, about ½ inch long; ripening about October.

RANGE. Coastal plain, southern Georgia and northern Florida west to Texas; north in Mississippi Valley to southern Illinois, central Missouri, and southeastern Kansas.

Also called Gum-elastic, Woolly-buckthorn, and Chittamwood.

SMALL BUMELIA *Bumelia smallii* R. B. Clark

A shrub similar to the preceding species but usually smaller; with leathery leaves 1 to 2½ inches long, and blue-black fruits ¼ to ⅜ inch long. It grows in low woods from Louisiana west to Texas, north to southeastern Missouri. (Not illustrated)

TOUGH BUMELIA *Bumelia tenax* (L.) Willd.

FIELD MARKS. An evergreen shrub or small tree 5 to about 20 feet high; growing in dry sandy pinelands and dunes near the coast. *Leaves* top-shaped or broadest well above the middle, wedge-shaped at base, rounded or sometimes notched at tip, untoothed on margin, lustrous green above, coated beneath with copper-colored or golden-brown silky hairs, ¾ to 2½ inches long. Flowers blooming May or June. *Fruits* black, oblong, about ½ inch long; ripening September or October.

RANGE. Coastal plain; South Carolina south to Florida.

Also called Ironwood.

NIGHTSHADE FAMILY (Solanaceae)

SALT MATRIMONY-VINE *Lycium carolinianum* Walt.

FIELD MARKS. A straggling shrub 1 to about 5 feet high, with lithe and recurving branches; growing among coastal sand dunes and about salt marshes. *Leaves* alternate, usually with smaller leaves clustered in the axils, narrow but broader toward the blunt tip, tapering to the base, fleshy in texture, 1 to 1½ inches long. *Flowers* blue or lilac purple, ½ to ¾ inch across, with 5 spreading lobes; blooming May to July. *Fruits* red, roundish egg-shaped berries, about ⅜ inch long; ripening September and October or later.

RANGE. Coastal plain; Georgia and Florida west to Texas.

Also called Christmasberry.

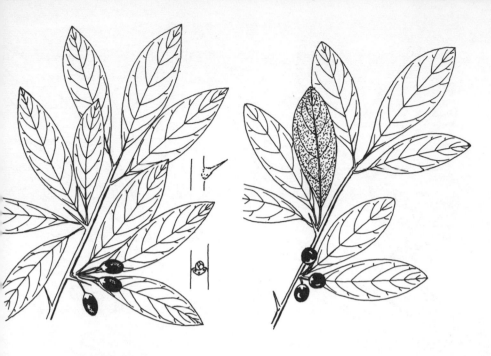

Buckthorn Bumelia

Woolly Bumelia

Tough Bumelia

Salt Matrimony-Vine

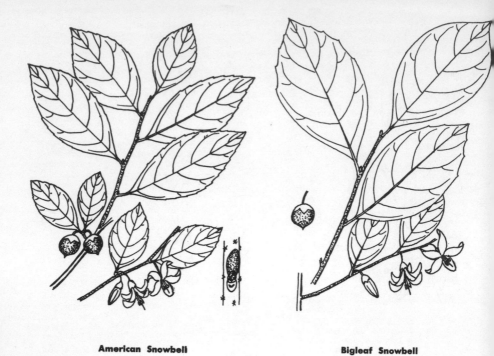

American Snowbell   Bigleaf Snowbell

Carolina Silverbell   Little Silverbell

AMERICAN SNOWBELL *Styrax americana* Lam.

FIELD MARKS. A leaf-losing shrub 3 to about 12 feet high; growing along streams and in swampy places. *Leaves* alternate, elliptic or sometimes broadest above the middle, pointed at both ends, margin untoothed or with rather widely spaced and low teeth, bright green and smooth above, paler and smooth or with scattered starry-branched hairs beneath (scaly and more densely hairy beneath in the variety *pulverulenta* [Michx.] Perkins), ¾ to 3 inches long. *Flowers* white, about ½ inch long, with 4 long and often recurved lobes, solitary or in leafy-bracted clusters of 5 to 20 in leaf axils or at ends of branchlets; blooming April to June. *Fruits* roundish, dry, 1-seeded, about ¼ inch in diameter.

RANGE. Southern Virginia to Ohio Valley region, Missouri, and Arkansas; south to Florida and Texas. Var. *pulverulenta* chiefly on Coastal Plain from Virginia and Arkansas southward.

Also called Mock-orange.

BIGLEAF SNOWBELL *Styrax grandifolia* Ait.

FIELD MARKS. A leaf-losing shrub or small tree 3 to about 12 feet high; growing in moist woods and along streams. *Leaves* alternate, broadly elliptic to oval or broadest above the middle, pointed at base, pointed or abruptly short-pointed at tip, margin untoothed or with some teeth chiefly above the middle, smooth or nearly so above, white-woolly or downy with starry-branched hairs beneath, 2 to about 7 inches long. *Flowers* similar to those of the preceding but almost 1 inch long and in fewer-flowered clusters; blooming April or May. *Fruits* roundish or oval, dry, 1-seeded, about ¼ inch in diameter.

RANGE. Southern Virginia, Tennessee, and Arkansas; south to Florida and Louisiana.

CAROLINA SILVERBELL *Halesia carolina* L.

FIELD MARKS. A leaf-losing shrub or small tree 5 to 30 feet or more high; growing in rich moist woods and along streams. *Leaves* alternate, elliptic to oblong or egg-shaped, broadly pointed to rounded at base, pointed or long-pointed at tip, finely toothed on margin, bright green and smooth or nearly so above, slightly paler and downy beneath, 2 to 5 inches long. *Flowers* white or pinkish, bell-shaped with 4 lobes, ⅓ to about 1 inch long, 2 to 5 in a cluster; blooming March to May. *Fruits* oblong-oval, dry, 4-winged, 1 to 1¾ inch long.

RANGE. Virginia and West Virginia to southern Ohio, southeastern and western Kentucky, and southern Illinois; south to northwestern Florida, Alabama, and western Tennessee. Also in Arkansas and southeastern Oklahoma.

Also called Snowdrop-tree and Opossumwood.

LITTLE SILVERBELL *Halesia parviflora* Michx.

FIELD MARKS. A leaf-losing shrub or small tree 4 to about 30 feet high; usually growing on dry sandy soils. *Leaves* alternate, elliptic or egg-shaped, pointed at base, pointed or long-pointed at tip, finely toothed on margin, smooth or nearly so above, downy at least on the veins beneath, 2 to 4 inches long. *Flowers* white, bell-shaped with 4 lobes, ¼ to ½ inch long; blooming March or April. *Fruits* club-shaped, rather narrowly 4-winged, dry, ⅝ to 1¼ inches long.

RANGE. Coastal plain; southern Georgia and northern Florida west to eastern Mississippi.

TWO-WING SILVERBELL *Halesia diptera* Ellis.

FIELD MARKS. A leaf-losing shrub or small tree 5 to about 30 feet high; growing in low woods, swamps, or along streams. *Leaves* alternate, oval to egg-shaped or broadest above the middle, broadly pointed to rounded at both ends or abruptly pointed at tip, margin with widely spaced teeth, smooth or nearly so above, usually somewhat downy on the veins beneath, 2½ to 4½ inches long. *Flowers* white, bell-shaped and deeply 4-lobed, 3 to 6 in a cluster; blooming April and May. *Fruits* oblong or broader toward the tip, broadly 2-winged and often with narrower wings or ridges between, 1½ to 2 inches long.

RANGE. Coastal plain; Georgia and northwestern Florida west to Texas; north in Mississippi Valley to central Arkansas and southeastern Oklahoma.

SWEETLEAF FAMILY (Symplocaceae)

SWEETLEAF *Symplocos tinctoria* (L.) L'Her.

FIELD MARKS. A leaf-losing or semi-evergreen shrub or small tree 5 to about 30 feet high; growing in moist rocky or sandy woods and along streams. *Leaves* alternate, oblong to narrowly elliptic, pointed at both ends, untoothed or with obscure wavy teeth on margin, thickish and somewhat leathery in texture, dark yellowish green and smooth above, paler and often slightly downy beneath, 2 to 6 inches long. *Flowers* small, creamy white or pale yellow, with very conspicuous stamens, fragrant, in showy clusters along the branchlets; blooming March to May, before the leaves appear. *Fruits* elliptic, orange brown, dry, 1-seeded, about ½ inch long; maturing August or September.

Also called Horse-sugar, both horses and cattle relishing the sweetish-tasting leaves. Sometimes called Yellowwood, as it yields a yellow dye.

RANGE. Delaware, North Carolina, Tennessee, and southern Arkansas; south to northern Florida and eastern Texas.

OLIVE FAMILY (Oleaceae)

SWAMP-PRIVET *Foresteria acuminata* (Michx.) Poir.

FIELD MARKS. A leaf-losing shrub or small tree 4 to (rarely) 25 feet high; growing in river swamps, borders of ponds, and along streams. *Leaves* opposite, slender-stalked, oblong egg-shaped or broadly lance-shaped, tapering to a point at both ends, margin usually finely toothed above the middle, thin in texture, light green and smooth on both surfaces, 1¼ to about 4 inches long. *Flowers* very small, greenish or yellowish, in dense clusters; blooming March to May. *Fruits* dark purple, narrowly ellipsoid and pointed at both ends, 1-seeded, with a rather thin flesh, about ½ inch long; ripening May to July.

RANGE. South Carolina to southern Indiana, Illinois and Missouri, and southeastern Kansas; south to Florida and Texas.

UPLAND SWAMP-PRIVET *Foresteria ligustrina* (Michx.) Poir.

FIELD MARKS. A leaf-losing shrub 3 to about 10 feet high; growing on rocky slopes and bluffs and the sandy banks of streams. *Branchlets* smooth to downy. *Leaves* opposite, short-stalked, elliptic to oblong or broadest above the middle, wedge-shaped at base, bluntly pointed at tip, finely and inconspicuously toothed on margin, light green and smooth above, slightly paler and more or less downy beneath, ⅜ to 1½ inches long. *Flowers* very small, greenish or yellowish, clustered; blooming April or May. *Fruits* dark purple, oval or egg-shaped, stalkless, 1-seeded and fleshy, about ¼ inch long; ripening June or July.

RANGE. Kentucky and Tennessee south to Florida and Alabama.

252

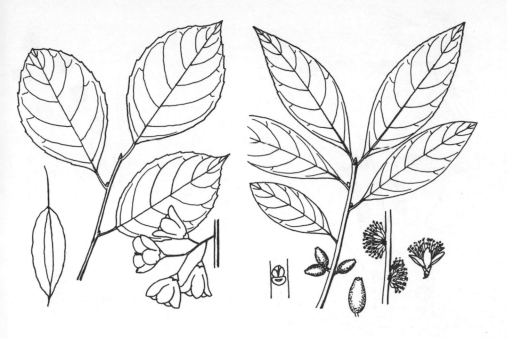

Two-wing Silverbell

Sweetleaf

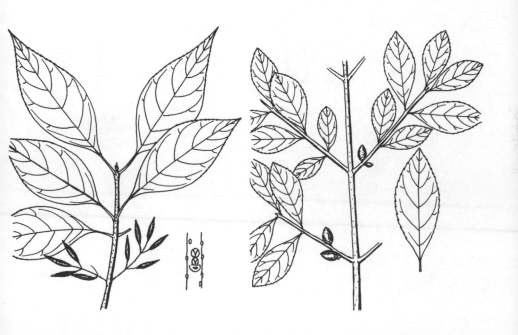

Swamp-privet

Upland Swamp-privet

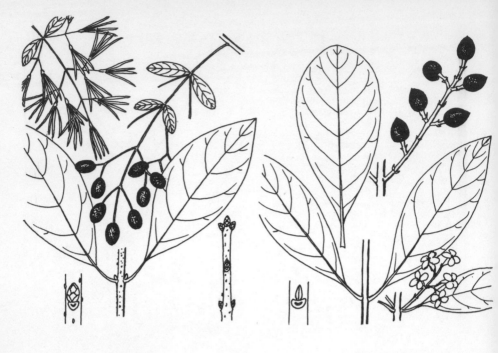

Fringetree

Devilwood

Yellow Jessamine

Beautyberry

FRINGETREE *Chionanthus virginica* L.

FIELD MARKS. A leaf-losing shrub or small tree to 20 or rarely 40 feet high; growing in woods, savannahs, and along streams. *Leaves* opposite, elliptic or broadest above the middle, pointed at both ends, untoothed on margin, thickish, smooth or nearly so and paler beneath, 3 to 8 inches long. *Flowers* white, petals 4 and ribbon-like, fragrant, ¾ to 1 inch long, in rather large and drooping clusters; blooming April or May. *Fruits* oval-shaped, olive-like, 1-seeded, bluish black, usually with a whitish bloom, ⅜ to ¾ inch long; ripening July to September.

RANGE. New Jersey to southern Ohio and Missouri, and southeastern Oklahoma; south to Florida and Texas.

Also called Flowering-ash, Old-man's beard, and Grancy-graybeard.

DEVILWOOD *Osmanthus americanus* (L.) Gray

FIELD MARKS. An evergreen shrub or small tree; growing in woods and borders of coastal swamps. *Leaves* opposite, narrowly elliptic or top-shaped, pointed at base, pointed to rounded at tip, untoothed on margin, leathery, lustrous above, paler beneath, smooth, 2½ to 4½ inches long. *Flowers* small, creamy white, in axillary clusters; blooming April or May. *Fruits* egg-shaped, olive-like, 1-seeded, dark bluish purple, ½ to ¾ inch long; ripening August to October.

RANGE. Coastal plain; Virginia south to Florida, west to Louisiana.

Also called Wild-olive.

LOGANIA FAMILY (Loganiaceae)

YELLOW JESSAMINE *Gelsemium sempervirens* (L.) Ait. f.

FIELD MARKS. A smooth, slender-stemmed, evergreen, twining vine; growing in borders of woods, swamps, and wayside thickets. *Leaves* opposite, lance-shaped or narrowly egg-shaped, broadly pointed to rounded at base, taper-pointed at tip, untoothed on margin, slightly leathery, lustrous above, paler beneath, smooth, 1½ to 3 inches long. *Flowers* bright yellow, trumpet-shaped, 5-lobed, very fragrant, about 1½ inches long, 1 to 3 on short stalks in leaf axils; blooming late February to May. *Fruits* oblong egg-shaped, pale-brown capsules ½ to ¾ inch long; containing flattened, winged seeds.

RANGE. Coastal plain and piedmont; Virginia south to Florida, west to Texas; north in Mississippi Valley to Arkansas.

Also called Carolina- or False-jessamine. Roots used medicinally. Children have been poisoned by sucking nectar from the flowers.

SCENTLESS YELLOW-JESSAMINE *Gelsemium rankinii* Small

A vine closely resembling the preceding, but the odorless flowers have pointed rather than blunt calyx lobes. The capsules are longer-beaked and seeds are wingless. Less common; southeastern North Carolina to Florida. (Not illustrated)

VERVAIN FAMILY (Verbenaceae)

BEAUTYBERRY *Callicarpa americana* L.

FIELD MARKS. A leaf-losing shrub 3 to about 6 feet high; usually growing in moist sandy or rocky woods. *Branchlets* ashy gray, hairy or roughish. *Leaves* opposite, elliptic to oval or egg-shaped, tapering to a point at both ends, sharply toothed on margin, roughish-hairy above, paler and woolly-hairy beneath, 3 to 6 inches long. *Flowers* small, bluish to lavender pink, funnel-shaped, clustered in leaf axils; blooming May to July. *Fruits* berry-like, violet or magenta purple, juicy, about ⅛ inch in diameter, in dense axillary clusters; ripening August to October.

RANGE. Maryland to Tennesee, Arkansas, and Oklahoma; south to Florida and Texas.

Also called French-mulberry. Handsome as an ornamental shrub.

DOGBANE FAMILY (Apocynaceae)

TRACHELOSPERMUM   *Trachelospermum difforme* (Walt.) Gray

FIELD MARKS. A slender, twining, high-climbing, soft-woody vine; growing in low moist woods, swamps, and along streams. *Leaves* opposite, oval to egg-shaped or lance-shaped, pointed at tip, usually pointed at base, untoothed on margin, thin in texture, 1½ to 3½ inches long. *Flowers* funnel-shaped, pale greenish yellow or cream-colored, about ½ inch long, in axillary or end clusters; blooming May to August. *Fruits* paired slender pods 5 to 9 inches long, containing a large number of small seeds with silky hairs at one end; maturing July to September.

RANGE. Delaware and southern Indiana and Illinois to Missouri and Oklahoma; south to Florida and Texas.

MINT FAMILY (Labiatae)

CONRADINA   *Conradina canescens* (T. & G.) Gray

FIELD MARKS. An evergreen shrub 1 to 1½ feet high, with numerous stiff and ascending branches; growing in dry sandy pinelands and among coastal sand dunes. *Leaves,* commonly with small leaves in the axils, narrow and somewhat club-shaped, the margins untoothed and tightly rolled, rounded or blunt at tip, very finely downy and grayish green in color, 3/16 to about ⅜ inch long. *Flowers* pale bluish, about ⅜ inch long, in axils of the upper leaves; blooming March to May. *Fruits* small, hard, dry nutlets in groups of 4 within the hairy calyx.

RANGE. Coastal plain; northwestern Florida and Alabama.

GEORGIA BASIL   *Satureja georgiana* (Harper) Ahles

FIELD MARKS. An aromatic shrub 8 inches to 2 feet high; growing in rocky or sandy woods and on stream banks. *Branchlets* erect, somewhat downy. *Leaves* opposite, elliptic, more or less pointed at both ends, shallowly toothed on margin, smooth or nearly so on both surfaces, paler beneath, ⅜ to about 1 inch long, commonly with smaller leaves clustered in the axils. *Flowers* white or pink, purple-spotted, ⅜ to ½ inch long, in axillary clusters; blooming July to October. *Fruits* small, hard, dry nutlets in groups of 4; within the persistent calyx.

RANGE. Piedmont and coastal plain; North Carolina south to Florida, west to Mississippi.

RED BASIL   *Satureja coccinea* Nutt.

FIELD MARKS. An evergreen, sparingly branched shrub 1 to 3 feet high; growing in sandy or rocky open woods and on sandhills. *Branchlets* slender, erect. *Leaves* narrowly top-shaped or elliptic, wedge-shaped at base, blunt or broadly pointed at tip, untoothed on margin, smooth or nearly so on both surfaces, ¼ to ¾ inch long. *Flowers* bright red, 1 to 1½ inches long, in axillary clusters; blooming May to September, or all year southward. *Fruits* small, hard, dry nutlets in groups of 4; within the persistent calyx.

RANGE. Coastal plain; southern Georgia and Alabama, south into Florida.

Trachelospermum

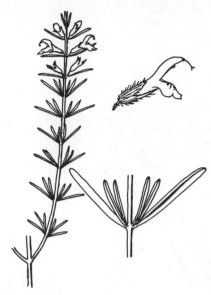

Conradina

Georgia Basil

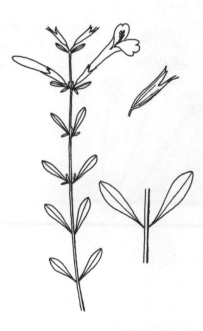

Red Basil

Cross-vine   **Trumpet-creeper**

Buttonbush   **Pinckneya**

BIGNONIA FAMILY (Bignoniaceae)

CROSS-VINE *Bignonia capreolata* L.

FIELD MARKS. A high-climbing vine which is evergreen southward; growing in moist woods and swamps. *Branchlets* show cross-shaped pith in cross-section. *Leaves* opposite, divided into 2 leaflets with a branched tendril between them; leaflets stalked, oblong-egg-shaped, heart-shaped at base, pointed at tip, untoothed on margin, smooth, paler beneath, 2 to 5 inches long. *Flowers* trumpet-shaped, orange red outside and yellow within, 5-lobed, 1½ to 2½ inches long, 2 to 5 in axillary clusters; blooming April to June. *Fruits* cylindrical, somewhat flattened, 2-celled capsules 4 to 6 inches long, containing many winged and flattened seeds; maturing July or August.

RANGE. Maryland to southern Ohio and Illinois, and Missouri; south to Florida and Louisiana.

TRUMPET-CREEPER *Campsis radicans* (L.) Seem

FIELD MARKS. A leaf-losing vine climbing by means of aerial rootlets in 2 short rows at the nodes; growing in moist woods, thickets, or along fence rows. *Leaves* opposite, compound, 8 to 15 inches long; the 9 to 11 leaflets almost stalkless, elliptic to oblong egg-shaped, pointed at both ends, coarsely and sharply toothed on margin, smooth above, slightly paler and often downy on the veins beneath, 1½ to 3 inches long. *Flowers* reddish orange, trumpet-shaped, 5-lobed, 2½ to 3½ inches long, in showy end clusters; blooming June to September. *Fruits* cylindrical, somewhat flattened, 2-ridged capsules 4 to 8 inches long, containing many winged and flattened seeds; maturing September or October.

RANGE. Connecticut and southeastern Pennsylvania to West Virginia, Kentucky, southern Illinois, and Iowa; south to Florida and Texas.

Also called Cow-itch, as the plant causes a severe skin irritation in some people. Often cultivated as an ornamental and sometimes escaping northward.

MADDER FAMILY (Rubiaceae)

BUTTONBUSH *Cephalanthus occidentalis* L.

FIELD MARKS. A leaf-losing shrub 3 to 10 or rarely 20 feet high; growing in swamps, shallow ponds, and along streams. *Leaves* opposite or in 3's, elliptic to egg-shaped or lance-shaped, pointed at both ends, untoothed on margin, often lustrous above, paler and sometimes downy beneath, 3 to 6 inches long. *Flowers* small, white, tubular, 5-lobed, fragrant, clustered in long-stalked ball-shaped heads 1 to 1½ inches across; blooming May to August. *Fruits* small, top-shaped, 2-seeded capsules in tight ball-shaped heads.

RANGE. Nova Scotia to southern Ontario, Minnesota, and California; south to Florida, Texas, and Mexico.

Also called Honeyballs. Often cultivated as an ornamental shrub.

PINCKNEYA *Pinckneya pubens* Michx.

FIELD MARKS. A leaf-losing shrub or small tree 5 to rarely 25 feet high; growing in sandy swamps or along streams. *Branchlets* more or less tawny- or rusty-hairy. *Leaves* opposite, elliptic to egg-shaped, pointed to roundish at base, pointed at tip, untoothed on margin, somewhat hairy above, paler and more densely hairy beneath, 5 to 8 inches long. *Flowers* tubular, greenish yellow spotted with red, 5-lobed; with 1 or 2 calyx lobes expanded into a broad pink to whitish, petal-like blade; borne in large and showy end clusters; blooming in May. *Fruits* roundish capsules about ¾ inch in diameter, containing many small seeds with wings.

RANGE. Coastal plain; southeastern South Carolina south to Florida.

Also called Georgia-bark and Fevertree. The bark was used by early settlers for the treatment of malaria.

PARTRIDGEBERRY   *Mitchella repens* L.

FIELD MARKS. A low evergreen plant with slightly woody, slender, creeping or trailing stems often rooting at the nodes; growing in moist to fairly dry woodlands. *Leaves* opposite, stalked, oval to broadly egg-shaped or roundish, rounded or heart-shaped at base, roundish or blunt at tip, untoothed on margin, smooth, lustrous above, paler beneath, ¼ to ¾ inch long and wide. *Flowers* funnel-shaped, 4-lobed, white (pinkish in bud), fragrant, borne in pairs at ends of branchlets; blooming April to June. *Fruits* berry-like bright red, about ¼ inch in diameter, partially joined together, edible; ripening August or September, often persisting until the following spring.
RANGE. Southwestern Newfoundland and southern Quebec to Ontario and Minnesota, south to Florida and Texas.
Also called Twinberry.

HONEYSUCKLE FAMILY (Caprifoliaceae)

BUSH-HONEYSUCKLES (Diervilla Mill.)

Bush-honeysuckles are rather low leaf-losing shrubs with opposite, simple leaves having toothed margins. Their flowers have yellow and tubular corollas with 5 short and spreading lobes at the summit. They are arranged in small clusters either at the tips of branchlets or in the axils of the uppermost leaves. The fruits are narrowly oblong or egg-shaped capsules, each ending in a beak with the remains of the 5 spreading calyx lobes at the tip. They are close relatives of the weigelias, commonly grown as ornamental shrubs.

NORTHERN BUSH-HONEYSUCKLE   *Diervilla lonicera* Mill.

FIELD MARKS. A bushy-branched shrub 1 to about 3 feet high; growing in dry, rocky, open woodlands and in wayside thickets. *Branchlets* nearly round with a hairy-lined ridge running down from a line connecting the bases of the leafstalks. *Leaves* obviously stalked, egg-shaped or lance-shaped, rounded or broadly pointed at base, long-pointed at tip, finely and sharply toothed and hairy-fringed on margin, smooth above, paler and sometimes downy on the veins beneath, 1½ to 5 inches long. *Flowers* pale yellow, usually 3 in a cluster; blooming June to August. Fruits slender, about ½ inch long.
RANGE. Newfoundland to Manitoba; south to Delaware, western North Carolina, Ohio, and Iowa.

SOUTHERN BUSH-HONEYSUCKLE   *Diervilla sessilifolia* Buckl.

FIELD MARKS. A bushy-branched shrub 1½ to 5 feet high; growing in moist rocky places and bogs in the southern Appalachians. *Branchlets* prominently 4-angled and with hairy lines. *Leaves* stalkless or nearly so, egg-shaped to broadly lance-shaped, rounded to somewhat heart-shaped at base, long-pointed at tip, sharply toothed and hairy-fringed on margin, smooth above, sometimes slightly downy beneath, 2 to 6 inches long. *Flowers* sulfur-yellow, in 3- to 7-flowered clusters; blooming June to August. *Fruits* oblong, ⅝ to ¾ inch long.
RANGE. Western Virginia and eastern Tennessee, south to northwestern Georgia and northern Alabama.

HAIRY BUSH-HONEYSUCKLE   *Diervilla rivularis* Gatt.

FIELD MARKS. A shrub 2 to about 4 feet high; growing in damp rocky woods, or on banks and cliffs in the southern Appalachians. *Branchlets* roundish, densely grayish-downy. *Leaves* short-stalked or the uppermost stalkless, egg-shaped to elliptic or lance-shaped, roundish or somewhat heart-shaped at base, long-pointed at tip, sharply and finely toothed on margin, somewhat hairy above, densely downy beneath, 1½ to about 4 inches long. *Flowers* pale yellow or greenish yellow, few to many in a cluster; blooming June to August. *Fruits* oblong, ¼ inch or slightly longer.
RANGE. Western North Carolina and eastern Tennessee, south to northwestern Georgia and northern Alabama.

Partridgeberry

Northern Bush-Honeysuckle

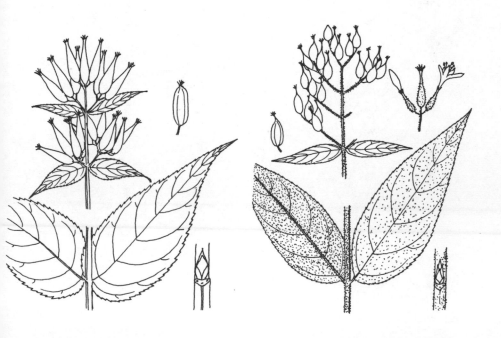

Southern Bush-Honeysuckle

Hairy Bush-Honeysuckle

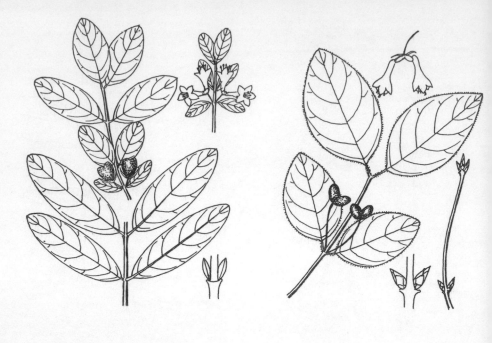

Mountain Fly Honeysuckle

American Fly Honeysuckle

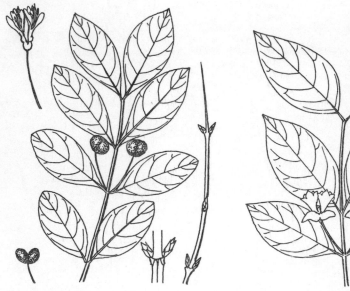

Swamp Fly Honeysuckle

Involucred Fly Honeysuckle

HONEYSUCKLES (Lonicera L.)

(Key Appendix O)

Honeysuckles are erect shrubs or often vines with simple, opposite, untoothed leaves. The flowers have tubular corollas, 5-lobed at the summit or sometimes 2-lipped; borne either in axillary pairs or in end clusters. The fruits are juicy few-seeded berries which are eaten by many kinds of wild birds. The introduced Japanese Honeysuckle (*Lonicera japonica* Thunb.) often escapes cultivation and is a pernicious weed in the southeastern states.

MOUNTAIN FLY HONEYSUCKLE *Lonicera villosa* (Michx.) R. & S.

FIELD MARKS. A leaf-losing shrub 1 to about 3 feet high, with ascending branches and shredding bark; growing in cold, moist, rocky woods or bogs. *Branchlets* may be hairy or smooth. *Leaves* short-stalked, elliptic to narrowly oblong, mostly roundish at both ends, margin untoothed but often hairy-fringed, usually hairy but sometimes quite smooth, veiny in appearance, pale or somewhat whitened beneath, ¾ to 1½ inches long. *Flowers* pale yellow, bell-shaped, 5-lobed, paired on axillary stalks less than ¼ inch long; blooming May or June. *Fruits* blue or bluish black, oval, 2-eyed berries about ¼ inch in diameter; ripening June to August.

RANGE. Newfoundland and southern Labrador to Manitoba; south to New England, northern Pennsylvania, Michigan, and Minnesota.

Also known as Blue Honeysuckle. The fruits are edible.

AMERICAN FLY HONEYSUCKLE *Lonicera canadensis* Marsh.

FIELD MARKS. A leaf-losing shrub 2 to 4 feet high; growing in cool, moist woodlands. *Branchlets* smooth, flexible, spreading. *Leaves* egg-shaped, rounded or heart-shaped at base, broadly pointed or blunt at tip, margin untoothed but hairy-fringed, smooth or nearly so on both surfaces, 1 to 3½ inches long. *Flowers* greenish yellow, funnel-shaped, 5-lobed, paired on long axillary stalks; blooming April to June. *Fruits* bright red, egg-shaped, paired but distinct berries about ¼ inch long; ripening July to September.

RANGE. Nova Scotia to Saskatchewan; south to northern New Jersey, northern Georgia, Indiana, and northeastern Iowa.

SWAMP FLY HONEYSUCKLE *Lonicera oblongifolia* (Goldie) Hook.

FIELD MARKS. A bushy leaf-losing shrub 2 to 5 feet high; growing in cold swamps and bogs. *Branchlets* stiff, ascending, smooth. *Leaves* short-stalked, oblong or elliptic, pointed at base, pointed or blunt at tip, untoothed on margin, paler beneath and smooth or nearly so on both surfaces, ¾ to 3 inches long. *Flowers* creamy white often tinged with purple, 2-lipped, paired on long axillary stalks; blooming May to July. *Fruits* red or purplish, egg-shaped berries about ¼ inch long, often somewhat united; ripening July to September.

RANGE. Southeastern Quebec to Manitoba; south to Maine, northwestern Pennsylvania, northern Ohio, Michigan, Wisconsin, and Minnesota.

INVOLUCRED FLY HONEYSUCKLE *Lonicera involucrata* (Richards.) Banks

FIELD MARKS. A leaf-losing shrub 3 to 10 feet high; growing in cool woods or along streams. *Branchlets* slightly 4-angled or 4-lined, smooth or downy. *Leaves* elliptic or oblong egg-shaped, pointed or rounded at base, pointed at tip, untoothed on margin, smooth or nearly so, 2 to 5 inches long. *Flowers* yellow, funnel-shaped, 5-lobed, sticky-hairy, paired on long stalks and with large leaflike bracts at base; blooming June or July. *Fruits* roundish or oval, blackish berries, paired on long axillary stalks and distinct; ripening August or September.

RANGE. New Brunswick to British Columbia and Alaska; south to western Ontario, Michigan, Utah, and California.

263

SMOOTH HONEYSUCKLE *Lonicera dioica* L.

FIELD MARKS. A somewhat twining to sprawling or reclining, leaf-losing shrub with stems 3 to 10 feet long. *Leaves* stalkless or short-stalked, oblong or oval, more or less pointed at base, rounded or bluntly pointed at tip, whitened and smooth or finely downy beneath, 1½ to 3½ inches long; at least the uppermost pair united at the base to form an oblong or rhombic disk. *Flowers* greenish yellow, often purplish-tinged, 2-lipped, the tube with a prominent swelling at the base, ½ to ¾ inch long, in 1 to 3 whorls in a nearly stalkless end cluster; blooming May to August. *Fruits* salmon-red, roundish, about ¼ inch in diameter; ripening July to September.

RANGE. Southwestern Maine to western Quebec and British Columbia; south to western North Carolina, Tennessee, Missouri, and Kansas.

Also called Glaucous Honeysuckle.

GRAPE HONEYSUCKLE *Lonicera prolifera* (Kirchn.) Rehd.

FIELD MARKS. A somewhat twining to almost bushy leaf-losing shrub, with stems 6 to 12 feet long; growing in rocky woods or along streams. *Leaves* stalkless or short-stalked, elliptic to oval or oblong, sometimes broadest above the middle, narrowed to a pointed base, blunt or broadly pointed at tip, untoothed on margin, dark green and slightly whitened above, very much whitened and more or less downy beneath, 2 to 3½ inches long; the upper pair united at base to form a roundish disk, 2 or 3 other pairs below it often united at base. *Flowers* pale yellow, 2-lipped, the tube scarcely swollen at the base, 1 to 1¼ inches long, in 1 to 4 whorls in a nearly stalkless end cluster; blooming May to July. *Fruits* coral red, roundish, about ¼ inch in diameter; ripening July to October.

RANGE. Southern Ontario to southeastern Manitoba; south to Tennessee, Arkansas, and eastern Kansas.

HAIRY HONEYSUCKLE *Lonicera hirsuta* Eat.

FIELD MARKS. A twining and often high-climbing leaf-losing shrub; growing in woods and thickets. *Branchlets* rough-hairy. *Leaves* stalked, oval or egg-shaped, untoothed but hairy-fringed on margin, roundish at base, bluntly or broadly pointed at tip, upper surface with some appressed hairs, lower surface grayish green and densely downy, 2 to 4 inches long; uppermost 1 or 2 pairs united at the base to form a roundish to oval or rhombic disk with pointed ends. *Flowers* orange yellow, sticky-hairy, 2-lipped, ¾ to 1 inch long, in a stalked or stalkless end cluster; blooming in July. *Fruits* red, roundish, about ¼ inch in diameter; ripening in September.

RANGE. Western Quebec to Saskatchewan; south to Pennsylvania, Ohio, Michigan, Minnesota, and Nebraska.

YELLOW HONEYSUCKLE *Lonicera flava* Sims

FIELD MARKS. A somewhat twining or reclining leaf-losing shrub; growing on rocky wooded slopes and bluffs. *Branches* smooth. *Leaves* short-stalked, oval to egg-shaped or broadly elliptic, roundish or abruptly pointed at base, broadly pointed or blunt at tip, bright green above, grayish green beneath, smooth on both surfaces, 1½ to 3½ inches long; the uppermost 1 or 2 pairs united at the base to form an oval or roundish disk. *Flowers* yellow to orange yellow, 2-lipped, fragrant, an inch or slightly longer, in a crowded and stalked end cluster; blooming April and May. *Fruits* red, roundish, about ¼ inch in diameter; ripening July and August.

RANGE. Southwestern North Carolina, northwestern South Carolina, and southeastern Tennessee; south to northern parts of Georgia and Alabama; also in the Ozark region of Arkansas, Missouri, and Oklahoma.

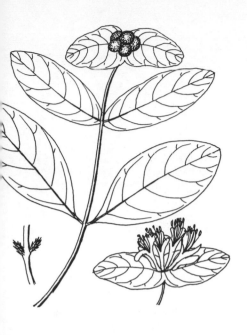

Smooth Honeysuckle

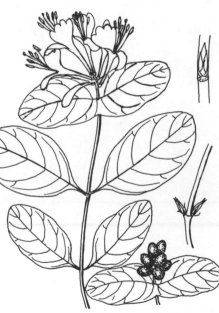

Grape Honeysuckle

Hairy Honeysuckle

Yellow Honeysuckle

Trumpet Honeysuckle

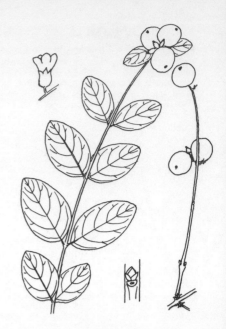

Snowberry

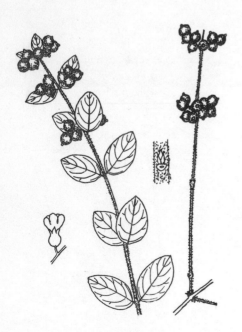

Coralberry

Wolfberry

TRUMPET HONEYSUCKLE   *Lonicera sempervirens* L.

FIELD MARKS. A twining and sometimes high-climbing, leaf-losing or (southward) evergreen shrub; growing in woodlands, thickets, and along fencerows. *Leaves* oval to egg-shaped or narrowly elliptic, short-stalked, pointed to roundish at base, rounded to bluntly pointed at tip, untoothed on margin, somewhat leathery in texture, dark green and smooth above, whitened and smooth or somewhat downy beneath, 1½ to 3½ inches long; the uppermost 1 or 2 pairs united at the base to form an oval-shaped or roundish disk. *Flowers* narrowly trumpet-shaped with 5 nearly equal lobes at summit, bright red outside, yellow within, 1½ to 2 inches long, in several whorls on an end stalk; blooming March to June or later. *Fruits* bright red, egg-shaped, about ¼ inch in diameter; ripening July to October.

RANGE. Southern Maine to New York, Ohio, Iowa, and Nebraska; south to Florida and Texas.

Also called Coral Honeysuckle. Often cultivated and frequently escaping.

SNOWBERRY   *Symphoricarpos albus* (L.) Blake

FIELD MARKS. A finely branched leaf-losing shrub 1 to about 5 feet high; growing on dry, rocky, wooded slopes and banks. *Branchlets* very slender, smooth or slightly hairy. *Leaves* opposite, short-stalked, oblong-elliptic to roundish, rounded or bluntly pointed at both ends, untoothed or somewhat wavy or margin (sometimes lobed on vigorous shoots), thin in texture, green on both surfaces, smooth above and smooth or slightly downy beneath, ¾ to 2 inches long. *Flowers* pink, about ¼ inch long, corolla 5-lobed, in leaf axils or end clusters; blooming May to July. *Fruits* roundish, white berries ¼ to ½ inch in diameter; ripening August to October.

RANGE. Eastern Quebec to British Columbia; south to Massachusetts, western Virginia, Michigan, Wisconsin, Nebraska, and Colorado.

Often cultivated as an ornamental shrub.

CORALBERRY   *Symphoricarpos orbiculatus* Moench.

FIELD MARKS. A finely branched leaf-losing shrub 2 to about 5 feet high; growing in low woods or dry, rocky, wooded slopes. *Branchlets* very slender, usually finely downy. *Leaves* opposite, short-stalked, egg-shaped to roundish, rounded or bluntly pointed at both ends, untoothed but often wavy on margin, dull green and smooth or nearly so above, paler and finely downy beneath, ½ to 2 inches long. *Flowers* pinkish, about 3/16 inch long, corolla 5-lobed, in short but dense clusters in the leaf axils; blooming July to September. *Fruits* roundish or slightly egg-shaped, purplish- to coral-red berries, about 3/16 inch in diameter; ripening September to November and persisting.

RANGE. Pennsylvania to Ohio, Illinois, Minnesota, South Dakota, and Colorado; south to northern Georgia, Alabama, and Mississippi.

Commonly cultivated as an ornamental and frequently escaping. Also called Indian-currant.

WOLFBERRY   *Symphoricarpos occidentalis* Hook.

FIELD MARKS. A bushy-branched, leaf-losing shrub 1 to about 3 feet high, spreading freely from the roots and often forming dense colonies; growing in dry open woods and on prairies. *Branchlets* slender, often minutely downy. *Leaves* opposite, short-stalked, egg-shaped, rounded to somewhat pointed at both ends, untoothed or sometimes lobed on margin, thickish in texture, dull green and often sparingly hairy above, paler and more or less downy beneath, 1 to 4 inches long. *Flowers* pinkish, stalkless, about 5/16 inch long, corolla 5-lobed, in dense axillary or end clusters; blooming June or July. *Fruits* roundish, dull-white berries about ⅜ inch in diameter, soon becoming blackish; ripening August or September.

RANGE. Ontario to British Columbia; south to northern Illinois, Missouri, Kansas, and New Mexico.

Locally escaping from cultivation eastward.

267

VIBURNUMS (Viburnum L.)

(Key Appendix P)

Viburnums are shrubs or small trees with opposite, simple leaves. The numerous small white or pinkish flowers are perfect and have a 5-lobed, short-tubed corolla. They are arranged in more or less flat-topped end clusters. The fruits are drupes with a large bony-covered seed surrounded by pulpy flesh. Most species are desirable ornamental plants, and the fruits provide food for wildlife.

HOBBLEBUSH *Viburnum alnifolium* Marsh.

FIELD MARKS. A leaf-losing shrub 3 to 10 feet high, the forked branches often bending over and rooting at the tip; growing in cool, moist, rocky woods or along streams. *Branchlets* and large naked end buds densely coated with cinnamon-colored, starry-branched hairs. *Leaves* roundish or heart-shaped, broadly pointed at tip, finely toothed on margin, veiny, becoming smooth or nearly so above but remaining rusty-hairy on the veins beneath, 4 to about 7 inches long. *Flowers* of 2 kinds; the marginal ones about ½ inch across and sterile; blooming April to June. *Fruits* egg-shaped, bright red becoming purplish black, about ⅜ inch long; ripening July to September.

RANGE. New Brunswick to Ontario; south to northern New Jersey, Pennsylvania, Ohio, and Michigan, and in the mountains to northern Georgia.

Also called Witch-hobble.

NORTHERN WITHEROD *Viburnum cassinoides* L.

FIELD MARKS. A leaf-losing shrub 3 to 8 feet high; growing in cool, moist, usually rocky woods and swamps. *Branchlets* slender, dull, rather flexible. *Leaves* narrowly egg-shaped to oblong-elliptic, pointed to roundish at base, pointed to blunt at tip, sometimes obscurely toothed on margin, dull above, paler and sometimes rusty-scurfy on midrib beneath, 1½ to 4 inches long. *Flowers* all alike, the cluster on a distinct *stalk;* blooming May or June. *Fruits* roundish or slightly oval, bluish black, whitened with a bloom, about 5/16 inch long; ripening August to October.

RANGE. Newfoundland to Ontario; south to Delaware, Maryland, northern Georgia, and Alabama, and the region of the Great Lakes.

Also called Wild-raisin.

SOUTHERN WITHEROD *Viburnum nudum* L.

FIELD MARKS. A leaf-losing shrub 5 to 15 feet high; growing in wet woods, swamps, and bogs. Similar to the preceding species. *Branchlets* rather lustrous. *Leaves* lustrous on the upper surface, paler and usually rusty-scurfy on midrib and veins beneath. *Flowers* all alike, the cluster on a stalk as long as or longer than its several branches; blooming April or May.

RANGE. Connecticut and southeastern Pennsylvania to Kentucky and Arkansas; south to Florida and Texas.

SWEET VIBURNUM *Viburnum lentago* L.

FIELD MARKS. A leaf-losing shrub or small tree 5 to 15 (rarely 30) feet high; growing in moist woods, thickets, and borders of swamps. *Branchlets* long, slender, flexible. *Leaves* oval or egg-shaped, rounded to broadly pointed at base, abruptly long-pointed at tip, finely and sharply toothed on margin, smooth, paler beneath, 2 to 4 inches long; leafstalks ½ to 1 inch long, prominenly winged. *Flowers* all alike, the cluster stalkless or nearly so; blooming May or June. *Fruits* oval-shaped, bluish black, whitened with a bloom, about ½ inch long; ripening September and October.

RANGE. New England and Quebec to Manitoba; south to New Jersey, West Virginia, Ohio, Missouri, and Colorado.

Also called Nannyberry and Sheepberry. The wood has a rank odor.

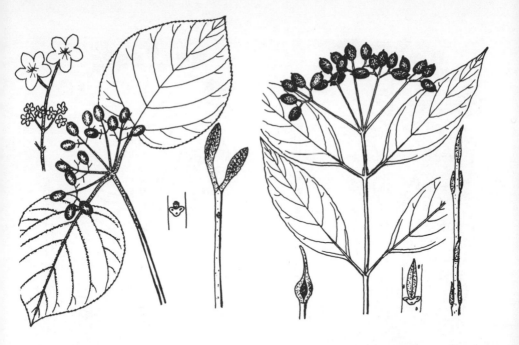

Hobblebush

Northern Witherod

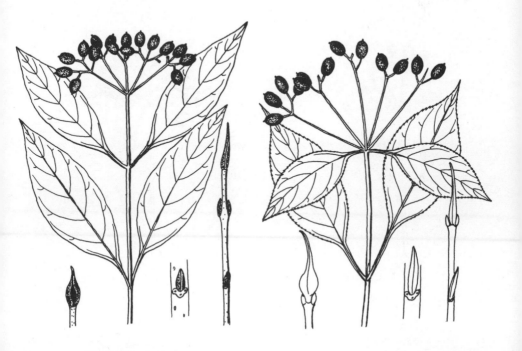

Southern Witherod

Sweet Viburnum

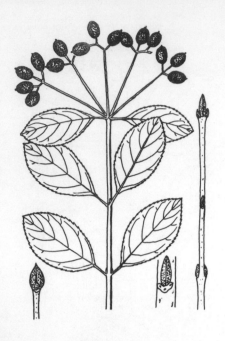

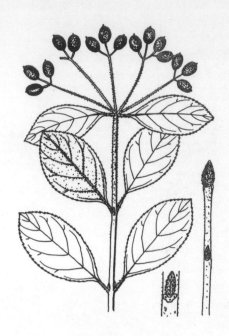

Black Haw

Rusty Black Haw

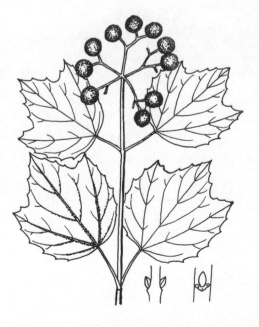

Small-leaf Viburnum

Squashberry

BLACK HAW *Viburnum prunifolium* L.

FIELD MARKS. A leaf-losing shrub or small tree 5 to about 15 feet high; growing chiefly in upland woods or thickets. *Branchlets* slender, rather stiff and spiky. *Leaves* elliptic to oval or egg-shaped, broadly pointed or roundish at base, blunt to broadly pointed at tip, finely and sharply toothed on margin, dull green above, paler beneath, smooth on both surfaces, 1 to 3 inches long; leafstalks grooved but not winged, ⅜ to ⅝ inch long. *Flowers* all alike, the cluster stalkless or nearly so; blooming April or May. *Fruits* oval-shaped, bluish black, sometimes with a slight whitish bloom, about ⅜ inch long, sweet and edible; ripening September or October.

RANGE. Connecticut to southern Michigan, Iowa, and eastern Kansas; south to northern Florida and Texas.

The bark of the roots is used medicinally.

RUSTY BLACK HAW *Viburnum rufidulum* Raf.

FIELD MARKS. A leaf-losing shrub or small tree 5 to about 25 feet high; growing in dry pine or deciduous woods and thickets. *Branchlets* slender, somewhat flexible, more or less rusty-scurfy. *Leaves* elliptic to oval or broadest above the middle, mostly pointed at base, blunt or abruptly short-pointed at tip, finely and sharply toothed on margin, rather thick in texture, lustrous above, paler and more or less rusty-scurfy beneath, 1½ to 3 inches long; leafstalks grooved and often slightly winged, rusty-scurfy, ¼ to ½ inch long. *Flowers* all alike, the cluster stalkless or nearly so; blooming late March to early May. *Fruits* oval-shaped, deep blue, often with a whitish bloom, about ⅜ inch long, sweet and edible; ripening September or October.

RANGE. Virginia to southern Ohio and Illinois, Missouri, and southeastern Kansas; south to central Florida and Texas.

Also called Southern Black Haw and Rusty Nannyberry.

SMALL-LEAF VIBURNUM *Viburnum obovatum* Walt.

FIELD MARKS. A shrub or small tree 5 to about 20 feet high with more or less persistent leaves; growing in swamps and low hammocks or along streams near the coast. *Branchlets* slender and rather flexible. *Leaves* stalkless or nearly so, top-shaped, broadest above the middle, wedge-shaped at base, rounded or broadly pointed at tip, untoothed or with some obscure and blunt teeth above the middle, lustrous above, paler and with some minute red hairs beneath, ¾ to 1½ inches long. *Flowers* all alike, the cluster somewhat dome-shaped and stalkless; blooming March or April. *Fruits* egg-shaped, bluish black, about ¼ inch long; ripening September or October.

RANGE. Coastal plain; South Carolina south to Florida.

Also called Walter Viburnum. Wood with a very rank odor.

SQUASHBERRY *Viburnum edule* (Michx.) Raf.

FIELD MARKS. A straggling or sprawling leaf-losing shrub 1 to 4 feet high; growing in cool moist woods and ravines. *Leaves* broadly oval or broadest above the middle, usually with 3 broadly pointed short lobes above the middle, rounded to somewhat heart-shaped at base, coarsely and irregularly toothed on margin, smooth above, slightly paler and more or less downy on the veins beneath, 1 to 2½ inches long; leafstalks ⅜ to ¾ inch long, often with a pair of small glands near the summit. *Flowers* all alike, the cluster less than 1½ inches broad; blooming May to August. *Fruits* roundish or slightly egg-shaped, light red or orange, about ⅜ inch in diameter; ripening August to October.

RANGE. Labrador to Alaska; south to Maine; northern New York, Michigan, and Minnesota; Colorado and Oregon.

The acid fruits are used for sauce and jelly.

HIGHBUSH-CRANBERRY *Viburnum trilobum* Marsh.

FIELD MARKS. A leaf-losing shrub 3 to about 12 feet high; growing in cool moist woods and cold swamps. *Leaves* broadly egg-shaped, with 3 broad and rather long-pointed lobes, rounded to very broadly pointed at base, margin with coarse and rather wavy teeth, sometimes sparingly hairy above, slightly paler and often hairy along the veins beneath, 2 to 4 inches long; leaf stalks grooved, ½ to 1½ inches long, often with small stalked glands at the summit. *Flowers* of 2 kinds, the marginal ones showy, ½ inch or so across, but sterile; blooming May to July. *Fruits* roundish or slightly oval-shaped, bright red, juicy, translucent, about ⅜ inch in diameter; ripening September or October.

RANGE. Newfoundland to British Columbia; south to New England, West Virginia, the region of the Great Lakes, northeast Iowa, South Dakota, and Washington.

The acid fruits are cooked and used like cranberries.

MAPLE-LEAF VIBURNUM *Viburnum acerifolium* L.

FIELD MARKS. A leaf-losing shrub 2 to 6 feet high; growing in moist to dry and often rocky woods. *Branchlets* smooth or minutely downy. *Leaves* egg-shaped to roundish, usually with 3 broad and pointed lobes but sometimes almost unlobed or the lobes very short, rounded to heart-shaped at base, coarsely toothed on margin, dull green and smooth or nearly so above, usually more or less downy (rarely nearly smooth) and with minute black dots beneath, 2 to 5 inches long; leafstalks ⅜ to 1 inch long, often with a pair of narrow stipules at base. *Flowers* all alike, sometimes pink-tinged; blooming late April to July. *Fruits* roundish or slightly oval-shaped, bluish black, about ¼ inch long; ripening September or October.

RANGE. Southwestern Quebec to Minnesota south to New England, Georgia, Alabama, and Mississippi.

The pinkish to magenta leaves are very attractive in the fall.

ARROWWOOD *Viburnum dentatum* L.

FIELD MARKS. A bushy leaf-losing shrub 3 to about 10 (rarely 15) feet high; growing along streams or on shores of lakes, and in low wet woods and swamps. *Branchlets* more or less ridged or angled, smooth or sometimes roughish-hairy. *Leaves* with leaf-stalks usually more than ¼ inch long, egg-shaped to roundish, rounded or slightly heart-shaped at base, pointed to blunt at tip, prominent lateral veins ending in the large and sharp-pointed marginal teeth, smooth or nearly so on the upper surface, paler and more or less downy beneath (or smooth except for occasional tufts of down in the axils of the veins in the variety *lucidulum* Ait.), 1½ to about 4 inches long. *Flowers* all alike; blooming late March to July. *Fruits* roundish or egg-shaped, bluish black, ¼ to ⅜ inch long; ripening July to October.

RANGE. New Brunswick to southern Ontario; south to Florida and Texas.

A variable shrub often divided into several species by some botanists.

SOFTLEAF ARROWWOOD *Viburnum molle* Michx.

FIELD MARKS. A leaf-losing shrub 4 to 12 feet high, with peeling grayish bark on the older stems; growing in rocky woods and on the banks of streams. *Branchlets* smooth and roundish. *Leaves* broadly egg-shaped or roundish, heart-shaped at base, abruptly pointed at tip, prominent lateral veins ending in the large and sharp-pointed marginal teeth, smooth above, paler and softly downy beneath, 2 to 5 inches long; leaf stalks ¾ to 2 inches long,, usually with a pair of narrow stipules at the base. *Flowers* all alike; blooming May and June. *Fruits* oval-shaped, bluish black, about ⅜ inch long; ripening August to October.

RANGE. Indiana and Illinois to Missouri; south to Kentucky and Arkansas.

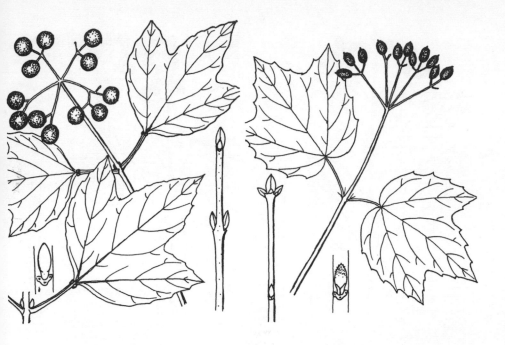

Highbush-cranberry

Maple-leaf Viburnum

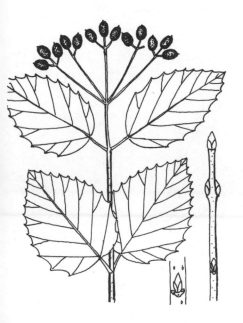

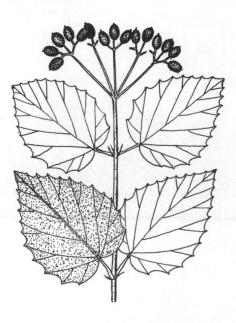

Arrowwood

Softleaf Arrowwood

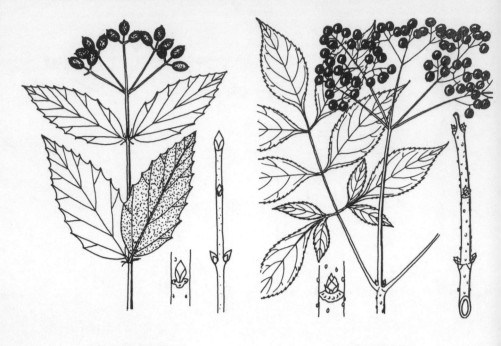

Downy Arrowwood

Common Elder

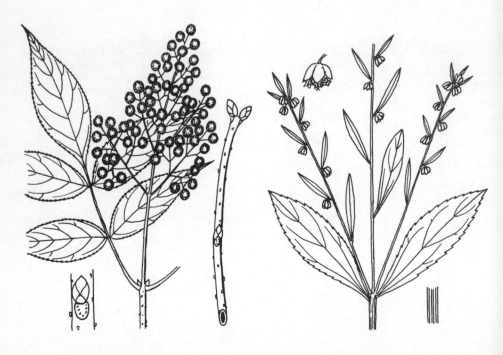

Red-berried Elder

Marsh Elder

DOWNY ARROWWOOD   *Viburnum rafinesquianum* Schultes

FIELD MARKS. A leaf-losing shrub 2 to 5 feet high, with slender grayish-barked stems; growing on dry wooded slopes and banks. *Branchlets* roundish, smooth or nearly so. *Leaves* stalkless or very short-stalked and with narrow stipules, egg-shaped or oblong egg-shaped, rounded at base, pointed at tip, with prominent lateral veins ending in coarse and sharp marginal teeth, smooth or nearly so above, softly downy beneath, 1½ to 3 inches long. *Flowers* all alike; blooming April to June. *Fruits* oval-shaped, purplish black, about ¼ inch long; ripening July to September.

RANGE. Quebec to Manitoba; south to central North Carolina, northern Georgia, Kentucky, and Missouri.

COMMON ELDER   *Sambucus canadensis* L.

FIELD MARKS. A leaf-losing shrub 4 to 12 feet high; widely distributed in moist rich soils. *Branchlets* stout, yellowish brown, with warty lenticels, large white pith, and small greenish or brown buds; odor rank when bruised. *Leaves* opposite, compound, 6 to 10 inches long; the 5 to 11 leaflets elliptic or lance-shaped, lower ones often 3-parted, mostly pointed at base and tip, margin sharply toothed, smooth above, paler and sometimes slightly downy beneath, 3 to 6 inches long. *Flowers* small, white, the short corolla tube 5-lobed, in broad flat-topped end clusters; blooming April to August. *Fruits* berry-like, round, purplish black, with 3 to 5 large seeds, about 3/16 inch in diameter; ripening July to October.

RANGE. Nova Scotia to Manitoba; south to Florida and Texas.

Fruits are eaten by birds and used for jelly, pies, and wine.

RED-BERRIED ELDER   *Sambucus pubens* Michx.

FIELD MARKS. A leaf-losing shrub 3 to 10 feet high; growing in cool, moist, rocky woods and ravines. *Branchlets* stout, light brown, with warty lenticels, large brownish pith, and egg-shaped purplish-red buds. *Leaves* opposite, compound, 5 to 8 inches long; the 5 to 7 leaflets lance-shaped, pointed to unevenly rounded at base, long-pointed at tip, finely and sharply toothed on margin, smooth above, paler and usually downy beneath, 2 to 5 inches long. *Flowers* small, creamy white, the short corolla tube 5 lobed, in pyramid-shaped end clusters; blooming April to June. *Fruits* berry-like, round, bright red, about 3/16 inch in diameter; ripening June to August.

RANGE. Newfoundland to Alaska; south to New Jersey, Pennsylvania, the region of the Great Lakes, Iowa, and along the mountains to northern Georgia.

COMPOSITE FAMILY (Compositae)

Composites have small flowers grouped in heads which are surrounded by bracts. Many like the goldenrods, asters, sunflowers, and daisies are familiar plants. Only a few species are more or less shrubby.

MARSH ELDER   *Iva frutescens* L.

FIELD MARKS. A woody-based plant 3 to about 10 feet high; growing in coastal salt marshes. *Leaves* mostly opposite, stalkless or nearly so, elliptic to narrowly lance-shaped, pointed at both ends, usually coarsely toothed on margin, somewhat fleshy, smooth or minutely rough-hairy, 1½ to 4 inches long. *Flowers* small, greenish, in nodding heads in axils of small leaves toward tips of branchlets; blooming August to November. *Fruits* small, dry, 1-seeded.

RANGE. Coastal plain; Newfoundland south to Florida, west to Texas.

SEACOAST MARSH ELDER   *Iva imbricata* Walt.

Similar to the preceding but usually less than 2 feet high and smoother; and with alternate, very narrow, untoothed leaves. Grows on coastal sand dunes from southeastern Virginia south to Florida, west to Texas. (Not illustrated)

GROUNDSEL TREE *Baccharis halimifolia* L.

FIELD MARKS. A more or less resinous, soft-wooded, semi-evergreen shrub 3 to 10 feet high; growing in swampy thickets, sandy open woods or fields, and on sea beaches. *Branchlets* green, longitudinally and finely furrowed, smooth or somewhat downy. *Leaves* alternate, elliptic to roundish or broadest above the middle, the upper ones often quite narrow, wedge-shaped at base, blunt or rather pointed at tip, margin (except in uppermost leaves) coarsely toothed from about the middle to tip, pale green and smooth or nearly so on both surfaces, 1 to 3 inches long. *Flowers* small, the heads mostly stalked and in a branching open end cluster; blooming September or October. *Fruits* small, dry, 1-seeded, with a conspicuous tuft of silky whitish hairs.

RANGE. Coastal plain and piedmont; eastern Massachusetts south to Florida, west to Texas.

Also called Groundselbush and Sea-myrtle.

SESSILE-FLOWERED GROUNDSEL TREE *Baccharis glomeruliflora* Pers.

FIELD MARKS. A barely resinous, soft-wooded, more or less evergreen shrub 3 to about 10 feet high; growing in low woods and brackish marshes near the coast. *Leaves* alternate, broadest above the middle and tapering to the base, blunt or broadly pointed at tip, usually with several coarse but sharp teeth above the middle, ¾ to about 2 inches long. *Flowers* small, the heads stalkless and mostly in groups of 3 in the axils of leaflike bracts; blooming October and November. *Fruits* small, dry, 1-seeded, with a tuft of silky whitish hairs.

RANGE. Coastal plain; North Carolina south to Florida.

FALSE WILLOW *Baccharis angustifolia* Michx.

FIELD MARKS. A more or less resinous, soft-wooded, evergreen shrub 2 to 8 feet high; growing in brackish coastal marshes. *Leaves* alternate, long and narrow with parallel sides, somewhat pointed at base and tip, untoothed or nearly so on margin, ¾ to 2 inches long, less than 3/16 inch wide. *Flowers* small, the heads mostly stalked and clustered at the ends of the branchlets; blooming late September and October, or later southward. *Fruits* small, dry, 1-seeded, with a tuft of silky whitish hairs.

RANGE. Coastal plain; North Carolina south to Florida, west to Texas.

SEA-OXEYE *Borrichia frutescens* (L.) DC.

FIELD MARKS. A shrub 1 to 2½ feet high, with the younger parts fleshy; growing in brackish marshes along the coast. *Leaves* opposite, narrow to quite broad and widest above the middle, somewhat pointed at both ends, untoothed or with some wavy teeth on margin, thickish, grayish green with short silky hairs on both surfaces, ¾ to 2¼ inches long. *Flowers* in daisy-like heads about 1½ inches across, with bright yellow rays and a brownish disk; blooming May to September. *Fruits* small, dry, 1-seeded.

RANGE. Coastal plain; southeastern Virginia south to Florida, west to Texas.

276

Groundsel Tree

Sessile-flowered Groundsel Tree

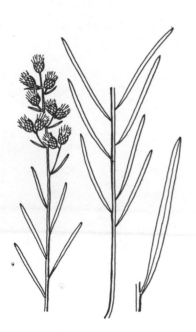

False Willow

Sea-oxeye

SELECTED REFERENCES

AMMONS, NELLE. *Shrubs of West Virginia.* (West Virginia Bulletin Ser. 50, No. 12-4.) Morgantown, W. Va., 1950.

BILLINGTON, CECIL. *Shrubs of Michigan.* Bloomfield Hills, Mich.: Cranbrook Institute of Science, 1949.

BRAUN, E. L. *The Woody Plants of Ohio.* Columbus, Ohio: Ohio State University Press, 1961.

BROWN, C. A. *Louisiana Trees and Shrubs.* (Louisiana Forestry Commission, Bulletin 1.) Baton Rouge, La., 1945.

CORE, E. L. and NELLE P. *Woody Plants in Winter.* Morgantown, W. Va.: The Book Exchange, 1958.

DEAM, C. C. *Shrubs of Indiana.* (Indiana Department of Conservation, Publication 44.) Indianapolis, Ind., 1931.
Flora of Indiana. Indianapolis, Ind.: Department of Conservation, Division of Forestry, 1940.

FERNALD, M. L. *Gray's Manual of Botany.* American Book Company, 1950.

GLEASON, H. A. *The New Britton and Brown Illustrated Flora of the Northeastern United States and Adjacent Canada.* New York: New York Botanical Garden, 1952.

GRIMM, W. C. *The Shrubs of Pennsylvania.* Harrisburg, Pa.: The Stackpole Company, 1952. Reissued in 1957 without change as *The Book of Shrubs.*

HARLOW, W. H. *Twig Key to the Deciduous Woody Plants of Eastern North America.* Published by the author, Syracuse, N.Y., 1949.

HARPER, R. M. *Economic Botany of Alabama.* Part 2: Catalog of the Trees, Shrubs, and Vines of Alabama, with their Economic Properties and Local Distribution. University, Ala.: Geological Survey of Alabama, 1928.

JONES, L. R., and RAND, F. V. *Vermont Shrubs and Woody Vines.* (Vermont Agricultural Experiment Station, Bulletin 145.) Burlington, Vt., 1909.

MATTHEWS, F. S. *Field Book of American Trees and Shrubs*. New York: G. P. Putnam's Sons, 1915.

MUENSCHER, W. C. *Keys to Woody Plants*. Ithaca, N. Y.: Comstock Publishing Co., 1950.

RADFORD, A. E., AHLES, H. E., and BELL, C. R. *Guide to the Vascular Flora of the Carolinas*. Chapel Hill, N. C.: University of North Carolina. The Book Exchange, 1964.

REHDER, ALFRED. *Manual of Cultivated Trees and Shrubs*. New York: The Macmillan Company, 1940.

SMALL, J. K. *Manual of the Southeastern Flora*. Chapel Hill, N. C.: University of North Carolina Press, 1933.

STUPKA, ARTHUR. *Trees, Shrubs, and Woody Vines of the Great Smoky Mountains National Park*. Knoxville, Tenn.: University of Tennessee Press, 1964.

TEHON, LEO R. *Fieldbook of Native Illinois Shrubs*. (Natural History Division, Manual 3.) Urbana, Ill., 1942.

APPENDICES

Keys for identifying particular plants within the larger native shrub families.

A

KEY TO THE GREENBRIERS (Smilax)

1 Stems and lower leaf surfaces woolly-hairy
WOOLLY GREENBRIER *(S. pumila)* 76
1 Stems and lower leaf surfaces otherwise—2

    2 Leaves white beneath
GLAUCOUS GREENBRIER *(S. glauca)* 72
    2 Leaves green on both surfaces or sometimes mottled with white—3

3 Leaves evergreen—4
3 Leaves deciduous—7

    4 Leaves lance-shaped and pointed at both ends—5
    4 Leaves commonly fiddle-shaped or triangular—6

5 Leaves thin, 5- to 7-veined
LANCELEAF GREENBRIER *(S. smallii)* 75
5 Leaves thickish, 3-veined
LAUREL-LEAF GREENBRIER *(S. laurifolia)* 75

    6 Leaves usually prickly on margin, sometimes mottled with white   CHINABRIER *(S. bona-nox)* 72
    6 Leaves not prickly on margin, sometimes notched at tip
WILD-BAMBOO *(S. auriculata)* 75

7 Leaves thickish; stems often angled and with stout broad-based prickles   COMMON GREENBRIER *(S. rotundifolia)* 72
7 Leaves thin; stems not angled, prickles slender when present—8

    8 Stems more or less thickly covered with needle-like blackish prickles; leaf margins roughish with minute bristly teeth; fruits black, on stalks longer than the leafstalks
BRISTLY GREENBRIER *(S. hispida)* 72
    8 Stems usually prickly only toward the base; leaf margins not roughish; fruits red, on stalks shorter than the leafstalks
RED-BERRIED GREENBRIER *(S. walteri)* 75

281

KEY TO THE WILLOWS (Salix)

1 Prostrate or creeping shrubs of arctic tundras and alpine mountain summits of the northeastern United States—2
1 Shrubs with erect or ascending stems—3

2 Leaves roundish, heart-shaped at base, bright green on both surfaces   DWARF WILLOW *(S. herbacea)*   91
2 Leaves elliptical or broadest above the middle, wedge-shaped at base, pale beneath
       BEARBERRY WILLOW *(S. uva-ursi)*   91

3 Leaf margins untoothed or nearly so—4
3 Leaf margins toothed—10

4 Leaves smooth on both surfaces—5
4 Leaves hairy at least beneath—6

5 Leaves green on both surfaces, narrowly elliptic or oblong, wedge-shaped at base, margin inrolled; northern bog shrub
       BOG WILLOW *(S. pedicellaris)*   87
5 Leaves whitened beneath, lustrous above, elliptic or oblong, pointed or blunt at both ends
       TEALEAF WILLOW *(S. planifolia)*   88

6 Branchlets smooth—7
6 Branchlets downy or woolly—8

7 Branchlets dark green and lustrous; leaves silvery-silky beneath, the margin inrolled   SILVER WILLOW *(S. argyrocarpa)*   88
7 Branchlets reddish to olive brown, usually whitened with a bloom; leaves often silky to velvety white beneath
       SATINY WILLOW *(S. pellita)*   88

8 Branchlets and lower leaf surfaces densely white-woolly, leaf margin inrolled; shrub of northern bogs
       HOARY WILLOW *S. candida*   88
8 Branchlets grayish-woolly; upland shrubs of wide distribution—9

9 Leaves mostly over 2 inches long, grayish-woolly to smooth and veiny beneath, margin usually wavy
       PRAIRIE WILLOW *(S. humilis)*   84
9 Leaves less than 2 inches long, white-woolly beneath, margin inrolled   DWARF GRAY WILLOW *(S. humilis* var. *microphylla)*   84

10 Upper leaf surfaces with a wrinkled appearance, margins with some wavy teeth—11
10 Upper leaf surfaces otherwise—12

11 Leaves more or less downy on both surfaces but more densely so beneath   BEBB WILLOW *(S. bebbiana)*   84
11 Leaves not hairy above, whitened and often with a few rusty hairs beneath   PUSSY WILLOW *(S. discolor)*   84

12   Leaves long, narrow, and almost stalkless, the margins with shallow and widely spaced teeth

                        SANDBAR WILLOW *(S. interior)*   80

12   Leaves rather regularly and finely toothed on margin—13

13   Leaves with short stout stalks, densely silky-hairy on both surfaces; branchlets woolly   FURRY WILLOW *(S. syrticola)*   87

13   Leaves otherwise—14

     14   Leaves less than 3 times as long as wide—15
     14   Leaves more than 3 times as long as wide—16

15   Leaves with a balsam-like odor when crushed, thin, dull above, smooth on both surfaces, margin with rather low glandular teeth; stipules small or absent   BALSAM WILLOW *(S. pyrifolia)*   87

15   Leaves not fragrant, thick, firm, lustrous above, whitened and sometimes woolly beneath; margin sharply toothed; stipules large

                 BLUELEAF WILLOW *(S. glaucophylloides)*   87

     16   Branchlets downy or woolly—17
     16   Branchlets smooth or nearly so—18

17   Leaves more or less grayish-hairy on both surfaces, more or less heart-shaped at base; stipules large and glandular-toothed; northern   HEARTLEAF WILLOW *(S. cordata)*   83

17   Leaves smooth but dull above, whitish and with some soft hairs beneath, mostly rounded to pointed at base; stipules moderate in size; midwestern MISSOURI RIVER WILLOW *(S. eriocephala)*   83

     18   Leafstalks with a pair of glands at the summit; leaves very lustrous on the upper surface—19
     18   Leafstalks otherwise; leaves but slightly if at all lustrous on the upper surface—20

19   Leaves whitish and smooth beneath

                   AUTUMN WILLOW *(S. serissima)*   80

19   Leaves green and sometimes with scattered rusty hairs beneath

                   SHINING WILLOW *(S. lucida)*   83

     20   Leaves smooth on both surfaces—21
     20   Leaves more or less silky-hairy beneath—22

21   Leaves gradually tapered to the tip; branchlets brittle at base; southern   WARD WILLOW *(S. caroliniana)*   83

21   Leaves rather abruptly pointed at the tip; branchlets not brittle-based; northern   PEACHLEAF WILLOW *(S. amygdaloides)*   83

     22   Leaves silvery-silky beneath, margins toothed quite to the base; branchlets brittle-based; widespread

                   SILKY WILLOW *(S. sericea)*   80

     22   Leaves whitened beneath and usually with scattered rusty or tawny hairs; margin not toothed toward the base; branchlets not brittle-based; northern

                   SLENDER WILLOW *(S. gracilis)*   80

KEY TO THE CURRANTS AND GOOSEBERRIES (Ribes)

1 Branchlets and stems unarmed—2
1 Branchlets and stems armed with spines or prickly bristles—6

    2 Main stems prostrate or creeping—3
    2 Main stems erect or ascending—4

3 Plant with a skunklike odor when bruised
                        SKUNK CURRANT (*R. glandulosum*)   120
3 Plant otherwise   SWAMP RED CURRANT (*R. triste*)   120

    4 Leaves and branchlets with small yellow resin dots
                  WILD BLACK CURRANT (*R. americanum*)   120
    4 Leaves and branchlets not resin-dotted—5

5 Branchlets downy   BUFFALO CURRANT (*R. odoratum*)   123
5 Branchlets smooth or with scattered bristles
                    SMOOTH GOOSEBERRY (*R. hirtellum*)   119

    6 Largest leaves less than 1 inch wide; southern—7
    6 Largest leaves more than 1 inch wide; northern or in mountains—8

7 Branchlets reddish brown; fruits smooth
                  GRANITE GOOSEBERRY (*R. curvatum*)   119
7 Branchlets grayish; fruits densely covered with gland-tipped spines
                  FLORIDA GOOSEBERRY (*R. echinellum*)   116

    8 Nodal spines less than ¼ inch long, the internodes smooth or with some short bristles—9
    8 Nodal spines more than ¼ inch long, the internodes often with prickles or bristles—11

9 Branchlets always smooth between the nodes
                  ROUNDLEAF GOOSEBERRY (*R. rotundifolium*)   116
9 Branchlets usually more or less bristly between the nodes—10

    10 Leaves with pointed lobes, smooth or nearly so on both surfaces   SMOOTH GOOSEBERRY (*R. hirtellum*)   119
    10 Leaves with bluntish lobes, somewhat hairy and glandular beneath NORTHERN GOOSEBERRY (*R. oxyacanthoides*)   119

11 Internodes thickly beset with long and prickly bristles
                  SWAMP BLACK CURRANT (*R. lacustre*)   120
11 Internodes smooth or with rather widely scattered spines or bristles—12

    12 Nodal spines less than ½ inch long; fruits prickly
                  PRICKLY GOOSEBERRY (*R. cynosbati*)   116
    12 Nodal spines often over ½ inch long; fruits smooth or bristly—13

13 Branchlets whitish or gray, sometimes bristly; leaves smooth above but usually downy beneath; fruits smooth
                  MISSOURI GOOSEBERRY (*R. missouriense*)   119
13 Branchlets reddish brown, usually bristly; leaves usually hairy on both surfaces; fruits often bristly
                  BRISTLY GOOSEBERRY (*R. setosum*)   119

KEY TO THE JUNEBERRIES (Amelanchier)

1   Leaves with pointed bases and stout leafstalks less than ⅜ inch long; fruits elongate, solitary or 2 to 3 together
OBLONG-FRUITED JUNEBERRY (*A. bartramiana*)   131
1   Leaves with rounded or heart-shaped bases and slender leafstalks up to ¾ inch long; fruits roundish or nearly so, several in a cluster—2

   2   Leaves coarsely toothed, the teeth about as many as the prominent straight primary veins—3
   2   Leaves finely toothed, the teeth at least twice as many as the irregular and branching veins—4

3   Low shrub forming colonies by creeping underground stems; leaf margins untoothed toward the base
LOW JUNEBERRY (*A. humilis*)   128
3   Tall shrub, straggling or with arching branches, not colony-forming; leaf margins toothed quite to the base
ROUNDLEAF JUNEBERRY (*A. sanguinea*)   128

   4   Colony-forming shrubs with creeping underground stems—5
   4   Shrubs growing in clumps, or small trees—6

5   Leaf margins untoothed toward the base; leaves smooth or slightly downy beneath; fruits with stalks of variable length
RUNNING JUNEBERRY (*A. spicata*)   128
5   Leaf margins toothed quite to the base; leaves downy beneath; fruits with stalks of about the same length
COASTAL JUNEBERRY (*A. obovalis*)   131

   6   Leaves very blunt or rounded at the tip
OBLONG-LEAF JUNEBERRY (*A. canadensis*)   131
   6   Leaves definitely pointed at the tip—7

7   Flowers and fruits in upright clusters; shrub with several stems in a clump   SWAMP JUNEBERRY (*A. intermedia*)   131
7   Flowers and fruits usually in drooping clusters; usually trees—8

   8   Mature leaves more or less downy beneath, at least on the midrib and veins   COMMON JUNEBERRY (*A. arborea*)   131
   8   Mature leaves smooth on both surfaces
SMOOTH JUNEBERRY (*A. laevis*)   131

E

KEY TO THE ROSES (Rosa)

1   Leaflets usually 3; stems scrambling or climbing
PRAIRIE ROSE (*R. setigera*)   144
1   Leaflets usually 5 or more; stems erect—2

   2   Stems with broad-based, usually hooked prickles
SWAMP ROSE (*R. palustris*)   143
   2   Stems unarmed or with slender needle-like or bristly prickles—3

3 Stems unarmed or with a few weak or bristly prickles; fruits smooth and with persistent stipules SMOOTH ROSE *(R. blanda)*   144
3 Stems well armed—4

    4 Stems with needle-like prickles at the nodes and others widely scattered; fruits glandular-bristly
                         PASTURE ROSE *(R. carolina)*   143
    4 Stems densely covered with bristly or needle-like prickles—5

5 Stems densely bristly; fruits bristly-hairy, the sepals soon shed
                         SHINING ROSE *(R. nitida)*   143
5 Stems densely covered with needle-like prickles; fruits smooth and with persistent sepals
                    PRICKLY WILD ROSE *(R. acicularis)*   144

F

KEY TO THE INDIGOBUSHES (Amorpha)

1 Lowest pair of leaflets close to the stem; shrubs usually less than 3 feet high—2
1 Lowest pair of leaflets ½ inch or more from the stem; shrubs usually over 3 feet high—4

    2 Branchlets smooth or nearly so; leaflets conspicuously glandular-dotted beneath
              GEORGIA INDIGOBUSH *(A. georgiana)*   152
    2 Branchlets and leaves grayish-downy or grayish-hairy—3

3 Leaflets and branchlets densely grayish-hairy; fruit pods densely hairy; midwestern shrub LEADPLANT *(A. canescens)*   151
3 Leaflets and branchlets grayish-downy; fruit pods grayish-downy and with conspicuous dark glands; southeastern coastal plain shrub PLUME-LOCUST *(A. herbacea)*   152

    4 Leaflets rather broadly egg-shaped or oval and smooth on both sides MOUNTAIN INDIGOBUSH *(A. glabra)*   151
    4 Leaflets rather narrow or oblong, often hairy at least beneath—5

5 Branchlets and upper surfaces of the leaflets both lustrous; fruit pods smooth or nearly so
              SHINING INDIGOBUSH *(A. nitens)*   152
5 Branchlets and upper surfaces of the leaflets not both lustrous; fruit pods either hairy or conspicuously glandular-dotted—6

    6 Branchlets and lower surfaces of the leaflets densely brownish-hairy
              SCHWERIN INDIGOBUSH *(A. schwerinii)*   152
    6 Branchlets and lower surfaces of the leaflets with pale to tawny hairs—7

7 Leaflets 9 to 19, rounded or slightly notched at tip, somewhat leathery and lustrous above; fruit pods nearly straight, dotted with small glands MOUNTAIN INDIGOBUSH *(A. virgata)*   151
7 Leaflets 11 to 35, with an abrupt little point at tip, firm and dull above; fruit pods curved and dotted with large raised glands COMMON INDIGOBUSH *(A. fruticosa)*   151

KEY TO THE LOCUSTS (Robinia)

1 Branchlets smooth or merely downy—2
1 Branchlets bristly-hairy or more or less glandular—5

    2 Shrub less than 2 feet tall; coastal plain.
                        DWARF LOCUST *(R. nana)*   156
    2 Shrubs more than 2 feet tall—3

3 Flower stalks merely downy; coastal plain
                        ELLIOTT LOCUST *(R. elliottii)*   155
3 Flower stalks more or less glandular-bristly; mountains and piedmont—4

    4 Branchlets unarmed or with very short nodal spines
                      BOYNTON LOCUST *(R. boyntonii)*   155
    4 Branchlets armed with slender nodal spines
                      KELSEY LOCUST *(R. kelseyi)*   156

5 Branchlets, leafstalks, and flower stalks densely covered with reddish-brown bristles   BRISTLY LOCUST *(R. hispida)*   155
5 Branchlets, leafstalks, and flower stalks with stalkless or short-stalked glands—6

    6 Branchlets, leafstalks, and flower stalks very sticky-glandular; tall shrub or small tree
                      CLAMMY LOCUST *(R. viscosa)*   152
    6 Branchlets, leafstalks, and flower stalks downy and with some short-stalked glands but not sticky; shrub 3 to 6 feet high   HARTWEG LOCUST *(R. hartwegii)*   155

KEY TO THE HOLLIES (Ilex)

1 Leaves evergreen, thick and leathery in texture—2
1 Leaves deciduous, thin or slightly thick in texture—6

    2 Leaf margins toothed quite to the base with bluntish or rounded teeth; fruits red or yellow
                      YAUPON HOLLY *(I vomitoria)*   172
    2 Leaf margins untoothed, or toothed only above the middle—3

3 Leaf margins with some low, blunt teeth toward the tip; fruits black   INKBERRY *(I. glabra)*   172
3 Leaf margins untoothed or with a few sharp, spiny, or minute teeth—4

    4 Leaves narrow, less than ⅜ inch wide, very stiff and sharp at tip MYRTLE-LEAF HOLLY *(I. cassine* var. *myrtifolia)*   175
    4 Leaves broader, often with a few small spiny teeth—5

5 Leaves minutely black dotted on the lower surface; fruits black
                LARGE GALLBERRY *(I. coriacea)*   172
5 Leaves not black-dotted beneath; fruits red or yellow
                   DAHOON HOLLY *(I. cassine)*   175

    6 Leaf margins with very small, blunt, and inconspicuous
      teeth   SARVIS HOLLY *(I. amelanchier)*   172
    6 Leaf margins with conspicuous sharp or bluntish teeth—7

7 Leaves and fruits clustered on short lateral spurlike branches—8
7 Leaves and fruits never clustered on short spurlike branches—11

    8 Leaf margins with rather low blunt teeth, the leaf bases
      quite sharply pointed—9
    8 Leaf margins with sharply pointed teeth, the leaf bases
      broadly pointed to roundish—10

9 Leaves less than 3 inches long, less than 1 inch wide; fruits on
  short stalks   DECIDUOUS HOLLY *(I. decidua)*   171
9 Leaves often over 3 inches long and over 1 inch wide; fruits on
  stalks ½ inch long or longer
           LONG-STALKED HOLLY *(I. decidua* var. *longipes)*   171

    10 Largest leaves less than 2½ inches long; coastal plain
       shrub   CAROLINA HOLLY *(I. ambigua)*   171
    10 Largest leaves more than 2½ inches long; chiefly mountain
       shrub   LARGELEAF HOLLY *(I. ambigua* var. *montana)*   171

11 Leaves thickish, dull above and downy beneath, with rather
  coarsely toothed margins   WINTERBERRY *(I. verticillata)*   168
11 Leaves thin, lustrous above, smooth or nearly so on both surfaces, with rather finely toothed margins
           SMOOTH WINTERBERRY *(I. laevigata)*   168

I

KEY TO THE GRAPES (Vitis)

1 Tendrils rarely present; plant low and bushy
                 BUSH GRAPE *(V. ruprestris)*   191
1 Tendrils always present; plants high-climbing—2

    2 Tendrils simple; branchlets with pith continuing through the
      nodes; bark not becoming loose or shredded
            MUSCADINE GRAPE *(V. rotundifolia)*   191
    2 Tendrils branched; branchlets with pith interrupted by a
      woody partition (diaphragm) at each node; bark becom-
      ing loose or shredded—3

3 A tendril or flower or fruit cluster opposite each leaf—4
3 Tendrils and flower or fruit clusters intermittent, none opposite
  every third leaf—5

    4 Leaves with permanent, matted, tawny or rusty wool on the
      lower surface   FOX GRAPE *(V. labrusca)*   187
    4 Leaves smooth or merely with some wool on the veins of
      the lower surface
           NEW ENGLAND GRAPE *(V. novae-angliae)*   188

5   Leaves green on the lower surface, smooth or somewhat hairy—6
5   Leaves not green on the lower surface—10

    6   Lower leaf surfaces conspicuously grayish-hairy—7
    6   Lower leaf surfaces smooth, or merely with axillary tufts or scattered hairs along the veins—8

7   Branchlets angled; southern   POSSUM GRAPE *(V. baileyana)*   191
7   Branchlets not angled; Great Lakes region
              DUNE GRAPE *(Vitis riparia* var. *syrticola)*   188

    8   Branchlets red; leaves deeply lobed
               RED GRAPE *(V. palmata)*   191
    8   Branchlets not red; leaves with shallow lobes if any—9

9   Leaves with broad U-shaped basal sinuses, the margins with narrowly pointed teeth; branchlets with thin nodal diaphragms
              RIVERBANK GRAPE *(V. riparia)*   188
9   Leaves with narrow V-shaped basal sinuses, the margins with rather broadly pointed teeth; branchlets with thick nodal diaphragms   FROST GRAPE *(V. vulpina)*   188

    10   Lower leaf surfaces smooth or nearly so and very white—11
    10   Lower leaf surfaces otherwise—12

11   Branchlets with thin nodal diaphragms; midwestern
             POST OAK GRAPE *(V. lincecumii)*   191
11   Branchlets with thick nodal diaphragms; eastern
           BLUELEAF GRAPE *(V. aestivalis* var. *argentifolia)*   187

    12   Young branchlets angled—13
    12   Young branchlets not angled—14

13   Leaves whitish-woolly beneath   WINTER GRAPE *(V. cinerea)*   188
13   Leaves reddish-hairy beneath
            PIGEON GRAPE *(V. cinerea* var. *floridana)*   188

    14   Branchlets with thin nodal diaphragms; midwestern
           POST OAK GRAPE *(V. lincecumii)*   191
    14   Branchlets with thick nodal diaphragms; eastern
           SUMMER GRAPE *(V. aestivalis)*   187

J

KEY TO THE ST. PETER'S-WORTS AND ST. JOHN'S-WORTS (Hypericum)

1   Flowers with 4 petals; sepals 2 or 4—2
1   Flowers with 5 petals; sepals 5—5

    2   Styles 3 or 4; sepals of nearly the same length but the outer pair much larger and broader
             ST. PETER'S *(H. stans)*   192
    2· Styles 2; the inner sepals very small or wanting—3

3   Flower stalks bending downward as fruits develop; bractlets near base of the flower stalk
            DWARF ST. PETER'S-WORT (*H. suffruticosum*)   192
3   Flower stalks remaining erect; bractlets near the base of the calyx—4

    4   Plant erect   ST. ANDREW'S-CROSS (*H. hypericoides*)   195
    4   Plant reclining
                RECLINING ST. ANDREW'S-CROSS (*H. stragalum*)   195

5   Leaves very narrow (about ⅛ inch wide) or almost needle-like; flowers in elongate end clusters—6
5   Leaves broader, usually more than ⅛ inch wide; flowers relatively few or, if numerous, in flat-topped clusters—10

    6   Leaves narrow but flat, the larger ones about ⅛ inch wide
                BEDSTRAW ST. JOHN'S-WORT (*H. galioides*)   199
    6   Leaves almost needle-like, about as wide as thick—7

7   Shrubs less than 1½ feet high—8
7   Shrubs usually over 2 feet high; growing in wet places—9

    8   Largest leaves ⅜ inch or less long; shrub of wet to dry coastal plain sands   SANDWEED (*H. reductum*)   199
    8   Largest leaves ½ inch or more long; shrub of dry, rocky, piedmont woodlands   SANDWEED (*H. lloydii*)   199

9   Stems with spongy bark peeling in thin layers; leaves with 2 longitudinal grooves beneath   SANDWEED (*H. fasciculatum*)   199
9   Stems with close thin bark; leaves not distinctly 2-grooved beneath   SANDWEED (*H. nitidum*)   199

    10   Flowers ½ inch or less across, usually numerous in flat-topped clusters; sepals all similar, narrow and not leaf-like—11
    10   Flowers larger, either not numerous or not in distinctly flat-topped clusters; sepals, or some of them, leaflike or larger—13

11   Principal leaves over ⅜ inch wide, seldom with axillary clusters of smaller leaves; flower cluster with very small bracts if any
            NAKED-FLOWERED ST. JOHN'S-WORT (*H. nudiflorum*)   199
11   Principal leaves ⅜ inch or less wide, usually with axillary clusters of smaller leaves; flower cluster with narrow but prominent bracts—12

    12   Leaves pointed at base; branchlets 2-edged; capsules much longer than broad
                BUSHY ST. JOHN'S-WORT (*H. densiflorum*)   196
    12   Leaves roundish at base; branchlets 4-angled; capsules about as broad as long
                ROUND-PODDED ST. JOHN'S-WORT (*H. cistifolium*)   199

13   Flowers stalkless, solitary or 2 to 3 at branchlet tips, 1 to 2 inches across   GOLDEN ST. JOHN'S-WORT (*H. frondosum*)   195
13   Flowers stalked, usually more numerous, mostly less than 1 inch across—14

K

KEY TO THE DOGWOODS (Cornus)

8 Leaves paler green beneath, smooth or nearly so; branchlets greenish or partly red, becoming gray; fruits pale blue; southeastern STIFF DOGWOOD *(C. stricta)* 207

8 Leaves whitened or densely woolly beneath; branchlets bright red to purplish red or reddish brown; fruits white; northern—9

9 Leaves smooth or nearly so
RED-OSIER DOGWOOD *(C. stolonifera)* 204

9 Leaves densely woolly beneath
BAILEY DOGWOOD *(C. stolonifera* var. *baileyi)* 204

L

KEY TO THE AZALEAS (Rhododendron)

When in flower

1 Flower red, orange, or yellow—2
1 Flowers white or pink—5

2 Flowers appearing before or with the young leaves—3
2 Flowers appearing in summer after the leaves mature—4

3 Corolla tubes with gland-tipped hairs; southern mountain shrub
FLAME AZALEA *(R. calendulaceum)* 216

3 Corolla tubes with simple, non-glandular hairs; southern lowland shrub SHOWY AZALEA *(R. speciosum)* 216

4 Corolla tubes hairy and with some short-talked glands; mountain shrub
CUMBERLAND AZALEA *(R. cumberlandense)* 216

4 Corolla tubes smooth or nearly so; southern coastal plain shrub RED AZALEA *(R. nudiflorum)* 220

5 Corolla tube very short, less than ¼ as long as the lobes—6
5 Corolla tubes as long as or longer than the lobes—7

6 Corolla strongly 2-lipped, with long and narrow lobes; stamens 10; northern shrub RHODORA *(R. canadense)* 216

6 Corolla slightly 2-lipped, the lobes broad and the upper one spotted, stamens usually 7; southern mountain shrub
PINKSHELL AZALEA *(R. vaseyi)* 215

7 Flowers appearing before or with the young leaves—8
7 Flowers appearing in summer after the leaves mature—12

8 Flower buds with stalked glands in prominent rows; colonial shrub of the coastal plain less than 2 feet high
DWARF AZALEA *(R. atlanticum)* 219

8 Flower buds otherwise; taller and non-colonial shrubs—9

9 Flowers white, the calyx glandular
ALABAMA AZALEA *(R. alabamense)* 216

9 Flowers pink, the calyx not glandular—10

With fruits and mature leaves

293

    6 Capsules and lower leaf surfaces grayish-downy and
      usually with some bristly hairs—7
    6 Capsules and lower leaf surfaces with bristly hairs but not
      downy—9

7 Most long hairs of the capsules gland-tipped; northern and mountain shrub   MOUNTAIN AZALEA *(R. roseum)*   219
7 Most long hairs of the capsules not gland-tipped—8

    8 Capsules with few or no long hairs; southern lowland shrub
                          HOARY AZALEA *(R. canescens)*   219
    8 Capsules with numerous long hairs; southern mountain
      shrub   FLAME AZALEA *(R. calendulaceum)*   216

9 Young branchlets grayish-downy as well as with scattered stiff
  hairs; leaves with scattered hairs beneath
                        ALABAMA AZALEA *(R. alabamense)*   216
9 Young branchlets smooth except for scattered bristly hairs; leaves
  hairy only along midrib beneath—10

    10 Leaves light green above; hairs of the capsules not gland-
       tipped   PINXTER-FLOWER *(R. nudiflorum)*   216
    10 Leaves lustrous dark green above; hairs of the capsules
       gland-tipped—11

11 Leaves mostly less than ¾ inch wide, pale or often whitened
   beneath, the margins merely hairy-fringed
                        SWAMP AZALEA *(R. viscosum)*   219
11 Leaves often over ¾ inch wide, green beneath, the margins
   minutely toothed as well as fairy-fringed
   SOUTHERN SWAMP AZALEA *(R. viscosum* var. *serrulatum)* 219

                                                              M

          KEY TO THE HUCKLEBERRIES (Gaylussacia)

1 Branchlets angled; leaves everygreen; toothed on margin, not
  resin-dotted   BOX HUCKLEBERRY *(G. brachycera)*   235
1 Branchlets not angled; leaves deciduous, untoothed on margin,
  dotted with small yellow resin globules at least on the lower
  surface—2

    2 Leaves resin-dotted on both surfaces but more densely so
      beneath; berries black, in short clusters
                       BLACK HUCKLEBERRY *(G. baccata)*   236
    2 Leaves resin-dotted only beneath; berries in rather long and
      more or less drooping clusters—3

3 Berries in the axils of large leaflike bracts—4
3 Berries not in the axils of such bracts—5

    4 Branchlets downy; berries smooth
                       DWARF HUCKLEBERRY *(G. dumosa)*   235
    4 Branchlets and berries both bristly-hairy
                     BRISTLY HUCKLEBERRY *(G. hirtella)*   235

294

5   Leaves green beneath; berries lustrous black
                    BUCKBERRY *(G. ursina)*   236
5   Leaves pale or whitened beneath; berries blue and whitened with
    a bloom—6

    6   Branchlets smooth; leaves smooth or nearly so beneath
                    DANGLEBERRY *(G. frondosa)*   235
    6   Branchlets and lower leaf surfaces downy or woolly—7

7   Branchlets and lower leaf surfaces merely downy; shrub with
    creeping underground stems
                    CREEPING DANGLEBERRY *(G. nana)*   236
7   Branchlets and lower leaf surfaces conspicuously woolly; shrub
    otherwise
          WOOLLY DANGLEBERRY *(G. frondosa var. tomentosa)*   236

N

KEY TO THE BLUEBERRIES, BILBERRIES, AND CRANBERRIES (Vaccinium)

1   Stems trailing, creeping, or tufted and mat-forming—2
1   Stems ascending or erect—5

    2   Leaves minutely black-dotted on the lower surface; stems
        tufted and mat-forming
            MOUNTAIN-CRANBERRY *(V. vitis-idea var. minima)*   247
    2   Leaves not black-dotted beneath, the margins more or less
        rolled inward on the lower side; stems very slender, creep-
        ing—3

3   Leaves green beneath; berries blue
                    CREEPING BLUEBERRY *(V. crassifolium)*   247
3   Leaves pale or whitened beneath; berries bright red—4

    4   Leaves elliptical, blunt at tip, margins but slightly rolled
        inward beneath LARGE CRANBERRY *(V. macrocarpum)*   247
    4   Leaves egg-shaped, pointed at tip, margins strongly rolled
        inward beneath   SMALL CRANBERRY *(V. oxycoccus)*   247

5   Fruits solitary in the axils of the leaves or of leaflike bracts—6
5   Fruits 2 to several together in a cluster; bracts, if present, very
    minute—12

    6   Branchlets 4-angled or 4-sided—7
    6   Branchlets round or nearly so—8

7   Leaves pale or whitened beneath, blunt at tip, the margins un-
    toothed; berries blue OVAL-LEAF BILBERRY *(V. ovalifolium)*   240
7   Leaves bright green on both surfaces, pointed at tip, the margins
    finely toothed; berries dark purple or black
                    THINLEAF BILBERRY *(V. membranaceum)*   240

    8   Leaves toothed—9
    8   Leaves untoothed or apparently so—10

9 Stems somewhat tufted, less than 1 foot high; fruits light blue; northern shrub DWARF BILBERRY *(V. caespitosum)* 239
9 Stems not tufted, 1 to 6 feet high; fruits purplish red; southern mountain shrub
SOUTHERN MOUNTAIN-CRANBERRY *(V. erythrocarpum)* 244

    10 Leaves leathery, margins often with minute teeth or slightly rolled inward beneath, lower surface sometimes minutely downy; fruits black, about ¼ inch in diameter
SPARKLEBERRY *(V. arboreum)* 239
    10 Leaves thin, margins always flat and untoothed, often whitened or downy beneath; fruits over ¼ inch in diameter—11

11 Fruits greenish or pale purplish, smooth and often with a whitish bloom; branchlets smooth or nearly so
DEERBERRY *(V. stamineum)* 239
11 Fruits purplish black and downy; branchlets downy
BLACK DEERBERRY *(V. stamineum* var. *melanocarpum)* 239

    12 Low shrubs less than 3 feet high—13
    12 Tall shrubs 3 or more feet high—19

13 Largest leaves less than ¾ inch long—14
13 Largest leaves more than ¾ inch long—15

    14 Arctic-alpine shrub; leaves dull above
BOG BILBERRY *(V. uliginosum* var. *alpinum)* 239
    14 Southern coastal plain shrub; leaves lustrous above.
EVERGREEN BLUEBERRY *(V. myrsinites)* 240

15 Branchlets and leaves conspicuously hairy—16
15 Branchlets minutely warty-dotted, slightly if at all hairy; leaves smooth to somewhat downy or sparingly hairy beneath—17

    16 Fruits smooth; northern shrub
VELVET-LEAF BLUEBERRY *(V. myrtilloides)* 240
    16 Fruits hairy; southern mountain shrub
HAIRY BLUEBERRY *(V. hirsutum)* 243

17 Leaves, or at least some of them, with small stalked glands on the lower surface SMALL BLACK BLUEBERRY *(V. tenellum)* 243
17 Leaves without such glands beneath—18

    18 Leaves pale or whitened beneath, the margins usually untoothed; widely distributed shrub
LATE LOW BLUEBERRY *(V. vacillans)* 243
    18 Leaves usually green beneath, the margins minutely toothed; northern shrub
EARLY LOW BLUEBERRY *(V. angustifolium)* 243

19 Leaves less than 1 inch long
ELLIOTT BLUEBERRY *(V. elliottii)* 244
19 Leaves more than 1 inch long—20

    20 Branchlets and lower leaf surfaces densely downy; berries black
BLACK HIGHBUSH BLUEBERRY *(V. atrococcum)* 244
    20 Branchlets and lower leaf surfaces smooth or nearly so; berries blue
HIGHBUSH BLUEBERRY *(V. corymbosum)* 244

KEY TO THE HONEYSUCKLES (Lonicera)

1 Scrambling shrubs or vines with flowers and fruits in end clusters, above disks formed by leaves with united bases—2
1 Erect shrubs with flowers and fruits paired on axillary stalks, the leaves all distinct—6

    2 Leaves merely grayish green beneath—3
    2 Leaves strongly whitened, at least on the lower surface—4

3 Branchlets rough-hairy; leaves densely downy beneath; northern
        HAIRY HONEYSUCKLE *(L. hirsuta)*   264
3 Branchlets and leaves both smooth; southern
        YELLOW HONEYSUCKLE *(L. flava)*   264

    4 Leaves whitened on both surfaces; midwestern
        GRAPE HONEYSUCKLE *(L. prolifera)*   264
    4 Leaves green on the upper surface; eastern or widespread—5

5 Branchlets whitened; flowers less than 1 inch long, 2-lipped, yellowish or purplish-tinged; fruits roundish, salmon red
        SMOOTH HONEYSUCKLE *(L. dioica)*   264
5 Branchlets not whitened; flowers over 1 inch long, trumpet-shaped and bright red; fruits egg-shaped and bright red
        TRUMPET HONEYSUCKLE *(L. sempervirens)*   267

    6 Leafy bracts present at the bases of the fruits
        INVOLUCRED HONEYSUCKLE *(L. involucrata)*   263
    6 Bracts at the bases of the fruits small and narrow or none—7

7 Leaves thin, usually egg-shaped; fruits distinct, bright red; branchlets flexible and spreading
        AMERICAN FLY HONEYSUCKLE *(L. canadensis)*   263
7 Leaves thickish, elliptical or oblong; fruits more or less united to form a 2-eyed berry; branchlets stiff and ascending—8

    8 Leaves usually rounded at the base, often hairy at least beneath; flowers and fruits with stalks less than ¼ inch long; fruits blue or bluish black
        MOUNTAIN FLY HONEYSUCKLE *(L. villosa)*   263
    8 Leaves usually pointed at the base, smooth or nearly so; flowers and fruits with stalks over ½ inch long; fruits red or purplish
        SWAMP FLY HONEYSUCKLE *(L. oblongifolia)*   263

KEY TO THE VIBURNUMS (Viburnum)

1   Leaves 3-lobed—2
1   Leaves not lobed—4

    2   Lower leaf surface with minute black dots, usually softly downy; leafstalks usually with stipules at the base
            MAPLE-LEAF VIBURNUM *(V. acerifolium)*   272
    2   Lower leaf surfaces not black-dotted, smooth or merely downy on the main veins; leafstalks commonly with a pair of glands at the summit—3

3   Leaves shallowly 3-lobed above the middle; low or straggling shrub   SQUASHBERRY *(V. edule)*   271
3   Leaves deeply 3-lobed; upright shrub
            HIGHBUSH-CRANBERRY *(V. trilobum)*   272

    4   Leaves usually over 4 inches wide, heart-shaped; branchlets and lower leaf surfaces with cinnamon-colored, starry-branched hairs   HOBBLEBUSH *(V. alnifolium)*   268
    4   Leaves less than 4 inches wide—5

5   Leaves with prominent straight veins running from the midrib into large marginal teeth—6
5   Leaf margins untoothed or with fine teeth, the veins not at all prominent toward the leaf margin—8

    6   Leaves stalkless or with stalks less than 3/16 inch long
            DOWNY ARROWWOOD *(V. rafinesquianum)*   275
    6   Leaves with stalks usually over ¼ inch long—7

7   Leafstalks with stipules at the base; bases of the leaves usually heart-shaped   SOFT ARROWWOOD *(V. molle)*   272
7   Leafstalks usually without stipules; bases of the leaves usually rounded   ARROWWOOD *(V. dentatum)*   272

    8   Leaf margins untoothed or the teeth very inconspicuous; flower and fruit clusters either stalkless or distinctly stalked—9
    8   Leaf margins quite finely, sharply, and regularly toothed the entire length; flower and fruit clusters stalkless or nearly so—11

9   Flower and fruit clusters stalkless; largest leaves seldom 1½ inches long, broadest toward the tip
            SMALL-LEAF VIBURNUM *(V. obovatum)*   271
9   Flower and fruit clusters distinctly stalked; largest leaves well over 2 inches long, usually broadest at or below the middle—10

    10   Stalk of the flower or fruit cluster shorter than its branches; leaves dull above, usually smooth beneath
            NORTHERN WITHEROD *(V. cassinoides)*   268
    10   Stalk of the flower or fruit cluster as long as or longer than its branches; leaves lustrous above, usually rusty-scurfy on the veins beneath
            SOUTHERN WITHEROD *(V. nudum)*   268

GLOSSARY OF TECHNICAL TERMS

ACHENE   A small, hard, dry, one-seeded fruit.

AERIAL ROOTLETS   Small rootlike structures along the stems of some climbing vines.

ALTERNATE   Arranged singly at intervals along the stems.

ANGLED   With several edges or evident ridges.

ANTHER   The part of a stamen containing the pollen.

ARMED   Provided with prickles, spines, or sharp thorns.

AROMATIC   With a pleasant spicy odor.

ASCENDING   Growing upward at an angle.

AWL-LIKE   Narrow and tapering to a sharp point.

AXIL   The upper angle formed by the leaf or leafstalk with the stem; or the similar angle formed by a principal vein of the leaf with the midrib.

AXILLARY   Situated in the axil of a leaf.

BEAKED   Ending in a prolonged tip.

BERRY   Botanically a fruit which is fleshy or pulpy throughout, with seeds imbedded in the pulp.

BERRY-LIKE   Resembling a berry but in many cases not a true berry.

BLADE   The flat or expanded portion of a leaf.

BLOOM   A white, waxy, powdery coating which is easily rubbed off.

BRACT   A small leaf or leaflike structure beneath a flower or flower cluster.

BRANCHLET   A small branch of the current season; a twig.

BRISTLE   A stiff hair; a weak outgrowth of a stem less formidable than a prickle.

BRISTLY   Having bristles.

BUD   An undeveloped stem or branch, flower, or flower cluster.

BUNDLE SCARS   Dotlike scars within a leaf scar, representing the broken ends of ducts which led into the leafstalk.

CALYX   The sepals of the flower taken collectively.

CAPSULE   A dry fruit which splits open into two or more parts at maturity.

CATKIN   A number of small, scaly-bracted flowers arranged in a long and often drooping cluster.

CHAFFY   Covered with small, branlike scales.

CHAMBERED PITH   Pith divided crosswise by woody plates or partitions.

COMPOUND LEAF   A leaf in which the blade is divided into smaller leaflike parts, or leaflets.

CONTINUOUS PITH   Pith which is not divided into compartments by cross plates.

COROLLA   The petals of a flower taken collectively.

DIAPHRAGM   A zone of denser or woody tissue in the pith.

DOUBLE-TOOTHED   Having large teeth which in turn have smaller teeth on them.

DOWNY   Coated with fine, soft hairs.

DRUPE   A fleshy fruit with the seed enclosed in a hard and bony covering.

DRUPELET   A tiny drupe.

EGG-SHAPED   Broadest below the middle.

ELLIPTIC   Having the outline of an ellipse; widest in the middle and tapering sharply at both ends.

ELONGATE   Much longer than broad.

END BUD   A bud formed at the precise tip of the twig.

EVERGREEN   With leaves remaining green throughout the winter.

FILAMENT   The stalk of a stamen.

FLAKY   With loose scales.

FRUIT   The seed-bearing portion of a plant.

GLAND   A small organ or protuberance having the function of secretion.

GLANDULAR   Bearing glands.

HAIRY   Covered with hairs.

HEAD   A dense cluster of stalkless or nearly stalkless flowers.

HEART-SHAPED   Shaped like a valentine heart; cordate.

HYBRID   A cross between two closely related species.

IMPERFECT   Flowers which lack either stamens or pistils.

INFLATED   Appearing blow up; bladdery.

INVOLUCRE   A circle or group of bracts below a flower cluster or surrounding a fruit.

LANCE-SHAPED   Long and narrow, broadest below the middle, and pointed at the tip; lanceolate.

LATERAL   Situated along the sides of a branchlet.

LEAFLET One of the small leaflike parts of a compound leaf.

LEAF SCAR The scar left on a twig when a leaf falls.

LEAFSTALK The stalk supporting a leaf; petiole.

LENTICEL A corky spot on the bark which originally permitted air to enter the branchlet.

LOBE A more or less rounded extension of an organ, such as a leaf.

LOBED Having lobes; a leaf with deep indentations.

LONG-POINTED With the tip gradually tapering to a point; acuminate.

LUSTROUS Shiny or glossy.

MARGIN The border or edge of a leaf.

MIDRIB The central or main vein of a leaf.

NAKED BUD A bud without bud scales.

NEEDLE-LIKE Very long, narrow, and pointed at the tip.

NODAL Pertaining to or situated at a node.

NODE The place on a stem where a leaf is attached.

NUT A hard-shelled, one-seeded fruit which does not split open at maturity.

NUTLET A very small and nutlike hard fruit.

OBLONG Longer than broad and with more or less parallel sides.

OPPOSITE Occurring in pairs at the nodes.

OVAL Broadly elliptic.

OVARY The ovule-bearing part of a pistil.

PALMATE With veins or lobes spreading from the summit of the leafstalk, like the fingers of a spread hand.

PALMATELY COMPOUND With leaflets radiating from the summit of the leafstalk.

PARASITIC Living on and obtaining food from another plant.

PARTITIONED PITH Pith divided crosswise by woody plates; chambered.

PERFECT A flower possessing both stamens and pistils.

PERSISTENT Remaining attached.

PETAL One of the modified leaves immediately outside the reproductive organs of a flower, usually brightly colored.

PINNATE Feather-like, with a main axis and branches along the side.

PINNATELY COMPOUND With leaflets arranged along a common rachis or midrib.

PISTIL The female organ of a flower which develops into the fruit and seeds.

PITH The soft or spongy tissue in the center of a twig or stem.

POD A dry fruit which splits open at maturity.

PRICKLE A small, sharp, needle-like outgrowth of the bark.

PROSTRATE Lying flat on the ground.

RECLINING With the lower part lying flat on the ground but the upper part curving upward.

RECURVED Curving downward or backward.

RESIN DOTS Minute globules or dots of resin exuded on the surface.

RESINOUS With small dots of resin on the surface.

ROLLED Curled under; revolute.

SCALE A small modified leaf on the outside of a bud.

SCALELIKE Resembling a scale.

SCURFY Covered with small, branlike scales.

SEED A ripened ovule.

SEMI-HERBACEOUS Only partly woody.

SEPAL One of the outermost modified leaves surrounding the reproductive organs of a flower, usually green or leaflike.

SHORT-POINTED Abruptly contracted into a sharp point.

SHREDDY Peeling off in thin, narrow, irregular strips.

SIMPLE LEAF A leaf with an undivided blade; not compound.

SIMPLE STEM A stem without branches.

SINUS The space or indention between the lobes of a leaf blade.

SPINE A sharp-pointed, rigid, thornlike structure.

SPRAWLING Spreading irregularly.

SPUR A short, slow-growing branch.

STALKED Borne on a stalk; with a narrow necklike base.

STAMEN The male element of a flower which produces pollen.

STARRY-BRANCHED Hairs with branches arranged like the points of a star.

STERILE Barren or unproductive.

STIGMA The part of a pistil which receives the pollen.

STIPULES Appendages at the base of a leafstalk, usually small and in pairs.

STIPULE SCAR A scar left on the twig by a fallen stipule.

STRAGGLING Spreading irregularly but semi-upright.

SUPERPOSED Placed one above the other.

TENDRIL A slender, twining organ by which a plant attaches itself to some support.

TERMINAL Borne at the tip of a stem or branch.

THORN A stiff, sharp, woody outgrowth of a stem.

THRICE COMPOUND Divided into leaflets which are in turn divided into leaflets, which are again divided into smaller leaflets.

TOOTHED Provided with teeth or small projections.

TOP-SHAPED Shaped like a toy top; widest toward the tip and tapering to the base.

TUBULAR A corolla or calyx of a flower with parts united to form a hollow tube, usually with lobes at the summit.

TWICE COMPOUND Divided into leaflets which are again divided into smaller leaflets.

TWIG A small shoot representing growth of the past season; a branchlet.

UMBEL A flower cluster in which the stalked flowers all arise from a common point.

WEDGE-SHAPED Shaped like a wedge; narrow and tapering to a sharp point.

WHORLED Arranged in a circle about the branchlet.

WINGED With thin, flat projections or corky outgrowths.

WOOLLY Coated with tangled or matted loose hairs.

INDEX

311